Irish Street Ballads

collected and annotated by Colm O Lochlainn
and illustrated with woodcuts

Pan Books London and Sydney

First published 1939 by The Three Candles Ltd, Dublin
This edition published 1978 by Pan Books Ltd,
Cavaye Place, London SW10 9PG
© Colm O Lochlainn 1939
ISBN 0 330 25316 6
Printed and bound in Great Britain by
Cox & Wyman Ltd, London, Reading and Fakenham

INTRODUCTION

In the life of eighteenth and nineteenth century Ireland
the ballad singer was an important person. Townsmen
and countrymen, being denied any instruction in their
own language, were turning more and more to English
for the spreading of news and the small amount of
culture that remained to them. So it came to pass that
ballads on every theme, from courtship to politics, were
carried through the country, to be sung and sold at fairs
and other rural gatherings. For the historian many of
them have a certain value. They record events of local
history, murders and burnings, deaths of priests and
political leaders (e.g. Lamentable lines on the death of
Father James Casey). They gave the popular view of
home and foreign affairs in peace and war; or acclaimed
the triumph of some popular idol, the erection of monu-
ments and the consecration of churches. Sometimes they
were in Irish, printed with strange phonetic spelling,
and sometimes they were bilingual. They soon became
part of the lore of the countryside. They were altered and
resung in the more intimate circle by the fireside or in
the ale house. Often they were sung to airs very
different from those which the professional ballad singer
had. It even happened that songs of definitely English

origin were sung to authentic Gaelic airs, in all their traditional beauty.

Many collections of ballads have been made in the past from oral and from printed sources, some recording words only, and others the airs only. The Journals of the Folk Song Societies have published many fine songs and interesting fragments, some of which are referred to in my commentary.

That indefatigable worker, the late P. W. Joyce, in his 1909 collection, OLD IRISH FOLK MUSIC AND SONGS (pages 175 to 242), printed 57 street ballads with airs, and also issued a pamphlet, IRISH PEASANT SONGS (1906, reprinted 1922), containing 7 songs with music.

In selecting material from my own 25 years' accumulation, I deliberately limited the scope of this book to ballads in English. I avoided repeating any songs that Joyce had already done—MOLLY BAWN being the only exception—even though I often had fuller and better versions than his. I had determined on 100, but found it very difficult not to exceed this number. All songs by known authors have been omitted, though many fine ballads by Samuel Lover, Michael Scanlan, P. J. MacCall almost demanded inclusion. Perhaps I shall do a book of these yet, if the Lord spares me.

Whether taken from printed or oral sources, variants are many. Where my own oral version seems satisfactory I have let it stand. Occasionally I have altered an obviously corrupt line and in one or two places a ribald or redundant verse has been omitted. The titles have been shortened. Most of them originally were announced as A NEW SONG ON THE LUCKY ELOPEMENT or THE MUCH ADMIRED SONG CALLED THE YOUNG MAID'S LOVE or, as already quoted, LAMENTABLE LINES ON THE DEATH OF FATHER JAMES CASEY.

In the scope and extent of my commentary I have disciplined myself rigorously, for indeed another book might be written on the history of these ballads and the many versions of their tunes. Regarding the dating of most of the songs here set down, it is difficult to dogmatise. LILLIBULERO, we know for certain, dates to the time of the accession of James II and its authorship is definitely ascribed to Lord Wharton.* The verse about the "old prophecy found in a bog" seems to have caught the popular fancy, for it is remembered still in rural Ulster, though the modern songs called THE PROTESTANT BOYS are more often heard sung.

Some others, DUNLAVIN GREEN and PATRICK BRADY, for instance, are authentic 1798 ballads. Of BOLD ROBERT EMMET I am a bit doubtful, but who will date me THE BONNY LABOURING BOY or THE SUIT OF GREEN or THE MAID WITH THE BONNY BROWN HAIR ? They are as likely to belong to 1720 as to 1820, and there are many such ageless songs in this book. DONNELLY AND COOPER is definitely datable, and I have such another, MORRISEY AND THE RUSSIAN SAILOR, in which the glories of the prize ring are sung.

* See " The Historical Songs of Ireland" by Crofton Croker (Percy Society, London, 1841) and "Songs that made History" by H. E. Pigott (Dent, London, 1937).

In the 60's and 70's of the last century, and ever since, the Irish element on both American and English variety stage (though we must not forget to honour Dan Lowry and Pat Kinsella—the Dublin free-and-easies) produced many songs of the rollicking type, represented here by LANIGAN'S BALL and FINNEGAN'S WAKE—a type that saw its downfall with the advent of the Gaelic League and a more virile nationality. Many such songs were written by Johnny Patterson, the clown of Batty's, Powell and Clarke's, and Lloyd's Circuses—author, I am told, of THE GARDEN WHERE THE PRATIES GROW, GOOD-BYE JOHNNY DEAR, BRIDGIE DONOHUE, and, no doubt, others. The late Percy French—most lovable of men—was a modern composer in the same strain.

Of one or two of our songs it may well be that the authors are still living. So strong the tradition, so true to type are such songs as BACHELOR'S WALK, THE NIGHT OF THE RAGMAN'S BALL, KEVIN BARRY, that it seems almost natural and fitting that no record should remain of their authors. If I have failed in any way to render due gratitude and acknowledgement to any living author, 'tis not for want of wishing, nor want of asking. I pay them what honour I can by setting them in this book with the greatest of ballad writers from 1690 to 1920.

One thing I can claim with confidence, that every song in the book can be sung by anyone who has the ordinary Irishman's ear for music. I have sung them all myself, and here they are set in keys to suit the average

x

voice. *Let the singer approach them with patience and sympathy. He must avoid all exaggeration of dialect and resist the temptation to burlesque, for it is fatally easy. He must sing them quietly and naturally, dropping a verse here and there, if he will, but telling the story completely. He will soon find that he has a rich store of entertainment, of a more universal appeal than any repertoire of operatic or classical song, and a sure bond of fellowship with Irishmen the world over. Furthermore, he will have gone a long way towards gaining an insight into the life and thought of our forebears, and he will link up with the genuine Gaelic tradition which we are seeking to restore.*

When the Irish language was fading, the Irish Street Ballad in English was the half-way-house between the Irish culture and the new English way. Now that the nation is retracing its steps, is it too much to hope that we may pause again at the half-way-house to find there the simple enjoyment of simple themes, to recapture the rhythm and the idiom of Gaelic poetry and music?

Colm O Lochlainn.

THE ILLUSTRATIONS

Elsewhere I have written of the printers in Dublin of the ballad sheets;* here I may say a word about the illustrations. They are all taken from Dublin-printed ballad sheets or from old wood-blocks in my possession. The old printers were most haphazard in the positioning of the wood-cuts, and so—as here— we are quite liable to find Donnelly and Cooper, the boxers, illustrating THE SPORTING YOUTH, *and a picture of a teapot facing* THE PARTING GLASS *just because it fits the page.*

Some of the cuts have quite a history. That on page 69 once adorned the cover of the first edition of Thomas Moore's IRISH MELODIES. *The picture of the stage coach on page 29 was in use in the old coaching days; while the sailing ships on pages 91 and 93 once headed the sailing bills of the cross-channel packet boats, and were later used by wine importers and coal merchants.*

---

* *Dublin Civic Week Handbook, 1929. See Addendum, p. 229.*
Some provincial imprints are: Mayne of Belfast, Haly of Cork Harrington of Johnstown, Co. Kilkenny and Kelly of Waterford.

Contents

ACKNOWLEDGMENT

To many generous singers I am indebted for much that is here set down. To two in particular I must express my gratitude. The name of one appears in the dedication; Denis Devereux, friend and fellow-worker of William Rooney and of Arthur Griffith; friend and fellow-craftsman to me, his junior; publisher for many years of Nugent's well-known song-sheets. Had he lived, his would have been the hand to introduce this book. As he has gone, it shall be my tribute to his memory. Suaimhneas Dé d'á anam.

The other is my young friend, Michael Bowles, B.MUS. (N.U.I.), who will yet, le cuidiú Dé, do great things for Irish music. Were it not for his interest and enthusiasm, added to his industry in transcribing the songs during the past three years, the book might never have been completed.

THE BALLADS FOLLOW HERE IN THE ALPHABETICAL ORDER OF THEIR FIRST LINES, A COMPLETE INDEX OF WHICH ENDS THE BOOK.

THE CONTENTS IN THE FRONT GIVES THE USUAL TITLES ALPHABETICALLY

1.—THE KERRY RECRUIT

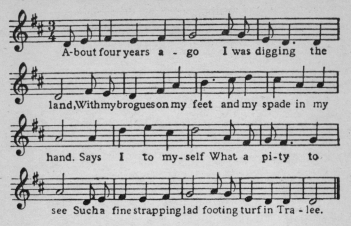

A-bout four years a-go I was digging the land, With my brogues on my feet and my spade in my hand. Says I to my-self What a pi-ty to see Such a fine strapping lad footing turf in Tra-lee.

So I buttered my brogues and shook hands with my spade,
And I went to the fair like a dashing young blade,
When up comes a sergeant and asks me to 'list,
"Arra, sergeant a grá, put the bob in my fist."

"O! then here is the shilling, as we've got no more,
When you get to head-quarters you'll get half a score."
"Arra, quit your kimeens," ses I, " sergeant, good-bye,
You'd not wish to be quartered, and neither would I."

And the first thing they gave me it was a red coat,
With a wide strap of leather to tie round my throat,
They gave me a quare thing I asked what was that,
And they told me it was a cockade for my hat.

The next thing they gave me they called it a gun,
With powder and shot and a place for my thumb;
And first she spit fire and then she spit smoke,
Lord, she gave a great lep and my shoulder near broke.

2

The next place they sent me was down to the sea,
On board of a warship bound for the Crimea.
Three sticks in the middle all rowled round with sheets,
Faith, she walked thro' the water without any feet.

When at Balaklava we landed quite sound,
Both cold wet and hungry we lay on the ground.
Next morning for action the bugle did call,
And we got a hot breakfast of powder and ball.

Sure it's often I thought of my name and my home
And the days that I spent cutting turf, och mavrone,
The balls were so thick and the fire was so hot,
I lay down in the ditch, boys, for fear I'd be shot.

We fought at the Alma, likewise Inkermann,
But the Russians they whaled us at the Redan.
In scaling the walls there myself lost my eye,
And a big Russian bullet ran off with my thigh.

It was there I lay bleeding, stretched on the cold ground,
Heads, legs and arms were scattered all around.
Says I, if my mam or my cleaveens were nigh
They'd bury me decent and raise a loud cry.

They brought me the doctor, who soon staunched my blood
And he gave me an elegant leg made of wood,
They gave me a medal and tenpence a day,
Contented with Sheela, I'll live on half-pay.

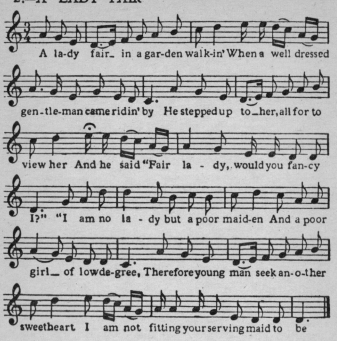

A la-dy fair— in a gar-den walk-in' When a well dressed gen-tle-man came ridin' by He stepped up to—her, all for to view her And he said "Fair la - dy, would you fan-cy I?" "I am no la - dy but a poor maid-en And a poor girl— of low de-gree, Therefore young man seek an-o-ther sweetheart I am not fitting your serving maid to be

And oh, kind sir, I have a lover
Tho' 'tis seven long years since I did him see.
And seven years more I will wait upon him
For if he's living he'll return to me."
" Perhaps your lover is dead or drownded
Or maybe sailing all on the sea.
Or maybe he is another's husband
And he will never return to thee."

" Oh, if he's married, I wish him happy,
And if he's dead, sure, I wish him rest;
No other young man will e'er enjoy me
For he's the one that I love the best."

He put his hand into his bosom
His lily-white fingers they were long and small;
He took out the ring that was broke between them
And when she saw that she down did fall.

He took her up all in his arms,
He gave her kisses most tenderly;
Saying " You're my jewel and I'm your single sailor
And now at last I've won home to thee.
I am your true and your single sailor
You thought was drownded all in the sea.
But I've passed over all my toil and trouble
And I've come home, love, to wed with thee."

Come all young maidens, now heed my story
Don't slight your true love and he on the sea;
And he'll come home and make you his own,
And he'll take you over to Americay.

3.—A NEW SONG CALLED GRANUAILE

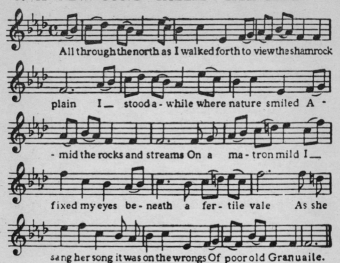

All through the north as I walked forth to view the shamrock plain I stood a-while where nature smiled A-mid the rocks and streams On a ma-tron mild I fixed my eyes be-neath a fer-tile vale As she sang her song it was on the wrongs Of poor old Granuaile.

Her head was bare and her gray hair over her eyes hung down
Her waist and neck, her hands and feet, with iron chains were bound
Her pensive strain and plaintive wail mingled with the evening gale
And the song she sung with mournful tongue was Poor Old Granuaile.

The gown she wore was stained with gore all by a ruffian band
Her lips so sweet that monarchs kissed are now grown pale and wan
The tears of grief fell from her eyes each tear as large as hail
None could express the deep distress of poor old Granuaile.

On her harp she leaned and thus exclaimed "My royal Brian is gone
Who in his day did drive away the tyrants every one

6

On Clontarf's plains against the Danes his faction did prepare
Brave Brian Boru cut their lines in two and freed old Granuaile.

But now, alas, I must confess, avengers I have none
There's no brave Lord to wave his sword in my defence—
   not one.
My enemies just when they please with blows they do assail,
The flesh they tore clean off the bones of poor old Granuaile.

Six hundred years the briny tears have flowed down from
   my eyes
I curse the day that Henry made of me proud Albion's prize
From that day down with chains I'm bound no wonder I
   look pale
The blood they drained from every vein of poor old Granuaile.

There was a lord came from the south he wore a laurel crown
Saying 'Grania dear, be of good cheer, no longer you'll be
   bound
I am the man they call great Dan, who never yet did fail
I have got the bill for to fulfil your wishes Granuaile.'"

With blood besmeared and bathed in tears her harp she
   sweetly strung
And oh the change, her mournful air from one last chord
   she wrung
Her voice so clear fell on my ear, at length my strength
   did fail
I went away and thus did say, " God help you, Granuaile."

[See Appendix, p. 205

4.—A NEW SONG ON THE TAXES

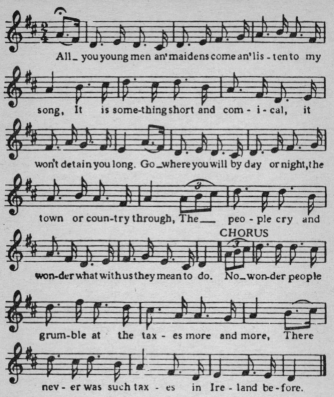

All you young men an' maidens come an' listen to my song, It is something short and comical, it won't detain you long. Go where you will by day or night, the town or country through, The people cry and wonder what with us they mean to do.

CHORUS

No wonder people grumble at the taxes more and more, There never was such taxes in Ireland before.

They're going to tax the farmers, and their horses, carts and ploughs,
They're going to tax the billygoats, the donkeys, pigs and cows;
They're going to tax the mutton, and they're going to tax the beef,
And they're going to tax the women if they do not try to read.

They will tax the ladies' chignons and their boas, veils and mats,
They're going to tax the mouse traps and the mousies, cats and rats;

They'll tax the ladies' flouncey gowns, their high-heeled boots
    and stays,
And before the sun begins to shine they'll tax the bugs and
    fleas.

They're going to tax the brandy, ale and whiskey, rum and
    wine,
They'll tax the tea and sugar, the tobacco, snuff and pipes;
They're going to tax the fish that swim and all the birds that fly,
An' they're going to tax the women who go drinking on the sly.

They're going to tax all bachelors as heavy as they can,
And they'll double tax the maidens who are over forty-one;
They'll tax the ground we walk on and the clothes that keep
    us warm,
And they're going to tax the childer on the night before
    they're born.

They're going to tax the crutches and they'll tax the wooden legs,
They're going to tax the bacon, bread and butter, cheese and
    eggs;
They're going to tax old pensioners as heavy as they can,
And they'll double tax young girls that go looking for a man.

They'll tax the ladies all that paint and those that walk with men,
They're going to tax the ducks and geese, and turkeys, cocks
    and hens;
They're going to tax the farmers' boys that work along the
    ditches,
And they'll double tax old drunken wives that try to wear
    the breeches.

They're going to tax the corn fields, potato gardens too,
They're going to tax the cabbage plants, the jackdaws and the
    crows;
They'll double tax the hobble skirts and table up some laws,
But the devil says he'll tax them if he gets them in his claws.

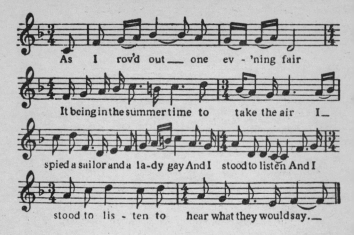

As I rov'd out — one ev-'ning fair
It being in the summer time to take the air I —
spied a sailor and a la-dy gay And I stood to listen And I
stood to lis - ten to hear what they would say. —

He said " Fair lady, why do you roam
For the day it is spent and the night is on."
She heaved a sigh, while the tears did roll
" For my dark-eyed sailor, for my dark-eyed sailor,
So young and stout and bold."

" 'Tis seven long years since he left this land,
A ring he took from off his lily-white hand,
One half of the ring is still here with me,
But the other's rolling, but the other's rolling
At the bottom of the sea."

He said, " Ye may drive him out of your mind,
Some other young man you'll surely find ;
Love turns aside and soon cold does grow,
Like a winter's morning, like a winter's morning,
The hills all white with snow."

She said " I'll never forsake my dear,
Although we're parted this many a year.
Genteel he was and no rake like you,
To induce a maiden, to induce a maiden
To slight the jacket blue."

One half of the ring did young William show,
She ran distracted in grief and woe,
Saying, " William, William, I have gold in store
For my dark-eyed sailor, for my dark-eyed sailor
Has proved his overthrow."

There is a cottage by yonder lea,
This couple's married and does agree;
So maids be loyal when your love's at sea,
For a cloudy morning, for a cloudy morning
Brings in a sunny day.

6.—THE MAID WITH THE BONNY BROWN HAIR

As once I roved out ve-ry ear-ly__ To view the green
meadows in Spring It was down by the side of a riv-er__
__ I__heard a fair damsel did sing__ And I
stood in com-pla-test a-maze-ment__ I gazed on that
maid-en so fair__ She appeared to me bright-er than
Ve-nus__ That maid with the bon-ny brown hair__

Her eyes they did shine like the diamonds
Her cheeks like the red rose in June,
Her skin was as white as the lily,
And her breath had the rarest perfume;
And a dress of the best speckled velvet
This charming wee lass she did wear,
And chains of bright gold and pure silver
Were twined in her bonny brown hair.

For a long while we courted together,
Till at last we named the wedding day,
And one day while conversing together
Very kindly to me she did say:

" Oh, it's I have another far kinder
My land and my fortune to share,
So farewell to you now, and forever,"
Said the maid with the bonny brown hair.

And once I went over the ocean,
Being bound for the proud land of Spain,
Some singing and dancing for pleasure,
But I had a heart full of pain;
And as the ship sailed down the river
I espied my old sweetheart so fair,
Quite content in the arms of another
Was the maid with the bonny brown hair.

So farewell to my friends and relations,
Perchance I shall see you no more,
And when I'm in far distant nations
Sure I'll sigh for my dear native shore;
When I'm in some far distant nation
My land and my fortune to share
I hope I'll get someone more kinder
Than the maid with the bonny brown hair.

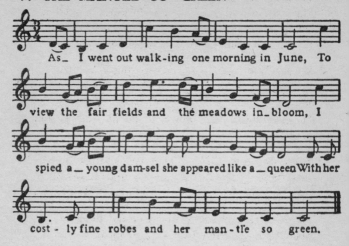

As I went out walk-ing one morning in June, To view the fair fields and the meadows in bloom, I spied a young dam-sel she appeared like a queen With her cost-ly fine robes and her man-tle so green.

I stood with amazement and was struck with surprise
I thought her an angel that fell from the skies,
Her eyes were like diamonds, her cheeks like the rose
She is one of the fairest that nature composed.

I said, " My pretty fair maid, if you will come with me
We'll both join in wedlock, and married we'll be,
I'll dress you in rich vesture, you'll appear like a queen,
With your costly fine robes and your mantle so green."

She answered me, " Young man, you must me excuse,
For I'll wed with no man, you must be refused;
To the woods I will wander to shun all men's view,
For the lad that I love fell in famed Waterloo."

" O, then, if you won't marry, tell me your love's name,
For I being in battle, I might know the same."
" Draw near to my garment and there will be seen,
His name all embroidered on my mantle of green."

14

In raising her mantle there I did behold
His name and his surname were in letters of gold;
Young William O'Reilly appeared to my view
He was my chief comrade in famed Waterloo.

"We fought so victorious where the bullets did fly
In the far field of honour your true love does lie,
We fought for three days till the fourth afternoon,
He received his death summons on the 16th of June.

But when he was dying I heard his last cry
'If you were here, Lovely Nancy, contented I'd die;'
Now Peace is proclaimed, and the truth I declare
Here is your love token, the gold ring I wear."

She stood in amazement, then pale did she grow,
She flew to my arms with a heart full of woe,
"To the woods I will wander for the lad I adore,"
"Rise up, lovely Nancy, your grief I'll remove.

Oh! Nancy, dear Nancy, 'tis I won your heart
In your father's garden that day we did part.
Now the wars are all over, no trouble is seen
And I'll wed with my true love in her mantle so green."

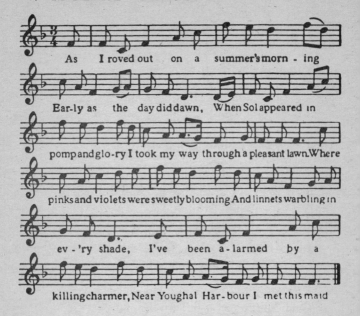

As I roved out on a summer's morn - ing
Ear-ly as the day did dawn, When Sol appeared in
pomp and glo-ry I took my way through a pleasant lawn. Where
pinks and violets were sweetly blooming And linnets warbling in
ev - 'ry shade, I've been a-larmed by a
killing charmer, Near Youghal Har-bour I met this maid

Her aspect pleasing, her smiles engaging,
I thought she really would distract my mind,
When I viewed her features, I thought on the fair one
That in Rathangan I left behind.
Her glancing eyes they seemed most pleasing,
" I think young man I saw you before,
Here in your absence in grief I languish,
My dear you're welcome to me once more.

" Don't you remember how you once deceived me,
And courted me with right good will,
But at your returning I'll now quit mourning,
In hopes your promise you will fulfil.

16

A darling babe for you I'll be rearing,
As in your travels you have never seen,
If you'll agree, love, and come with me, love,
We'll all live happy in Cappoquin."

" Oh no, fair maid, I will tell you plainly,
Here to remain I will not agree,
For when your parents would not receive me,
It made me leave this countery.
And when your parents would not receive me
It's then to Leinster I did repair,
Where I fell a-courting another fair one,
In sweet Rathangan, near to Kildare.

And now I'm going to leave off roving
For I am hoping her love to win,
To her I'll go now, and I'll bid adieu, now,
Saying ' Fare you well, sweet Cappoquin.'
So now he has left me in grief bewailing,
That he my tender young heart did win.
So all fair maidens, beware of strangers,
And think on Mary of Cappoquin."

[See Appendix, p. 206

9.—THE BONNY LABOURING BOY

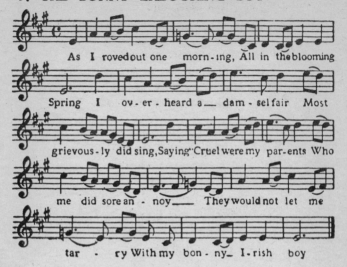

As I roved out one morn-ing, All in the blooming Spring I ov-er-heard a damsel fair Most grievous-ly did sing, Saying "Cruel were my par-ents Who me did sore an-noy They would not let me tar-ry With my bon-ny Irish boy

His cheeks are like the roses red,
His eyes are black as sloes,
He is meek in his behaviour
Wherever that he goes.
He is well sized both neat and wise
Like a maiden's chastity,
If I had my will I would be still
In my love's company.

Says the mother to her daughter
" Why do you stoop so low,
To marry a poor labouring boy,
Around the world to go?
Some noble lord might fancy you
Great riches to enjoy,
So do not throw yourself away,
On a poor labouring boy."

Says the daughter to the mother
"Your talk is all in vain,
For knights, and lords, and dukes, and earls
Their efforts I disdain;
I'd sooner live a humble life
Where time I would employ,
Still waiting happy prospects
With my bonny labouring boy.

"If I had all the riches now
Which great men have in store,
'Tis freely I'd bestow them all
On the lad that I adore;
His beauty so entangled me,
The same I'll ne'er deny,
In the arms of my labouring boy
I mean to live and die."

We'll fill our glasses to the brim,
And let the toast go round.
Here's health to every labouring boy
That ploughs and sows the ground,
Who, when his work is over
It is home he'll go with joy,
And happy is the girl that weds
The bonny labouring boy.

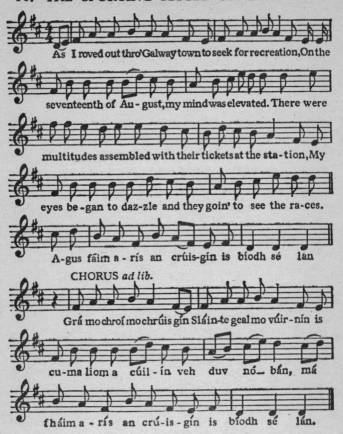

As I roved out thro' Galway town to seek for recreation, On the
seventeenth of Au-gust, my mind was elevated. There were
multitudes assembled with their tickets at the sta-tion, My
eyes be-gan to daz-zle and they goin' to see the ra-ces.
A-gus fáim a-rís an crúis-gín is biodh sé lán

CHORUS *ad lib.*

Grá mo chroí mo chrúis gín Sláin-te geal mo vúir-nín is
cu-ma liom a cúil-ín veh duv nó— bán, má
fháim a-rís an crú-is-gín is biodh sé lán.

There were passengers from Limerick and passengers from
Nenagh
And passengers from Dublin and sportsmen from Tipp'rary.
There were passengers from Kerry and all quarters of the
Nation
And our member Mr. Hasset for to join the Galway Blazers.

There were multitudes from Aran and members from New
  Quay shore
The boys from Connamara and the Clare unmarried maidens
There were people from Cork city who were loyal, true and
  faithful
That brought home Fenian prisoners from dying in foreign
  nations.

It's there you'll see confectioners with sugarsticks and dainties
The lozenges and oranges, the lemonade and raisins.
The gingerbread and spices to accommodate the ladies
And a big crubeen for threepence to be picking while you're
  able.

It's there you'll see the gamblers, the thimbles and the garters
And the sporting Wheel of Fortune with the four and twenty
  quarters
There was others without scruple pelting wattles at poor Maggy
And her father well contented and he looking at his daughter.

It's there you'll see the pipers and the fiddlers competing
And the nimble-footed dancers and they tripping on the daisies
There was others crying cigars and lights, and bills of all the
  races
With the colours of the jockeys and the prize and horses' ages.

It's there you'd see the jockeys and they mounted on most stately
The pink and blue, the red and green, the Emblem of our nation.
When the bell was rung for starting, all the horses seemed
  impatient,
I thought they never stood on ground, their speed was so
  amazing.

There was half a million people there of all denominations
The Catholic, the Protestant, the Jew and Presbyterian.
There was yet no animosity, no matter what persuasion
But fáilte and hospitality inducing fresh acquaintance.

11.—THE PIPER'S TUNES

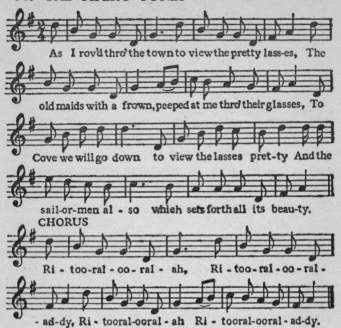

As I rov'd thro' the town to view the pretty lass-es, The old maids with a frown, peeped at me thro' their glasses, To Cove we will go down to view the lasses pret-ty And the sail-or-men al - so which sets forth all its beau-ty.

CHORUS

Ri - too-ral - oo - ral - ah, Ri - too-ral - oo - ral - ad-dy, Ri - tooral-ooral - ah Ri - tooral-ooral - ad-dy.

There's Captain Burke of Grove, a very famous name, sirs,
He keeps the buck and doe, and hunts the sporting game, sirs,
He winds the whip and spur, and makes the hunters rattle,
And when that home he comes he'll surely crack a bottle.

John Blake for to promote, he plays some tunes so merry;
He gave some charming notes to banish melancholy,
He'll then blow up the pipes to play the tune " Brave Larry,"
You'd laugh until you'd die to hear " Sweet Paddy Carey."

He'd play the Prussian Wars, the falls of the Boyne Water,
Jeannette and Jeannot and the March of Alexander,
The blooming White Cockade, the Old Brigade is coming,
O'Connell's in for Clare, and All the bells were ringing.

He played the Colleen Bawn, the banks of Kitty's Cottage,
The affermonious jig, called—My mother's mess of pottage.
The Wexford Rakes in style, and Trip the world before him,
The Sailor's Hornpipe, and Garryowen and Glory.

He played Kitty from Athlone, with Moreen móra Glanna,
Noreen on the road, and the flashy Rakes of Mallow.
Aughrim's overthrow, and the fall of Carrig Castle,
Brave Sarsfield took command at many a famous battle.

He played the Chorus jig, the ancient Ladies' Fancy,
Jack and the Jug of Punch, and the Bonnie highland laddie
The Ale house in great glee, with the Glass of brandy
The Roving sporting wheel—My love he is a dandy.

Nora Creena, he can play with all the variations,
The Rambler from Tralee, the De'il among the Tailors.
The Job of journey work, and the Boy she left behind her,
The song of Paddy Whack, and Tally hi ho the grinder.

He played up Bob and Joan, with Ju Ju Joice the joker
The famous jig Tow row, that was kept for Captain Croker.
The Ball of Ballinafad, and the Banks of Bannow
Plunkett's Moll in the wad, and Shawn O'Deer a'Glana.

He played of Bonaparte who crossed the Alps in winter,
The Union hornpipe, and the Killinick fox hunters,
The song of Patrick's Day, and the jig of Paddy Carroll
And each boy will Kiss the Maid behind the whiskey barrel.

So now I'll sing no more, because my song is ended
If I said anything wrong I hope you're not offended
Of hornpipes, jigs and reels, I'm sure I told you many,
Get up and shake your heels, 'tis better sport than any.

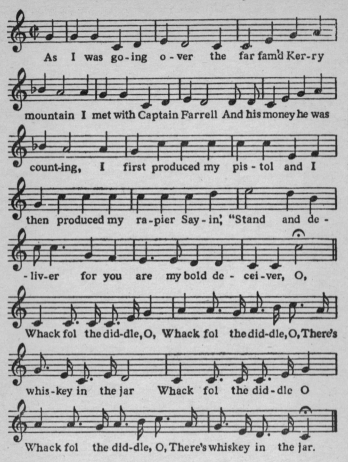

As I was go-ing o-ver the far fam'd Ker-ry mountain I met with Captain Farrell And his money he was count-ing, I first produced my pis-tol and I then produced my ra-pier Say-in', "Stand and de--liv-er for you are my bold de-cei-ver, O, Whack fol the did-dle, O, Whack fol the did-dle, O, There's whis-key in the jar Whack fol the did-dle O Whack fol the did-dle, O, There's whiskey in the jar.

He counted out his money and it made a pretty penny
I put it in my pocket and I gave it to my Jenny
She sighed and she swore that she never would betray me
But the devil take the women for they never can be easy.

I went unto my chamber all for to take a slumber
I dreamt of gold and jewels and for sure it was no wonder
But Jenny drew my charges and she filled them up with water
An' she sent for Captain Farrell, to be ready for the slaughter.

And 'twas early in the morning before I rose to travel,
Up comes a band of footmen and likewise Captain Farrell;
I then produced my pistol, for she stole away my rapier
But I couldn't shoot the water so a prisoner I was taken.

And if any one can aid me 'tis my brother in the army
If I could learn his station, in Cork or in Killarney.
And if he'd come and join me we'd go roving in Kilkenny
I'll engage he'd treat me fairer than my darling sporting Jenny.

13.—GRÁ GEAL MO CHROÍ

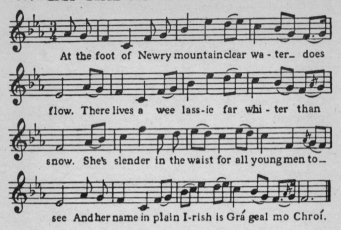

At the foot of Newry mountain clear wa-ter- does flow. There lives a wee lass-ie far whi-ter than snow. She's slender in the waist for all young men to- see And her name in plain I-rish is Grá geal mo Chroí.

'Twas on a summer's morning, as I walked along.
Down by yon green valley, I heard a fine song;
It was a fair damsel, and her voice rang most clear,
Saying, " How blest would I be if my darling was here."

I then drew anear to a shade that was green,
Where the leaves grew about her and she scarce could be seen ;
And it was her whole cry, " O ! my darling come away,
For without your loving company no longer can I stay.

That the moon it may darken and show us no light,
And the bright stars of heaven fall down from their height ;
That the rocks may all melt, and the mountains remove
The hour I prove false to the fair one I love.

If I were an empress and had the care of a crown,
And had I all the money that's for it laid down,
I would freely return it to the boy that I love,
And my mind I'd resign to the great God above."

Like a sheet of white paper is her neck and her breast,
Her bright eyes a-shining have robbed me of rest,
She's a pattern of virtue wherever she goes,
And her cheeks I compare to the red blushing rose.

Oh, the ships on the ocean may go without sails,
And the smallest of fishes turn into great whales,
In the middle of the ocean there will grow an apple tree,
If e'er I prove false to my Grá geal mo chroí.

14.—A NEW SONG ON THE MANCHESTER MARTYRS; or THE SMASHING OF THE VAN

At-tend you gal-lant I-rishmen and lis-ten for a while I'll sing to you the praises of the sons of Er-in's Isle It's of those gal-lant he-roes Who volun tar-i-ly ran To re - lease two I - rish Shamrocks, From an Eng-lish pris-on van.

CHORUS

Hur-rah my lads for freedom, let's all join heart and hand, May the Lord have mercy on the boys that helped to smash the van.

On the eighteenth of September, it was a dreadful year.
When sorrow and excitement ran throughout all Lancashire,
At a gathering of the Irish boys they volunteered each man,
To release those Irish prisoners out of the prison van.

Kelly and Deasy were their names, I suppose you knew them
    well,
Remanded for a week they were in Bellvue Gaol to dwell,
When taking of the prisoners back, their trial for to stand,
To make a safe deliverance they conveyed them in a van.

28

William Deasy was a man of good and noted fame,
Likewise Michael Larkin, we'll never forget his name,
With young Allen and O'Brien they took a part so grand,
In that glorious liberation and the smashing of the van.

In Manchester one morning those heroes did agree,
Their leaders, Kelly and Deasy, should have their liberty,
They drank a health to Ireland, and soon made up the plan,
To meet the prisoners on the road and take and smash the van.

With courage bold those heroes went and soon the van did stop,
They cleared the guards from back and front and then smashed
    in the top,
But in blowing open of the lock, they chanced to kill a man,
So three men must die on the scaffold high for smashing of
    the van.

One cold November morning in eighteen sixty-seven,
These martyrs to their country's cause a sacrifice were given,
" God save Ireland," was the cry, all through the crowd it ran,
The Lord have mercy on the boys that helped to smash the van.

So now kind friends I will conclude, I think it would be right,
That all true-hearted Irishmen together should unite,
Together should sympathise, my friends, and do the best we can
To keep the memories ever green, of the boys that smashed
    the van.

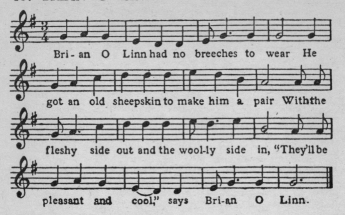

Bri-an O Linn had no breeches to wear He
got an old sheepskin to make him a pair With the
fleshy side out and the wool-ly side in, "They'll be
pleasant and cool," says Bri-an O Linn.

Brian O Linn had no shirt to his back,
He went to a neighbour's, and borrowed a sack,
Then he puckered the meal bag in under his chin—
"Sure they'll take them for ruffles," says Brian O Linn.

Brian O Linn was hard up for a coat,
So he borrowed the skin of a neighbouring goat,
With the horns sticking out from his oxsters, and then,
"Sure they'll take them for pistols," says Brian O Linn.

Brian O Linn had no hat to put on,
So he got an old beaver to make him a one,
There was none of the crown left and less of the brim,
"Sure there's fine ventilation," says Brian O Linn.

Brian O Linn had no brogues for his toes,
He hopped in two crab-shells to serve him for those.
Then he split up two oysters that match'd like a twin,
"Sure they'll shine out like buckles," says Brian O Linn.

Brian O Linn had no watch to put on,
So he scooped out a turnip to make him a one.
Then he placed a young cricket in under the skin—
" Sure they'll think it is ticking," says Brian O Linn.

Brian O Linn to his house had no door,
He'd the sky for a roof, and the bog for a floor
He'd a way to jump out, and a way to swim in,
" 'Tis a fine habitation," says Brian O Linn.

Brian O Linn went a-courting one night,
He set both the mother and daughter to fight ;
To fight for his hand they both stripped to the skin,
" Sure ! I'll marry you both," says Brian O Linn.

Brian O Linn, his wife and wife's mother,
They all lay down in the bed together,
The sheets they were old and the blankets were thin,
" Lie close to the wall," says Brian O Linn.

Brian O Linn, his wife and wife's mother,
Were all going home o'er the bridge together,
The bridge it broke down, and they all tumbled in,
" We'll go home by the water," says Brian O Linn.

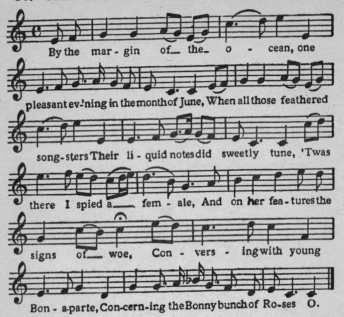

By the mar-gin of the o-cean, one pleasant ev-'ning in the month of June, When all those feathered song-sters Their li-quid notes did sweetly tune, 'Twas there I spied a female, And on her fea-tures the signs of woe, Con-vers-ing with young Bon-a-parte, Con-cern-ing the Bonny bunch of Ro-ses O.

Then up speaks young Napoleon, and takes his mother by the hand,
Saying: "Mother dear, be patient until I'm able to take command;
And I'll raise a mighty army, and through tremendous dangers go,
And I never will return again till I've conquered the Bonny Bunch of Roses, O.

"When first you saw great Bonaparte, you fell upon your bended knee,
And you asked your father's life of him, he granted it right manfully.

And 'twas then he took his army, and o'er the frozen Alps
    did go,
And he said : ' I'll conquer Moscow, and return for the Bonny
    Bunch of Roses, O.'

" He took three hundred thousand men, and kings likewise
    to bear his train,
He was so well provided for, that he could sweep the world
    for gain ;
But when he came to Moscow, he was overpowered by the
    sleet and snow,
With Moscow all a-blazing, and he lost the Bonny Bunch
    of Roses, O."

" Now son, be not too venturesome, for England is the heart
    of oak,
And England, Ireland, Scotland, their unity shall ne'er be broke ;
Remember your brave father, in Saint Helena he lies low,
And if you follow after, beware of the Bonny Bunch of
    Roses, O."

" O mother, adieu for ever, for now I lie on my dying bed,
If I lived I'd have been clever, but now I droop my youthful head ;
But when our bones lie mouldering and weeping willows o'er
    us grow,
The name of young Napoleon will enshrine the Bonny
    Bunch of Roses, O."

17.—THE BLACK HORSE

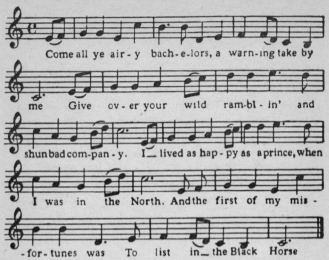

Come all ye air-y bach-e-lors, a warn-ing take by me Give ov-er your wild ram-bl-in' and shun bad com-pan-y. I lived as hap-py as a prince, when I was in the North. And the first of my mis-for-tunes was To list in the Black Horse

Now it being of a Thursday morn to Galway I did go,
Meeting with a small officer which proved my overthrow;
I met with Sergeant Atkinson in the market going down,
And says he: "Young man, would you enlist to be a Light
Dragoon?"

"Oh no, kind sir, a soldier's life with me would not agree,
Nor neither will I bind myself down from my libertie.
I live contented at my ease, my mind does tell me so,
So fare thee well, I'm just going down my shuttle for to
throw."

"So are you in a hurry now or are you going away,
Or won't you stand and listen to those words I'm going to say;
Or do you live far from this place, the same I'd wish to know,
Your name, kind sir, now if you please, give me before you go?"

34

"Oh, then, I am in a hurry, and my dwelling is not far,
My place of habitation lies six miles behind Armagh;
Charles Egan is my name, from Armagh town I came
I ne'er intend to do a crime that I should deny my name."

He says: "Now Cousin Charlie, perhaps you might do worse,
Now leave your native counterie and list in the Black Horse";
And with all his kind persuasiveness with him I did agree,
And I left my native country, boys, and fought for libertie.

Farewell unto my father, dear, likewise my sisters three,
Farewell unto my mother, her kind face I ne'er will see;
As I ride down through Armagh town, they all run in my mind
So farewell unto my country, boys, and the girl I left behind.

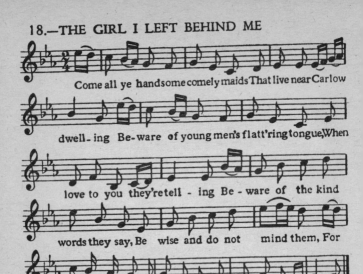

Come all ye handsome comely maids That live near Carlow dwell-ing Be-ware of young men's flatt'ring tongue, When love to you they're tell-ing Be-ware of the kind words they say, Be wise and do not mind them, For if they were talking till they die They'd leave you all be-hind them

In Carlow town I lived I own
All free from debt and danger.
Till Colonel Reilly listed me
To join the Wicklow Rangers.
They dressed me up in scarlet red
And they used me very kindly
But still I thought my heart would break
For the girl I left behind me.

I was scarcely fourteen years of age
When I was broken-hearted
For I'm in love these two long years
Since from my love I parted
These maidens wonder how I moan
And bid me not to mind him
That he might have more grief than joy
For leaving me behind him.

So now my love is gone from me
I own I do not blame him
For oftentimes he told to me
That he never would deceive me
But now he's gone across the foam
Unto some distant island
But in course of time he may come home
To the girl he left behind him.

'Tis not my love I claim I own
All for our separation
That left me wandering far from home
All in a distant station
But when e'er I get my liberty
No man shall ever bind me
I'll see my native land once more
And the girl I left behind me.

19.—THE MAID OF THE SWEET BROWN KNOWE

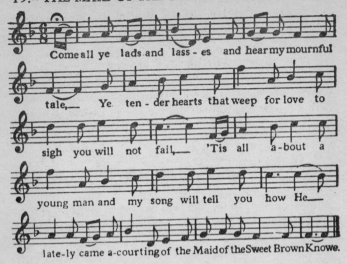

Come all ye lads and lass-es and hear my mournful tale,— Ye ten-der hearts that weep for love to sigh you will not fail,— 'Tis all a-bout a young man and my song will tell you how He— late-ly came a-courting of the Maid of the Sweet Brown Knowe.

Said he, " My pretty fair maid, could you and I agree,
To join our hands in wedlock bands, and married we will be ;
We'll join our hands in wedlock bands, and you'll have my
    plighted vow,
That I'll do my whole endeavours for the Maid of the Sweet
    Brown Knowe."

Now this young and pretty fickle thing, she knew not what to
    say,
Her eyes did shine like silver bright and merrily did play ;
Says she, " Young man, your love subdue, I am not ready now,
And I'll spend another season at the foot of the Sweet Brown
    Knowe."

" Oh," says he, " My pretty fair maid, now why do you
    say so ?
Look down in yonder valley where my verdant crops do grow

38

Look down in yonder valley at my horses and my plough
All at their daily labour for the Maid of the Sweet Brown
    Knowe."

" If they're at their daily labour, kind sir, it is not for me,
I've heard of your behaviour, I have, kind sir," says she ;
" There is an inn where you drop in, I've heard the people say,
Where you rap and you call and you pay for all, and go home
    at the dawn of day."

" If I rap and I call and I pay for all, my money is all my own,
I've never spent aught o' your fortune, for I hear that you've
    got none.
You thought you had my poor heart broke in talking to me now,
But I'll leave you where I found you, at the foot of the Sweet
    Brown Knowe."

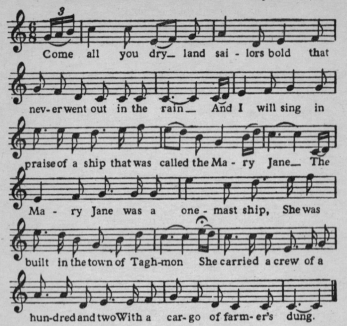

Come all you dry land sai-lors bold that
nev-er went out in the rain And I will sing in
praise of a ship that was called the Ma-ry Jane The
Ma-ry Jane was a one-mast ship, She was
built in the town of Tagh-mon She carried a crew of a
hun-dred and two With a car-go of farm-er's dung.

The captain he was a Dutchman,
  And he hailed from Barrack-lane,
And his wife was " man behind the mast,"
  On board of the *Mary Jane*.
The mate was a great navigator,
  And his nose was as red as a tart;
He belonged to the Wexford Militia,
  And he knew every pub on the chart.

We had a French cook from Mullinavat,
  Pat Murphy was his name;
And he was chief cook for spoiling the soup
  On board of the *Mary Jane*.

The morning that we left Taghmon
  Our ship ran short of wind,
So the crew had to get right out in the wet,
  And everyone shove behind.

When going around by the Long Stone Cross,
  A terrible storm now blew,
So we tightened her sails with a horse's reins,
  And we steered for Timbuctoo.
Next morning our cargo shifted,
  So the captain cried " We're done,"
But every man took a sprong in his hand,
  And went down for to turn the dung.

Next day we ran short of tobacco,
  We had not a bit in our bag ;
So when captain and crew had ne'er a chew,
  They started to " chaw the rag."
So now we were short of lime-juice,
  And the herrings they were so salt,
The skipper he told our mate so bold,
  When he'd come to a pub to halt.

The mate he kept a sharp look-out,
  For he was fond of a drop.
When he saw the green light he shouted " Hold
      tight !
  We're into a doctor's shop."
The *Mary Jane* took a stitch in her side,
  And so did the rest of the crew,
So she went ashore at the doctor's door,
  And she never reached Timbuctoo.

[*See Appendix*, p. 206

41

21.—VAN DIEMEN'S LAND

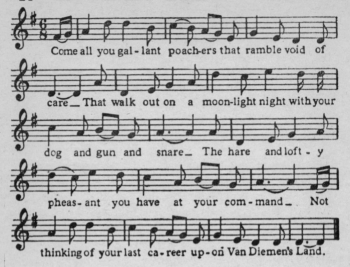

Come all you gal-lant poach-ers that ramble void of care — That walk out on a moon-light night with your dog and gun and snare — The hare and loft-y pheas-ant you have at your com-mand — Not thinking of your last ca-reer up-on Van Diemen's Land.

Poor Thomas Brown from Nenagh town, Jack Murphy and
    poor Joe
Were three determined poachers as the county well does know
By the keepers of the land, my boys, one night they were
    trepanned
And for fourteen years transported unto Van Diemen's Land.

The first day that we landed upon that fatal shore
The planters came around us there might be twenty score.
They ranked us off like horses and they sold us out of hand
And they yoked us to the plough, brave boys, to plough
    Van Diemen's Land.

The cottages we live in are built with sods of clay
We have rotten straw for bedding but we dare not say nay.
Our cots we fence with firing and slumber when we can
To keep the wolves and tigers from us in Van Diemen's Land.

Oft times when I do slumber I have a pleasant dream
With my sweet girl sitting near me close by a purling stream
I am roaming through old Ireland with my true love by the
 hand
But awaken broken-hearted upon Van Diemen's Land.

God bless our wives and families, likewise that happy shore
That isle of sweet contentment which we shall ne'er see more
As for the wretched families see them we seldom can
There are twenty men for one woman in Van Diemen's Land.

There was a girl from Nenagh town, Peg Brophy was her name,
For fourteen years transported was, we all well knew the same
But our planter bought her freedom and married her out of hand
And she gives to us good usage upon Van Diemen's Land.

But fourteen years is a long time, that is our fatal doom
For nothing else but poaching for that is all we done
You would leave off both dog and gun and poaching every man
If you but knew the hardship that's in Van Diemen's Land.

Oh, if I had a thousand pounds all laid out in my hand
I'd give it all for liberty if that I could command,
Again to Ireland I'd return and be a happy man
And bid adieu to poaching and to Van Diemen's Land.

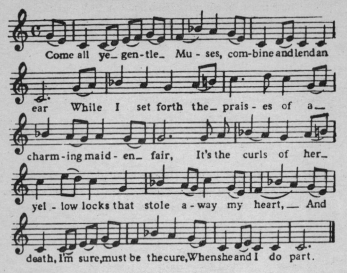

Come all ye gentle Muses, combine and lend an ear While I set forth the praises of a charming maiden fair, It's the curls of her yellow locks that stole away my heart, And death, I'm sure, must be the cure, When she and I do part.

The praises of this lovely maid I mean for to unfold,
Her hair hangs o'er her shoulders like lovely links of gold.
Her carriage neat, her limbs complete, which fractured quite
    my brain,
Her skin is whiter than the swan that swims on the purling
    stream.

Her eyes are like the diamonds that shine with crystal sheen
So modest and so tender she's fit to be a queen,
How many pleasant hours I spent all in the garden field,
She's won my heart, I cannot part with the maid of sweet
    Gurteen.

It was my cruel father that caused my grief and woe.
For he took and locked her in a room and would not let her go.
Her windows I have daily watched, thinking she might be seen
In hopes some time to get a sight of the maid of sweet Gurteen.

My father he arose one day and this to me did say
Oh son, dear son, be advised by me, don't throw yourself away
For to marry a poor servant girl whose parents are so mean,
So stay at home and do not roam, but always with me remain.

O father, dearest father, don't deprive me of my dear,
I would not lose my darling for a thousand pounds a year.
Was I possessed of England's crown I would make her my
    queen,
In high renown I'd wear the crown with the maid of sweet
    Gurteen.

My father in a passion flew, and this to me did say,
Since it is the cause within this place no longer she shall stay,
Mark what I say, from this very day you ne'er shall see her face,
For I will send her far away unto some other place.

'Twas in a few days after that a horse he did prepare
And sent my darling far away to a place I know not where,
I may go view my darling's room where oft times she has been
In hopes to get another sight of the maid of sweet Gurteen.

Now to conclude and make an end, I take my pen in hand.
Young Johnny Reilly is my name, and Flower Hills my land,
The days I spent in merriment since my darling first I seen,
And while I live I'll always think of the maid of sweet Gurteen,

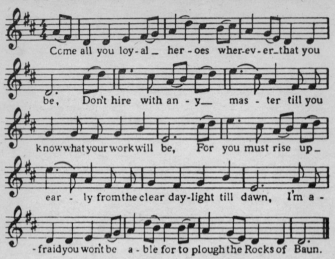

Come all you loy-al — her-oes wher-ev-er—that you
be, Don't hire with an-y— mas-ter till you
know what your work will be, For you must rise up—
ear - ly from the clear day-light till dawn, I'm a-
-fraid you won't be a - ble for to plough the Rocks of Baun.

My shoes they are well worn now and my stockings they are thin,
My heart is always trembling afeared that I'd give in
My heart is nearly broken from the clear daylight till dawn,
And I never will be able for to plough the rocks of
    Baun.

My curse attend you, Sweeney, for you have me nearly robbed,
You're sitting by the fireside with your feet upon the hob,
You're sitting by the fireside from the clear daylight till dawn,
But you never will be able for to plough the rocks of
    Baun.

O rise up, lovely Sweeney, and give your horse its hay,
And give him a good feed of oats before you start away,
Don't feed him on soft turnips, take him down to your green
    lawn,
And then you might be able for to plough the rocks of Baun.

I wish the Queen of England would write to me in time,
And place me in some regiment all in my youth and prime,
I'd fight for Ireland's glory from the clear daylight till dawn,
And I never would return again to plough the rocks of Baun.

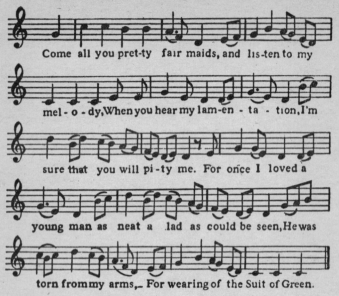

Come all you pret-ty fair maids, and lis-ten to my mel - o - dy, When you hear my lam-en - ta - tion, I'm sure that you will pi -ty me. For once I loved a young man as neat a lad as could be seen, He was torn from my arms,— For wearing of the Suit of Green.

It was on a Summer's evening as my love and I did chance to roam
Folded in each other's arms, as we strayed thro' yon shady grove,
He laid his hands against my breast, and most feelingly to me did say,
My life it lies in danger, for wearing of the suit of green.

If this be true, dear Willy, if this you tell to me be true,
I pray you throw aside your clothes, and I'll buy for you a suit of blue
No, no, my charming fair one, no cowardice shall e'er be seen,
For I am son to Grania and I always will adore the green.

It was of a summer's evening, as my love and I sat in a room,
Thinking it was no harm, immediately the guards did come,

It's with their guns the door they broke, the moment that
   my love was seen
He was torn from my arms for wearing of the suit of green.

I was sent for by my master, a man that I did wish to see,
He brought me up to Dublin, the rights of law to give to me,
He brought me to a merchant's shop, the neatest clothes that
   could be seen
Embroidered all with gold lace, he bought for me a suit of green.

I went unto the Colonel, down on my bended knees I fell
Begging your honour's pardon for the story I am going to tell.
You have a clever young man, the bravest boy that e'er was seen
And he lies in cold irons for the wearing of the suit of green.

Pick out six of your best men, to stand before my love and me
A thousand pounds I will lay down, that he will answer
   manfully
He says rise up my blooming girl, your true love I shall set free
I'll restore him to your arms, and give him leave to wear the
   green.

It is now my trial is over, thanks be to God who set me free,
Prosperity attend on him, that has restored my love to me.
It is now I'll wed my Phoenix bright, a faithful girl she proved
   to me,
And she shall have gold ear-rings, and her mantle shall be of
   the green.

25.—THE BOLD BELFAST SHOEMAKER

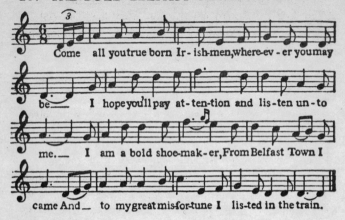

Come all you true born Ir-ish-men, where-ev-er you may
be— I hope you'll pay at-ten-tion and lis-ten un-to
me.— I am a bold shoe-mak-er, From Belfast Town I
came And— to my great mis-for-tune I lis-ted in the train.

I had a fair young sweetheart Jane Wilson was her name
She said it grieved her to the heart to see me in the train.
She told me if I would desert to come and let her know
She would dress me up in her own clothes that I might go
    to and fro.

We marched to Chapelizod like heroes stout and bold.
I'd be no more a slave to them, my officer I told,
For to work upon a Sunday with me did not agree
That was the very time, brave boys, I took my liberty.

When encamped at Tipperary, we soon got his command
For me and for my comrade bold, one night on guard to stand.
The night it was both wet and cold and so we did agree
And on that very night, brave boys, I took my liberty.

The night that I deserted I had no place to stay,
I went into a meadow and lay down in the hay.
It was not long that I lay there until I rose again,
And looking all around me I espied six of the train.

We had a bloody battle but soon I beat them all
And soon the dastard cowards for mercy loud did call.
Saying spare our lives brave Irewin and we will pray for thee,
By all that's fair we will declare for you and liberty.

As for George Clarke of Carrick, I own he's very mean,
For the sake of forty shillings he had me took again
They locked me in a strong room my sorrows to deplore,
With four on every window and six on every door.

I being close confined then I soon looked all around
I leaped out of the window and knocked four of them down
The light horse and the train, my boys, they soon did follow me
But I kept my road before them and preserved my liberty.

I next joined Father Murphy as you will quickly hear
And many a battle did I fight with his brave Shelmaliers.
With 400 of his croppy boys we beat great Lord Mountjoy
And at the battle of New Ross we made 8,000 fly.

I am a bold shoemaker and Irewin is my name
I could beat as many Orangemen as listed in a train;
I could beat as many Orangemen as could stand in a row
I would make them fly before me like an arrow from a bow.

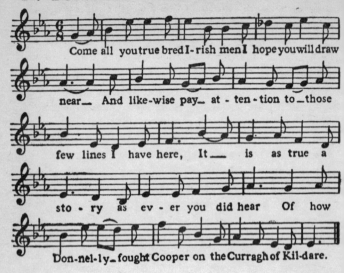

Come all you true bred Irish men I hope you will draw near. And likewise pay attention to those few lines I have here, It is as true a story as ever you did hear Of how Don-nel-ly fought Cooper on the Curragh of Kildare.

It was on the third of June, brave boys, the challenge was sent o'er,
From Britannia to old Grania for to raise her son once more
To renew the satisfaction and the credit to record,
They are all in deep distraction since Daniel conquered all.

Old Grania read the challenge and received it with a smile,
" You'd better haste unto Kildare my well-beloved child,
It is there you'll reign victorious as you often did before;
And your deeds will shine most glorious around sweet Erin's shore."

The challenge was accepted of, those heroes did prepare
To meet brave Captain Kelly on the Curragh of Kildare,
Those Englishmen bet ten to one that day against poor Dan,
Such odds as this could ne'er dismay the blood of an Irishman.

When those two bully champions were stripped off in the ring,
They were then full determined on each other's blood to spill,
From six to nine they parried that time till Donnelly knocked
    him down
Here Grania smiled, " Well done my child, that is 10,000
    pounds."

The second round that Cooper fought he knocked down
    Donnelly
And Dan likewise being of true game, he rose most furiously,
Right active then was Cooper he knocked Donnelly down
    again,
Those Englishmen they gave three cheers saying " The battle
    is all in vain."

Long life to brave Miss Kelly 'tis recorded on the plain,
She boldly stepped into the ring saying, " Dan, what do you
    mean ?
Well done," says she, " brave Donnelly, my Irish boy," said she
"My whole estate I have laid out on you, brave Donnelly."

Then Donnelly rose up again and meeting with great might,
For to stagnate those nobles all, he continued on the fight.
Tho' Cooper stood in his own defence exertion proved in vain,
For he soon received a temple blow that hurled him o'er the
    rails.

You sons of proud Britannia, your boasting now recall,
Since Cooper by Dan Donnelly has met his sad downfall,
In eleven rounds he got nine knock-downs likewise a
    broke jaw-bone,
" Shake hands," said she, " brave Donnelly, the battle is all
    our own."

Come all you warriors and renownèd no-bles, give ear un-to my warlike theme, And I will sing you how Father Mur-phy late-ly a-roused from his sleep-y dream Sure Ju-lius Cae-sar and Al-ex-and-er Nor brave King Ar-thur ev-er equalled him For arm-ies for-mid-a-ble he did con-quer tho' with two gun-men he did be-gin.

Camolin cavalry he did unhorse them,
Their first lieutenant he cut them down,
With shattered ranks, and with broken columns,
They soon returned to Camolin town,
On the hill of Oulart he displayed his valour,
Where a hundred Corkmen lay on the plain
At Enniscorthy his sword he wielded
And I hope to see him once more again,

When Enniscorthy became subject to him,
'Twas then to Wexford we marched our men,
And on the Three Rock took up our quarters,
Waiting for daylight the town to win.
The loyal townsmen gave their assistance
We'll die or conquer, they all did say,
The yeomen cavalry made no resistance,
For on the pavement their corpses lay,

With drums a-beating the town did echo,
And acclamations came from door to door;
On the Windmill Hill we pitched our tents,
And we drank like heroes, but paid no score.
On Carraig Rua for some time we waited,
And next to Gorey we did repair,
At Tubberneering we thought no harm,
The bloody army was waiting there,

The issue of it was a close engagement,
While on the soldiers we played warlike pranks;
Thro' sheepwalks, hedgerows and shady thickets,
There were mangled bodies and broken ranks,
The shuddering cavalry I can't forget them;
We raised the brushes on their helmets straight—
They turned about, and they bid for Dublin,
As if they ran for a ten-pound plate.

Some crossed Donnybrook and more through Blackrock
And some up Shankill without wound or flaw
And if Barry Lawless be not a liar
There's more went groaning up Luggelaw.
To the Windmill Hill of Enniscorthy,
The British Fencibles they fled like deers;
But our ranks were tattered, and sorely scattered,
By the loss of Kyan and the Shelmaleers.

[cont. on p. 207

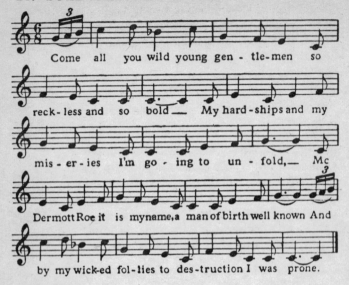

Come all you wild young gen-tle-men so
reck-less and so bold— My hard-ships and my
mis-er-ies I'm go-ing to un-fold,— Mc
Dermott Roe it is my name, a man of birth well known And
by my wick-ed fol-lies to des-truction I was prone.

I headed the Defenders, as their captain 'tis the truth,
In the County of Roscommon I was called the undaunted
youth
One thousand men at my command, no rent I'd let be paid,
For to face an army I was brought, and of them was not afraid.

Part of my men being taken, I swore I'd rescue them with speed,
Like Hector bold I ventured, but in it did not succeed,
I fought as brave as any, till half my face was shot away,
Nor did I turn a traitor, or from my brave boys run away.

So McDermott Roe was taken and laid in Roscommon gaol,
Although my friends were rich and great for me they'd take
no bail,
Twice I was at assizes tried, and each time guilty found,
But yet they dare not hang me for fear of the country round.

There are numbers in the country would shed salt tears for me,
Would venture life and limb to save me from the gallows tree
Farewell dear honoured father, you've thousands lost by me,
Your trouble grieves me more than going to face the gallows tree.

To Dublin I was brought to hang upon the gallows tree,
'Tis little thought I at the time of my nativity,
My father was a gentleman and my mother a lady gay,
One thousand was her fortune upon her wedding day.

There were estated gentlemen, that do belong to me,
And did I lead a sober life it's hanged I ne'er would be,
To back the poor against the rich with them did not agree,
And so McDermott Roe must die in shame and misery.

29.—YOUNG MOLLY BÁN

Come all you young fellows That fol-low the gun
Be-ware of goin' a shoot-in' By the late set-ting sun
It might happen to an-y-one As it hap-pened to me
To shoot your own true love In-un-der a tree.

She was going to her uncle's, when the shower it
came on
She went under a bush, the rain for to shun.
With her apron all around her, I took her for a swan
And I levelled my gun and I shot Molly Bán.

I ran to her uncle's in haste and great fear,
Saying Uncle, dear Uncle, I've shot Molly dear,
With her apron all around her I took her for a swan,
But oh and alas ! it was my Molly Bán.

I shot my own true love—alas I'm undone
While she was in the shade by the setting of the sun
If I thought she was there I'd caress her tenderly,
And soon I'd get married to my own dear Molly.

My curse on you, Toby, that lent me your gun
To go out a-shooting by the late setting sun,
I rubbed her fair temples and found she was dead
A fountain of tears for my Molly I shed.

Up comes my father and his locks they were grey,
Stay in your own country and don't run away,
Stay in your own country till your trial comes on
And I'll see you set free by the laws of the land.

Oh the maids of this country they will all be very glad
When they hear the sad news that my Molly is dead.
Take them all in their hundreds, set them all in a row,
Molly Bán she shone above them like a mountain of snow.

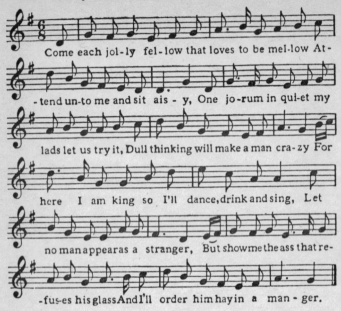

Come each jol-ly fel-low that loves to be mel-low At-tend un-to me and sit ais-y, One jo-rum in qui-et my lads let us try it, Dull thinking will make a man cra-zy For here I am king so I'll dance, drink and sing, Let no man appear as a stranger, But show me the ass that re-fus-es his glass And I'll order him hay in a man-ger.

By ploughing and mowing, by reaping and sowing
Kind nature supplies me with plenty,
I've a cellar well stored and a plentiful board,
And a garden affords every dainty,
Were it not for my seeding you'd have but poor feeding,
You'd surely be starved without me,
I am always content when I pay up my rent,
I am happy when friends are about me.

Draw near to my table, my boys, when you're able,
Let me hear not one word of complaining,
For the jingling of glasses all music surpasses,
I love to see bottles a-draining.

Let the mighty and great roll in splendour and state
I envy them not, I declare it,
I eat my own ham, my own chicken and lamb,
I shear my own fleece, and I wear it.

I have all things in season both woodcock and pheasant,
I am here as a Justice of Quorum,
At my cabin fore-end I've a bed for a friend,
A clear fireside and a jorum;
I've a lawn and I've bowers, I've fruit and I've flowers,
The lark is my morning alarmer,
So jolly boys now, that follow the plough,
Drink life and success to the Farmer.

31.—THE SORROWFUL LAMENT FOR CALLAGHAN, GREALLY AND MULLEN

Killed at the Fair of Turloughmore

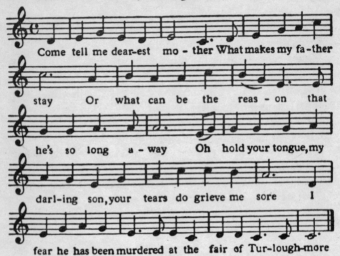

Come tell me dear-est mo - ther What makes my fa-ther
stay Or what can be the reas - on that
he's so long a - way Oh hold your tongue, my
darl-ing son, your tears do grieve me sore I
fear he has been murdered at the fair of Tur-lough-more

Come all you tender Christians I hope you will draw near
It's of this dreadful murder I mean to let you hear;
Concerning those poor people whose loss we do deplore
(The Lord have mercy on their souls) they died at Turloughmore.

'Twas on the first of August the truth I will declare
Those people they assembled that day all at the fair;
But little was their notion what evil was in store
All by the bloody Peelers at the fair of Turloughmore.

Were you to see that dreadful sight 'twould grieve your heart
   I know
To see the comely women and the men all lying low;
God help their tender parents, they will never see them more,
For cruel was their murder at the fair of Turloughmore.

It's for that base bloodthirsty crew remark the word I say
The Lord He will reward them against the Judgment Day,
The blood they've taken innocent for it they'll suffer sore,
And the treatment that they gave to us that day at Turloughmore.

The morning of their trial as they stood up in the dock,
The words they spoke were feeling, the people round them
    flock,
" I tell you, Judge and Jury, the truth I will declare
It was Brew that ordered us to fire, that evening at the fair."

Now to conclude and finish this sad and doleful lay,
I hope their souls are happy against the Judgment Day,
It was little time they got, we know, when they fell like new-
    mown hay,
May the Lord have mercy on their souls against the Judgment-
    Day.

32.—COORTIN' IN THE KITCHEN

Come sin-gle belle and beau To me now pay at-

-ten-tion And love I'll plain-ly show Is the

div-il's own in-ven-tion For once in love I

fell With a maiden's smiles be-witching, Miss

Hen-ri-et-ta Bell Down in Captain Phibbs's kitchen

CHORUS

Ri-tooral oor-al lah Ri-tooral-ooral addy Ri-

-tooral-oor-al lah Ri-tooral-ooral addy.

At the age of seventeen I was tied unto a grocer,
Not far from Stephen's Green, where Miss Bell for tea would
 go, sir.
Her manners were so free, she set my heart a-twitching,
She invited me to tea, down in Captain Phibbs's kitchen.

Next Sunday being the day, we were to have the flare-up,
I dressed myself quite gay, an' I frizz'd and oiled my
 hair up.

As the captain had no wife, he had gone out a-fishin',
So we kicked up high life, below-stairs in the kitchen.

Just as the clock struck six we sat down to the table;
She handed tea and cakes—I ate while I was able.
I ate cakes, drank punch and tea, till my side had got a stitch in,
And the hours flew quick away, while coortin' in the kitchen.

With my arms round her waist I kissed—she hinted marriage—
To the door in dreadful haste came Captain Phibbs's carriage.
Her looks told me full well, that moment she was wishin'
That I'd get out to H——, or somewhere far from the kitchen.

She flew up off my knees, full five feet up or higher,
And over head and heels, threw me slap into the fire.
My new Repealer's coat, that I bought from Mr. Stitchen
With a thirty-shilling note, went to blazes in the kitchen.

I grieved to see my duds, all besmeared with smoke and ashes,
When a tub of dirty suds, right in my face she dashes.
As I lay on the floor still the water she kept pitchin',
Till the footman broke the door, and marched down into the
   kitchen.

When the captain came down stairs, though he seen my
   situation,
In spite of all my prayers I was marched off to the station.
For me they'd take no bail, tho' to get home I was itchin',
But I had to tell the tale, of how I came into the kitchen.

I said she did invite me, but she gave a flat denial,
For assault she did indict me, and I was sent for trial.
She swore I robbed the house in spite of all her screechin'.
So I six months went round the rack for courtin' in the kitchen.

33.—A BALLAD OF MASTER McGRATH

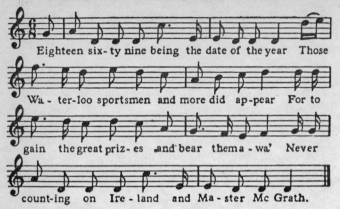

Eighteen six-ty nine being the date of the year Those
Wa-ter-loo sportsmen and more did ap-pear For to
gain the great priz-es and bear them a-wa' Never
count-ing on Ire-land and Ma-ster Mc Grath.

On the 12th of December, that day of renown,
McGrath and his keeper they left Lurgan town;
A gale in the Channel, it soon drove them o'er,
On the thirteenth they landed on fair England's shore.

And when they arrived there in big London Town,
Those great English sportsmen they all gathered round—
And some of the gentlemen gave a " Ha ! Ha ! "
Saying : " Is that the great dog you call Master McGrath ? "

And one of those gentlemen standing around
Says : " I don't care a damn for your Irish greyhound "
And another he laughs with a scornful " Ha ! Ha !
We'll soon humble the pride of your Master McGrath."

Then Lord Lurgan came forward and said : " Gentlemen,
If there's any amongst you has money to spend—
For you nobles of England I don't care a straw—
Here's five thousand to one upon Master McGrath."

Then McGrath he looked up and he wagged his old tail.
Informing his lordship, " I know what you mane,
Don't fear, noble Brownlow, don't fear them, agra,
For I'll tarnish their laurels," says Master McGrath.

And Rose stood uncovered, the great English pride,
Her master and keeper were close by her side;
They have let her away and the crowd cried: " Hurrah!"
For the pride of all England—and Master McGrath.

As Rose and the Master they both ran along.
" Now I wonder," says Rose, " what took you from your
        home;
You should have stopped there in your Irish demesne,
And not come to gain laurels on Albion's plain."

" Well, I know," says McGrath, " we have wild heather bogs
But you'll find in old Ireland there's good men and dogs.
Lead on, bold Britannia, give none of your jaw,
Snuff that up your nostrils," says Master McGrath.

Then the hare she went on just as swift as the wind
He was sometimes before her and sometimes behind,
Rose gave the first turn according to law;
But the second was given by Master McGrath.

The hare she led on with a wonderful view,
And swift as the wind o'er the green field she flew.
But he jumped on her back and he held up his paw
" Three cheers for old Ireland," says Master McGrath.

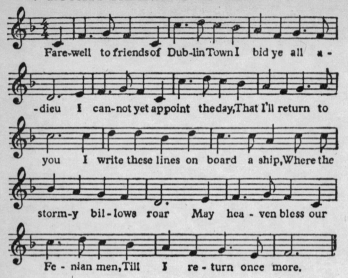

Fare-well to friends of Dub-lin Town I bid ye all a-

-dieu I can-not yet appoint the day, That I'll return to

you I write these lines on board a ship, Where the

storm-y bil-lows roar May hea-ven bless our

Fe - nian men, Till I re - turn once more.

I joined the Fenian Brotherhood
 In the year of Sixty-four,
Resolved to save my native land
 Or perish on the shore;
My friends and me we did agree
 Our native land to save,
And to raise the flag of freedom
 O'er the head of Emmet's grave.

My curse attend those traitors
 Who did our cause betray;
I'd throw a rope around their necks,
 And drown them in the Bay.
There was Nagle, Massey, Corydon,
 And Talbot—he makes four;
Like demons for their thirst of gold,
 They're punished evermore.

Let no man blame the turnkey
  Nor any of the men;
There's no one knows but two of us
  The man who served my friend.
I robbed no man, I spilt no blood,
  Tho' they sent me to jail;
Because I was O'Donovan Rossa,
  And a son of Granuaile.

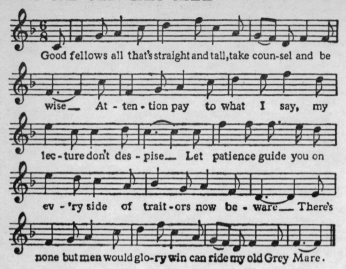

Good fellows all that's straight and tall, take coun-sel and be wise— At - ten - tion pay to what I say, my lec - ture don't des - pise— Let patience guide you on ev - 'ry side of trait - ors now be - ware— There's none but men would glo-ry win can ride my old Grey Mare.

In Erin's Isle in ancient times,
She was rode by Brian Boru,
Phelim O'Neill with sword of steel,
Owen Roe and Sarsfield, too,
Brave Michael Dwyer not long ago
Ranged Wicklow and Kildare
Tone, Tandy, Sheares, and other peers
Rode on my old grey mare.

Brave Bonaparte on her did start
He rode too fast, 'tis true.
She lost a shoe at Moscow fair
And fell lame at Waterloo.
When she comes o'er to Erin's shore,
She'll have good farriers' care
At the very next 'chase she'll win the race,
My sporting old grey mare.

Here's to the man that's six foot one,
And more then if you choose,
That stands up straight without deceit,
In Spanish leather shoes.
Likewise the youth that tells the truth
That he may have Liberty fair
And to every man in Ireland
That rides my old grey mare.

36.—LILLIBULERO

(—) Ho bro-ther Teig, dost hear the de - cree

Lil-li - bu - lè - ro bul-len a la Dat we shall have a

new De-bitt-ie Lilli - bu - lè - ro bul-len a la.

CHORUS

Lè - ro lè - ro lè - ro lè - ro Lil-li - bu - le - ro

bul-len a la Lil-li-bu-lè - ro lè - ro lè - ro

Lil-li - bu - lè - ro bul - len a la.

Ho, by my Soul, it is a Talbot;
Lillibuléro, etc.
And he will cut all de English throat,
Lillibuléro, etc.

Though, by my Soul, de English do prate,
Lillibuléro, etc.
De Law's on dere side and de divil knows what
Lillibuléro, etc.

But if Dispence do come from the Pope,
Lillibuléro, etc.
We'll hang Magna Cart and demselves in a rope,
Lillibuléro, etc.

And the good Talbot is now made a Lord,
 Lillibuléro, etc.
And with his brave lads he's coming aboard,
 Lillibuléro, etc.

Who all in France have taken a swear,
 Lillibuléro, etc.
Dat day will have no Protestant heir.
 Lillibuléro, etc.

O but why does he stay behind?
 Lillibuléro, etc.
Ho, by my Soul, 'tis a Protestant wind,
 Lillibuléro, etc.

Now that Tyrconnel is come a-shore,
 Lillibuléro, etc.
And we shall have Commissions *go leór*,
 Lillibuléro, etc.

And he dat will not go to the Mass,
 Lillibuléro, etc.
Shall be turned out and look like an ass.
 Lillibuléro, etc.

Now, now de hereticks all will go down,
 Lillibuléro, etc.
By Christ and St. Patrick the nation's our own.
 Lillibuléro, etc.

Dere was an old prophecy found in a bog,
 Lillibuléro, etc.
Dat our land would be ruled by an ass and a dog.
 Lillibuléro, etc.

So now dis old Prophecy's coming to pass,
 Lillibuléro bullen a la,
For James is de dog and Tyrconnel's de ass.
 Lillibuléro, etc.

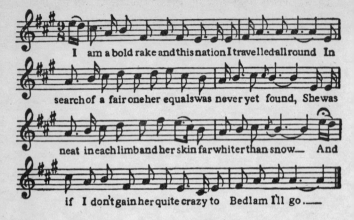

I am a bold rake and this nation I travelled all round In search of a fair one her equals was never yet found, She was neat in each limb and her skin far whiter than snow— And if I don't gain her quite crazy to Bedlam I'll go.—

One fine summer's morning to Culgreany chapel I strayed,
Where I fell a courting this innocent harmless maid,
She was so fair a creature, that I could her senses beguile,
I took her in my arms saying, " Darling, don't leave me
behind."

That very night up to the town of Roscrea we did stray
And the night after that in the sweet town of Thurles
we lay;
When her money was out it was then she began to condole
And I said, " My sweet fair maid, it's better to part and
go home."

" O Johnny, if you leave me, that the great God may pity
my moan,
How could you deceive me and bring me so far from my
home
You promised to marry me and never to alter your mind,
That you'd wed lovely Sally and leave other sweethearts
behind."

" Indeed if I said it I'm sure it was far from my heart,
To wed lovely Sally and all other maids for to part,
Let this be a warning to all other maids of your kind,
To beware of a rake or a rambler will leave you behind.

I will go to my clergy and tell him the bad life I led,
Hoping for pardon for never with you could I wed,
And if he forgives me I'll lead a correct sober life,
I ll go home to Longacre and live with my own lawful wife."

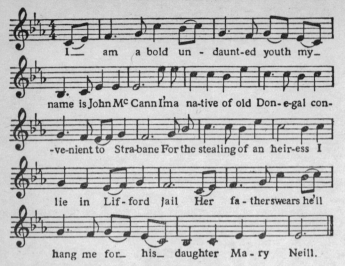

I— am a bold un-daunt-ed youth my—
name is John McCann I'm a na-tive of old Don-e-gal con-
-ve-nient to Stra-bane For the stealing of an heir-ess I
lie in Lif-ford Jail Her fa-ther swears he'll
hang me for— his— daughter Ma-ry Neill.

Whilst I lay in cold irons, my love she came to me:
"Don't fear my father's anger, for I will set you free."
Her father soon gave his consent to let me out on bail,
And I was to stand my trial for his daughter Mary Neill.

Her father kept her close confined, for fear I should her see,
And on my trial day, my prosecutor was to be;
But like a loyal lover, to appear she did not fail,
She freed me from all dangers; she's my charming Mary Neill.

With wrath and indignation, her father loud did call,
And when my trial was over, I approached the garden wall,
My well-known voice soon reached her ears, which echoed hill
    and dale,
"You're welcome here, my Johnny dear," says charming
    Mary Neill.

We both sat on a sunny bank, and there we talked awhile.
I says, "My dear, if you will comply, I'll free you from exile.

The *Shamrock* now is ready from Derry to set sail;
So come with me, off to Quebec, my charming Mary Neill."

She gave consent, and back she went, and stole the best of clothes,
And to nobody in the house her secret she made known;
Five hundred pounds of ready gold from her father she did steal,
And that was twice I did elope with charming Mary Neill.

Our coach it was got ready to Derry for to go,
And there we bribed the coachman for to let no one know;
He said he would keep secret, and never would reveal.
So off to Derry then I went with charming Mary Neill.

It was to Captain Nelson our passage money paid,
And in the town of Derry it was under cover laid.
We joined our hands in wedlock bands before we did set sail.
And her father's wrath, I value not—I love my Mary Neill.

It was o'er the proud and swelling seas our ship did gently glide,
And on our passage to Quebec, six weeks a matchless tide;
Until we came to Whitehead Beach we had no cause to wail,
On Crossford Bay I thought that day I lost my Mary Neill.

On the ninth of June, in the afternoon, a heavy fog came on;
The captain cries, " Look out, my boys ! I fear we are all gone."
Our vessel on a sandy bank was driven by a gale,
And forty were washed overboard, along with Mary Neill.

With the help of boats and the ship's crew, five hundred they
       were saved,
And forty more of them also have met a watery grave.
I soon espied her yellow locks come floating down the waves:
I jumped into the boiling deep and saved my Mary Neill.

Her father wrote a letter as you may understand,
That if I would go back again he would give me all his land.
I wrote him back an answer, and said that without fail,
" I am the heir of your whole estate, by your daughter
       Mary Neill."

39.—THE HACKLER FROM GROUSE HALL

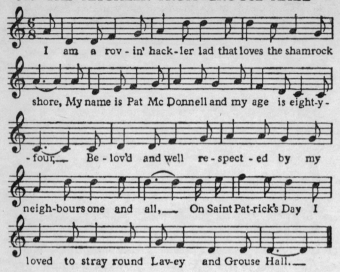

I am a rov-in' hack-ler lad that loves the shamrock shore, My name is Pat Mc Donnell and my age is eight-y-four. Be-lov'd and well re-spect-ed by my neigh-bours one and all, On Saint Pat-rick's Day I loved to stray round Lav-ey and Grouse Hall.

When I was young I danced and sung and drank good
    whiskey, too,
Each shebeen shop that sold a drop of the real old mountain dew
With the poteen still on every hill the peelers had no call
Round sweet Stradone I am well known, round Lavey and
    Grouse Hall.

I rambled round from town to town for hackling was my trade
None can deny I think that I an honest living made
Where'ere I'd stay by night or day the youth would always call
To have some crack with Paddy Jack the Hackler from
    Grouse Hall.

I think it strange how times have changed so very much of late
Coercion now is all the row and Peelers on their bate
To take a glass is now alas the greatest crime of all
Since Balfour placed that hungry beast the Sergeant of
    Grouse Hall.

The busy tool of Castle rule he travels night and day
He'll seize a goat just by the throat for want of better prey
The nasty skunk he'll swear you're drunk tho' you took none
    at all
There is no peace about the place since he came to Grouse
    Hall.

'Twas on pretence of this offence he dragged me off to jail
Alone to dwell in a cold cell my fate for to bewail;
My hoary head on a plank bed such wrongs for vengeance call
He'll rue the day he dragged away the Hackler from Grouse
    Hall.

He haunts the League, just like a plague, and shame for
    to relate
The Priest can't be on Sunday free the Mass to celebrate;
It's there he'll kneel encased in steel prepared on duty's call
For to assail and drag to jail our clergy from Grouse Hall.

Down into hell he'd run pelmell to hunt for poteen there
And won't be loth to swear an oath 'twas found in Killinkere.
He'll search your bed from foot to head, sheets, blankets, tick
    and all
Your wife undressed must leave the nest for Jemmy of Grouse
    Hall.

He fixed a plan for that poor man who had a handsome wife
To take away without delay her liberty and life
He'd swear quite plain that he's insane and got no sense at all
As he has done of late with one convenient to Grouse Hall.

His raid on dogs I'm sure it flogs it's shocking to behold
How he'll pull up a six-month's pup and swear it's a two-
    year old;
Outside of hell a parallel can't be found for him at all
For that vile pimp and devil's imp the ruler of Grouse Hall.

[cont. on p. 207/9

40.—DUBLIN JACK OF ALL TRADES

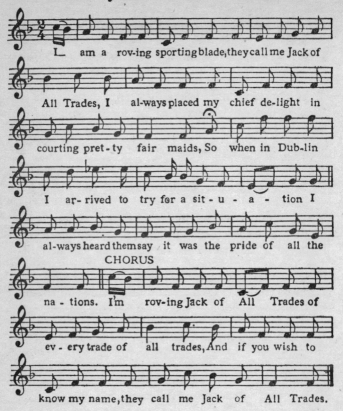

I am a rov-ing sporting blade, they call me Jack of All Trades, I al-ways placed my chief de-light in courting pret-ty fair maids, So when in Dub-lin I ar-rived to try for a sit-u-a-tion I al-ways heard them say it was the pride of all the na-tions.

CHORUS

I'm rov-ing Jack of All Trades of ev-ery trade of all trades, And if you wish to know my name, they call me Jack of All Trades.

On George's Quay I first began and there became a porter,
Me and my master soon fell out which cut my acquaintance
shorter
In Sackville Street a pastry cook—in James's Street a baker,
In Cook Street I did coffins make, in Eustace Street a preacher.

In Baggot Street I drove a cab and there was well requited,
In Francis Street had lodging beds to entertain all strangers.

For Dublin is of high renown or I am much mistaken,
In Kevin Street I do declare sold butter, eggs and bacon.

In Golden Lane I sold old shoes—in Meath Street was a grinder
In Barrack Street I lost my wife—I'm glad I ne'er could find her,
In Mary's Lane I've dyed old clothes of which I've often boasted
In that noted place Exchequer Street sold mutton ready roasted.

In Temple Bar I dressed old hats, in Thomas Street a sawyer,
In Pill Lane I sold the plate—in Green Street an honest lawyer.
In Plunkett Street I sold cast clothes—in Bride's Alley a broker,
In Charles Street I had a shop, sold shovel, tongs and poker.

In College Green a banker was—and in Smithfield a drover,
In Britain Street a waiter and in George's Street a glover,
On Ormond Quay I sold old books—in King Street a nailer,
In Townsend Street a carpenter and in Ringsend a sailor.

In Cole's Lane a jobbing butcher—in Dame Street a tailor,
In Moore Street a chandler and on the Coombe a weaver.
In Church Street I sold old ropes—on Redmond's Hill a draper,
In Mary Street sold 'bacco pipes—in Bishop Street a Quaker.

In Peter Street I was a quack—in Greek Street a grainer,
On the harbour I did carry sacks, in Werburgh Street a glazier,
In Mud Island was a dairyboy where I became a scooper,
In Capel Street a barber's clerk—in Abbey Street a cooper.

In Liffey Street had furniture with fleas and bugs I sold it,
And at the Bank a big placard I often stood to hold it.
In New Street I sold hay and straw and in Spitalfields made
    bacon,
In FishambleStreet was at the grand old trade of basketmaking.

In Summerhill a coachmaker, in Denzille Street a gilder,
In Cork Street was a tanner—in Brunswick Street a builder,
In High Street I sold hosiery, in Patrick Street sold all blades,
So if you wish to know my name they call me Jack of all trades.

I am a ram-blin' hay-ro, and by love I— am be-trayed, Near to the town of— Balt-inglass, there dwells a love-ly— maid, She's fair-er than Hy-pa-tia bright, and she's free from earthly— pride. She's a dar-lin' mald, her dwell-in' place is— down by the tan-yard side.

Her lovely hair in ringlets rare lies on her snow-white neck,
And the tender glances of her eyes would save a ship from
wreck
Her two red lips so smiling and her teeth so pearly white
Would make a man become her slave down by the Tanyard
side.

I courteously saluted her and I viewed her o'er and o'er,
And I said, " Are you Aurora bright descending here
below ? "
" Oh, no, kind sir, I'm a maiden poor," she modestly
replied,
" And I daily labour for my bread down by the Tanyard
side."

So for twelve long years I courted her till at length we did agree
For to acquaint her parents and married we should be.
But 'twas then her cruel father to me proved most unkind
Which makes me sail across the sea and leave my love behind.

Farewell, my aged parents, to you I bid adieu.
I'm crossing the main ocean all for the sake of you.
But whenever I return again I will make her my bride
And I'll roll her in my arms down by the Tanyard side.

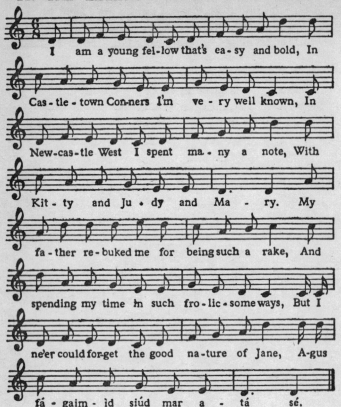

I am a young fellow that's easy and bold, In Castletown Conners I'm very well known, In Newcastle West I spent many a note, With Kitty and Judy and Mary. My father rebuked me for being such a rake, And spending my time in such frolicsome ways, But I ne'er could forget the good nature of Jane, A-gus fágaimíd siúd mar a tá sé.

My parents had rear'd me to shake and to mow,
To plough and to harrow to reap and to sow.
But my heart being too airy to drop it so low
I set out on a high speculation
On paper and parchment they taught me to write
In Euclid and Grammar they opened my eyes
And in multiplication in truth I was bright.
　　Agus fágaimid siúd mar atá sé.

If I chance for to go to the town of Rathkeal
The girls all round me do flock on the square
Some give me a bottle and others sweet cakes
To treat me unknown to their parents.
There is one from Askeaton and one from the Pike
Another from Arda my heart has beguiled
Tho' being from the mountains her stockings are white
    Agus fágaimid siúd mar atá sé.

To quarrel for riches I ne'er was inclin'd
For the greatest of misers must leave them behind
I'll purchase a cow that will never run dry
And I'll milk her by twisting her horn.
John Damer of Shronel had plenty of gold
And Devonshire's treasure is twenty times more
But he's laid on his back among nettles and stones
    Agus fágaimid siúd mar atá sé.

This cow can be milked without clover or grass
For she's pamper'd with corn, good barley and hops
She's warm and stout, and she's free in her paps
And she'll milk without spancel or halter.
The man that will drink it will cock his caubeen
And if any one cough there'll be wigs on the green
And the feeble old hag will get supple and free
    Agus fágaimid siúd mar atá sé.

If I chance for to go to the market of Croom
With a cock in my hat and my pipes in full tune
I am welcome at once and brought up to a room
Where Bacchus is sporting with Vénus
There's Peggy and Jane from the town of Bruree
And Biddy from Bruff and we all on the spree
Such a combing of locks as there was about me
    Agus fágaimid siúd mar atá sé.

[cont. on p. 210

43.—THE LUCKY ELOPEMENT

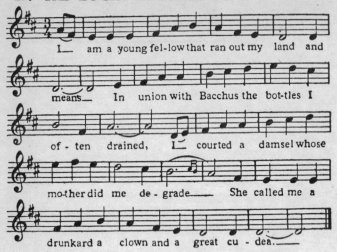

I am a young fel-low that ran out my land and means— In union with Bacchus the bot-tles I of-ten drained, I courted a damsel whose mo-ther did me de-grade— She called me a drunkard a clown and a great cu-dea.—

When I was offended I bid the old dame good-bye
I winked at the daughter who gave me the same reply
I told her in private to meet me in Mohill fair
And she never drew back till we met about noon next day.

My love was so loyal and came with such noble speed,
The moment I met her I told her to mount the steed,
The day being advanc'd and we having time to spare
That she reach'd me a bottle and told me to have a drain.

When we finished the bottle to Carrick we made our way
We call'd to an inn where our dinner got no delay
A steak on the pan and we drank so much Congo tea
That our slumbers were restless until the first dawn of day.

Next day when we started by auction I sold my mare;
We took an excursion to Ballysodare by train.
In a second-class carriage my lover and I engaged
And the steam was so pushing I thought she could fly
   to Spain.

One night on my pillow I dreamt that we both were seized.
It was then I consulted my lover to cross the sea.
Our ship she weighed anchor from Sligo we both set sail
And we dreaded no storm whilst Neptune did rule the waves.

When we reached up to London we thought we were mighty safe,
When a pair of policemen on Peggy and I did gaze
They gave our description and the colour of both our hair,
For our warrant was issued by telegraph news that day.

When we were detected they brought us before the mayor
He signed our committal and sent us to Carrick Jail
Her mother then swore that I was both a fool and knave
That I spoiled her young daughter and stole all her gold away.

The bench was consulting, her mother no more could say,
They called on the daughter to know what on me she'd swear
She said that I was a most loving genteel young swain
That's able and willing to work for her night and day.

When I was acquitted my lover I did embrace
We went to the clergy who joined us in love and peace.
We gave him three guineas to join us in wedlock bands,
And we're living near Carrick as happy as days are long.

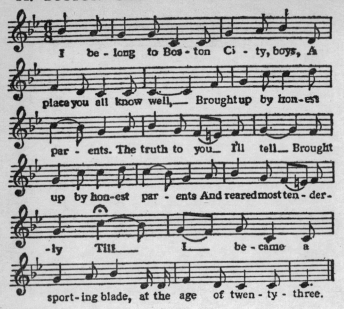

I be-long to Bos-ton Ci-ty, boys, A place you all know well,— Brought up by hon-est par-ents. The truth to you— I'll tell— Brought up by hon-est par-ents And reared most ten-der--ly Till— I— be-came a sport-ing blade, at the age of twen-ty-three.

My chárácter it was taken,
And I was sent to jail,
My parents thought to bail me out,
But they found it all in vain;
The jury found me guilty,
And the clerk he wrote it down,
The judge he passed my sentence,
And I was sent to Charlestown.

I see my aged Father,
And he standing by the Bar,
Likewise my aged Mother,
And she tearing of her hair,

The tearing of her old grey locks,
And the tears came mingled down,
Saying, " John my son, what have you done,
That you're bound for Charlestown."

There's a girl in Boston City, boys,
A place you all know well,
And if e'er I get my liberty,
It's with her I will dwell,
If e'er I get my liberty,
Bad company I will shun,
The robbing of the Munster Bank,
And the drinking of rum.

You lads that are at liberty
Should keep it while you can,
Don't roam the street by night or day,
Or break the laws of man.
For if you do you're sure to rue,
And become a lad like me,
A serving up your twenty-one years
In the Royal Artillery.

[See Appendix, p. 210

45.—A NEW SONG CALLED THE YOUNG MAID'S LOVE

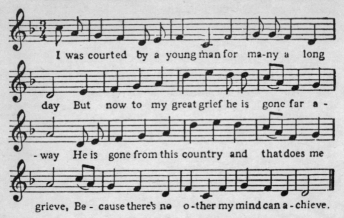

I was courted by a young man for ma-ny a long day But now to my great grief he is gone far a-way He is gone from this country and that does me grieve, Be-cause there's no o-ther my mind can a-chieve.

O how came I to court him, ye powers let me know,
Like the great Alexander for my love's sake I'll go ;
Like a pilgrim to wander in search of my dear
King Cupid direct me my love's course to steer.

His father being a rich merchant of wealth and renown,
He purchased ten hundred acres of land near the town,
But I a poor weaver of a low degree,
I courted his daughter and she did love me.

It was down in a room all alone as we sat,
Still thinking on love, 'tis not easy forgot ;
For love is a root that's well-grounded in my heart,
It's a pleasure to meet but great sorrow to part.

Some marry for riches but it often brings woe,
Others for beauty—for my love's sake I'll go,
But if I ever marry I'll marry for love,
And I'll be as true as the sweet turtle dove.

It's I got an order for to be transported,
And was straightway sent on board of a great man-of-war,
To become a sailor and plough the raging main,
Farewell, dear Eliza, will we never meet again.

Now to conclude and to finish my song,
I hope to get married and that before long,
For I have a spirit above my degree,
I'd scorn to love any that would not love me.

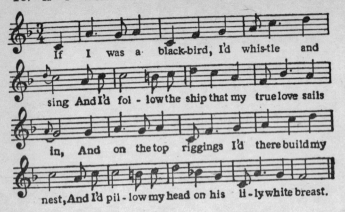

If I was a black-bird, I'd whis-tle and sing And I'd fol-low the ship that my true love sails in, And on the top riggings I'd there build my nest, And I'd pil-low my head on his li-ly white breast.

I am a young maiden and my story is sad
For once I was courted by a brave sailor lad.
He courted me strongly by night and by day,
But now my dear sailor is gone far away.

(Chorus).

He promised to take me to Donnybrook fair
To buy me red ribbons to bind up my hair.
And when he'd return from the ocean so wide,
He'd take me and make me his own loving bride.

(Chorus).

His parents they slight me and will not agree
That I and my sailor boy married should be.
But when he comes home I will greet him with joy
And I'll take to my bosom my dear sailor boy.

(Chorus).

I'm a stranger to this country From A-meri-ca I came, There is few in it knows me or can tell my name, It's here in this coun-try I will tar-ry a-while For my true love I will wan-der a-ma-ny a long mile.

"Some says I'm foolish and more says I'm wise
And more says I'm guilty fair maids to beguile.
But to make them all liars let you come along with me
To the shores of America, my true love," says he.

If I would leave my parents and go along with you
My friends would be afraid that you would not prove true;
I will leave all my sweethearts and comrades behind
And to sail to America it is my design.

That the moon it may darken and show no more light
The day I'd be false to my own heart's delight;
In the middle of the ocean may there grow a willow tree
The hour I prove false to the maid that loves me.

Bring my love to Susanna she's the girl I adore,
And my love to Sally although she is poor;
But I have got Mary, she's my joy and heart's delight
I would roll her in my arms on a cold winter's night.

The ships are on the ocean just ready for to sail
I wish her safe landed with a sweet and pleasant gale;
And when that we are landed we will sit down and sing
In that beautiful country where no dangers can bring.

So now we are landed and married we be—
We will live in contentment and sweet unity;
Here's a health to old Ireland, that runs in my mind,
And to all my true-lovers I have left behind.

In comes the captain's daughter, the captain of the yeos Saying "Brave U-ni-ted Ir-ish-men, we'll ne'er a-gain be foes. A thousand pounds I'll give you and fly from home with thee I'll dress myself in man's at-tire and fight for lib-er-ty.

CHORUS

We are the Boys of Wexford who fought with heart and hand, To burst in twain the gall-ing chain and free our na-tive land.

And when we left our cabins, boys,
   We left with right good will,
To see our friends and neighbours
   That were at Vinegar Hill !
A young man from our ranks,
   A cannon he let go ;
He slapt it into Lord Mountjoy—
   A tyrant he laid low !

            Chorus.

We bravely fought and conquered
  At Ross, and Wexford town;
And, if we failed to keep them,
  'Twas drink that brought us down,
We had no drink beside us
  On Tubberneering's day,
Depending on the long bright pike,
  And well it worked its way!

Chorus

They came into the country
  Our blood to waste and spill;
But let them weep for Wexford,
  And think of Oulart Hill!
'Twas drink that still betrayed us—
  Of them we had no fear;
For every man could do his part
  Like Forth and Shelmalier!

Chorus

My curse upon all drinking!
  It made our hearts full sore;
For bravery won each battle,
  But drink lost evermore;
And if, for want of leaders,
  We lost at Vinegar Hill,
We're ready for another fight,
  And love our country still!

Chorus

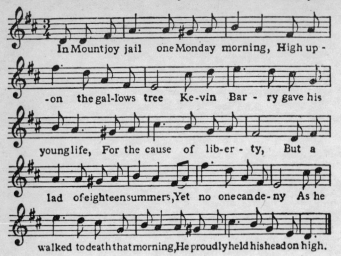

In Mountjoy jail one Monday morning, High up-on the gal-lows tree Ke-vin Bar-ry gave his young life, For the cause of lib-er-ty, But a lad of eighteen summers, Yet no one can de-ny As he walked to death that morning, He proudly held his head on high.

Just before he faced the hangman,
  In his dreary prison cell,
British soldiers tortured Barry,
  Just because he would not tell
The names of his brave companions,
  And other things they wished to know,
" Turn informer or we'll kill you,"
  Kevin Barry answered " No."

Calmly standing to ' attention,'
  While he bade his last farewell
To his broken-hearted mother,
  Whose grief no one can tell.
For the cause he proudly cherished,
  This sad parting had to be ;
Then to death walked softly smiling,
  That old Ireland might be free.

Another martyr for old Ireland,
   Another murder for the crown,
Whose brutal laws may kill the Irish,
   But can't keep their spirit down.
Lads like Barry are no cowards,
   From the foe they will not fly,
Lads like Barry will free Ireland,
   For her sake they'll live and die.

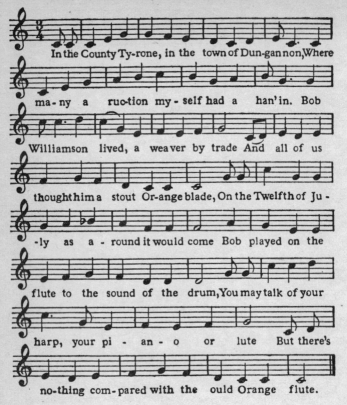

In the County Ty-rone, in the town of Dun-gan non, Where ma-ny a ruc-tion my-self had a han' in. Bob Williamson lived, a weaver by trade And all of us thought him a stout Or-ange blade, On the Twelfth of Ju-ly as a-round it would come Bob played on the flute to the sound of the drum, You may talk of your harp, your pi-an-o or lute But there's no-thing com-pared with the ould Orange flute.

But Bob the deceiver he took us all in,
For he married a Papish called Brigid McGinn,
Turned Papish himself, and forsook the old cause
That gave us our freedom, religion, and laws.
Now the boys of the place made some comment upon it,
And Bob had to fly to the Province of Connacht
He fled with his wife and his fixings to boot,
And along with the latter his old Orange flute.

At the chapel on Sundays, to atone for past deeds,
He said *Paters* and *Aves* and counted his beads,
Till after some time, at the priest's own desire,
He went with his old flute to play in the choir.
He went with his old flute to play for the Mass,
And the instrument shivered, and sighed: "Oh, alas!"
And blow as he would, though it made a great noise,
The flute would play only "The Protestant Boys."

Bob jumped, and he started, and got in a flutter,
And threw his old flute in the blest Holy Water;
He thought that this charm would bring some other sound
When he blew it again, it played "Croppies lie down";
And for all he could whistle, and finger, and blow,
To play Papish music he found it no go;
"Kick the Pope," "The Boyne Water," it freely would
    sound,
But one Papish squeak in it couldn't be found.

At a council of priests that was held the next day,
They decided to banish the old flute away
For they couldn't knock heresy out of its head
And they bought Bob a new one to play in its stead.
So the old flute was doomed and its fate was pathetic,
'Twas fastened and burned at the stake as heretic,
While the flames roared around it they heard a strange
    noise—
'Twas the old flute still whistling "The Protestant Boys."

51.—THE ROCKY ROAD TO DUBLIN

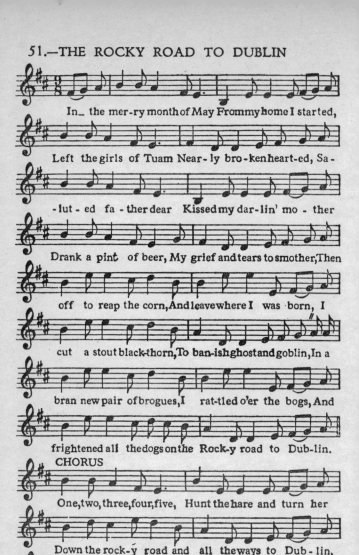

In_ the mer-ry month of May From my home I started,

Left the girls of Tuam Near-ly bro-ken heart-ed, Sa-

-lut-ed fa-ther dear Kissed my dar-lin' mo-ther

Drank a pint of beer, My grief and tears to smother, Then

off to reap the corn, And leave where I was born, I

cut a stout black-thorn, To ban-ish ghost and goblin, In a

bran new pair of brogues, I rat-tled o'er the bogs, And

frightened all the dogs on the Rock-y road to Dub-lin.

CHORUS

One, two, three, four, five, Hunt the hare and turn her

Down the rock-y road and all the ways to Dub-lin,

Whack - fol - lol - de - ra.

In Mullingar that night I rested limbs so weary,
Started by daylight next mornin' light and airy,
Took a drop of the pure, to keep my heart from sinkin',
That's an Irishman's cure, whene'er he's on for drinking.
To see the lasses smile, laughing all the while,
At my curious style, 'twould set your heart a-bubblin'.
They ax'd if I was hired, the wages I required,
Till I was almost tired of the rocky road to Dublin.

In Dublin next arrived, I thought it such a pity,
To be so soon deprived a view of that fine city.
Then I took a stroll all among the quality,
My bundle it was stole in a neat locality;
Something crossed my mind, then I looked behind
No bundle could I find upon my stick a wobblin'.
Enquirin' for the rogue, they said my Connacht brogue,
Wasn't much in vogue on the rocky road to Dublin.

From there I got away, my spirits never failin'
Landed on the quay as the ship was sailin';
Captain at me roared, said that no room had he,
When I jumped aboard, a cabin found for Paddy,
Down among the pigs; I played some funny rigs,
Danced some hearty jigs, the water round me bubblin'
When off Holyhead, I wished myself was dead,
Or better far instead, on the rocky road to Dublin.

The boys of Liverpool, when we safely landed,
Called myself a fool, I could no longer stand it;
Blood began to boil, temper I was losin'
Poor ould Erin's isle they began abusin',
" Hurrah my soul," sez I, my shillelagh I let fly;
Some Galway boys were by, saw I was a hobble in,
Then with a loud hurray, they joined in the affray.
We quickly cleared the way, for the rocky road to Dublin.

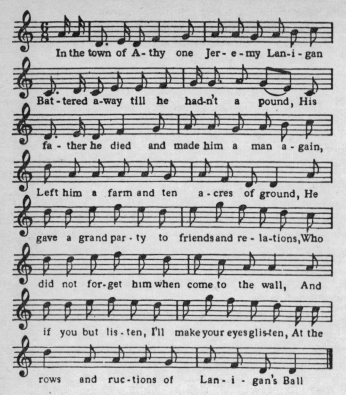

In the town of A-thy one Jer-e-my Lan-i-gan
Bat-tered a-way till he had-n't a pound, His
fa-ther he died and made him a man a-gain,
Left him a farm and ten a-cres of ground, He
gave a grand par-ty to friends and re-la-tions, Who
did not for-get him when come to the wall, And
if you but lis-ten, I'll make your eyes glis-ten, At the
rows and ruc-tions of Lan-i-gan's Ball

Myself to be sure got free invitations,
For all the nice girls and boys I might ask.
And just in a minute both friends and relations,
Were dancing as merry as bees round a cask.
Miss Judy O'Daly that nice little milliner,
Tipped me the wink for to give her a call
And soon I arrived with Peggy McGilligan,
Just in time for Lanigan's ball.

There was lashings of punch and wine for the ladies
Potatoes and cakes there was bacon and tea,
There were the Nolans, Dolans, O'Gradys
Courting the girls and dancing away
The songs they went round as plenty as water,
From the Harp that once sounded in Tara's old Hall,
To sweet Nelly Gray and the Rat-catcher's daughter,
All singing together at Lanigan's ball.

They were doing all kinds of nonsensical polkas
All round the room in a whirligig,
But Julia and I soon banished their nonsense.
And tipped them a twist of a real Irish jig.
Och mavrone, how the girls they got mad on me
And danced till you'd think the ceilings would fall,
For I spent three weeks at Brooks's Academy,
Learning steps for Lanigan's ball.

The boys were as merry the girls all hearty.
Dancing away in couples and groups
Till an accident happened young Terence Macarthy,
He put his right leg through Miss Finerty's hoops.
The creature she fainted and cried " Meelia murther"
Called for her brothers and gathered them all
Carmody swore that he'd go no further
Till he'd have satisfaction at Lanigan's ball.

In the midst of the row Miss Kerrigan fainted
Her cheeks at the same time as red as the rose,
Some of the lads decreed she was painted,
She took a small drop too much I suppose,
Her sweetheart Ned Morgan so powerful and able
When he saw his fair colleen stretched by the wall,
He tore the left leg from under the table,
And smashed all the chaneys at Lanigan's ball.

[cont. on p. 211

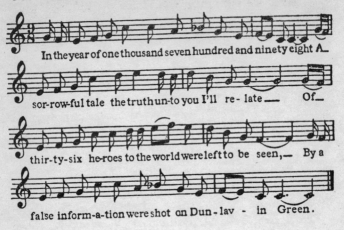

In the year of one thousand seven hundred and ninety eight A sor-row-ful tale the truth un-to you I'll re-late — Of thir-ty-six he-roes to the world were left to be seen, — By a false inform-a-tion were shot on Dun-lav-in Green.

Bad luck to you, Saunders, for you did their lives betray;
You said a parade would be held on that very day,
Our drums they did rattle—our fifes they did sweetly play;
Surrounded we were and privately marched away.

Quite easy they led us as prisoners through the town,
To be slaughtered on the plain, we then were forced to kneel
     down,
Such grief and such sorrow were never before there seen,
When the blood ran in streams down the dykes of Dunlavin
     Green.

There is young Matty Farrell, has plenty of cause to
     complain,
Also the two Duffys, who were shot down on the plain,
And young Andy Ryan, his mother distracted will run
For her own brave boy, her beloved eldest son.

Bad luck to you, Saunders, bad luck may you never shun !
That the widow's curse may melt you like snow in the sun,
The cries of the orphans whose murmurs you cannot screen,
For the murder of their dear fathers, on Dunlavin Green.

Some of our boys to the hills they are going away,
Some of them are shot, and some of them going to sea,
Micky Dwyer in the mountains to Saunders he owes a spleen,
For his loyal brothers, who were shot on Dunlavin Green.

[See Appendix p. 212

Is it true that the women are worse than the men
Right fol right fol tid-dy fol lay Is it
true that the women are worse than the men, That they
went down to hell and were thrown out a-gain, With your
right fol-lol tid-dy fol lol
Fol-the-dol-lol-the-dol, lol-the-dol-lay.

Now there was an old man lived at Kellyburn braes
And he had a wife was the plague of his days.

The divil he came to the man at the plough,
Saying, " One of your family I must take now."

Said he, " My good man, I've come for your wife,
For I hear she's the plague and torment of your life."

So the divil he hoisted her up on his back,
And landed at Hell's hall-door with a crack.

There were two little divils a playing with chains,
She upp'd with her stick, and knocked out their brains.

There were two other divils looked over the wall
They said, " Take her away or she'll murder us all."

So the divil he hoisted her up on his back,
And back to the old man hurried the pack.

They were seven years going and nine coming back,
Yet she asked for the scrapings she left in the pot.

Said he, " My good man, here's your wife back again,
For she wouldn't be kept, not even in Hell !

Now, I've been a divil the most of my life,
But I ne'er was in Hell till I met with your wife."

So it's true that the women are worse than the men,
For they went down to Hell and were threw out again.

55.—LOVELY WILLIE

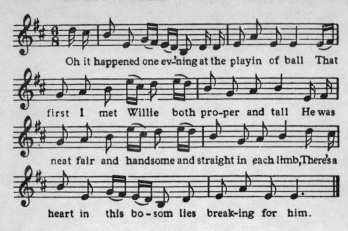

Oh it happened one ev-'ning at the playin of ball That
first I met Willie both pro-per and tall He was
neat fair and handsome and straight in each limb, There's a
heart in this bo-som lies break-ing for him.

" Oh will you go with me a short piece of the road
To see my father's dwelling and place of abode ? "
He knew by her look and her languishing eye
That he was the young man she valued most high.

" There's a place in my father's garden, lovely Willie," said she
" Where lords, dukes and earls they wait upon me,
But when they are sleeping in their long silent rest,
I'll go with you, lovely Willie, you're the boy I love best."

Her father being listening in ambush he lay,
To hear those fond words these young lovers did say,
Then with a sharp rapier he pierced her love through,
And the innocent blood of her darling he drew.

The grave was made ready, lovely Willie laid in,
The Mass it was chanted to cleanse his soul from sin.
And its " Oh, honoured father you may talk as you will
But the innocent blood of my love you did spill."

" And I shall go off to some far counterie,
  Where I shall know no one and no one know me
  And there I shall wander till I close my eyes in death
  For you, lovely Willie, you're the boy I love best "

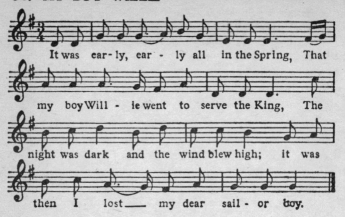

It was ear-ly, ear-ly all in the Spring, That my boy Will-ie went to serve the King, The night was dark and the wind blew high; it was then I lost my dear sail-or boy.

The night is long and I can find no rest,
The thought of Willie runs in my breast,
I'll search the green woods and village wide,
Still hoping my true love to find.

" Oh, father, father, give me a boat,
Out on the ocean that I may float,
To watch the big boats as they pass by,
That I might enquire for my sailor boy."

She was not long out upon the deep,
When a man-o'-war vessel she chanced to meet,
Saying, " Captain, captain, now tell me true,
If my boy Willie is on board with you."

" What sort of a boy is your Willie dear,
Or what sort of a suit does your Willie wear ? "
" He wears a suit of the royal blue,
And you'll easy know him for his heart is true."

" Oh, then your boy Willie, I am sorry to say,
Has just been drownéd the other day,
On yon green island that we pass by,
'Twas there we laid your poor sailor boy."

She wrung her hands and she tore her hair,
And she sobbed and sighed in her despair,
And with every sob she let fall a tear,
And every sigh was for her Willie dear.

" O, father, make my grave both wide and deep,
With a fine tombstone at my head and feet;
And in the middle a turtle dove
That the world may know that I died of love."

Come all you sailors who sail along
And all you boatmen who follow on.
From the cabin-boy to the mainmast high
Ye must mourn in black for my sailor boy.

It was on a fine summer's morning When the birds sweetly tuned on each bow, I heard a fair maid sing most charming As she sat a-milk-ing her cow; Her voice it was chant-ing mel-o-dious, She left me scarce a-ble to go, My heart it is sooth-ed in so-lace, My cai-lín deas crúite na mbó.

With courtesy I did salute her,
"Good morrow most amiable maid,
I'm your captive slave for the future."
"Kind sir, do not banter," she said,
"I'm not such a precious rare jewel,
That I should enamour you so,
I am but a plain country girl,"
Says Cailín deas crúite na mBó.

" The Indies afford no such jewels,
  So precious and transparently fair,
  Oh ! do not to my flame add fuel,
  But consent for to love me my dear,
  Take pity and grant my desire,
  And leave me no longer in woe,
  Oh ! love me or else I'll expire,
  Sweet Cailín deas crúite na mBó.

" Or had I the wealth of great Damer,
  Or all on the African shore,
  Or had I great Devonshire treasure,
  Or had I ten thousand times more,
  Or had I the lamp of Alladin,
  Or had I his genie also,
  I'd rather live poor on a mountain,
  With Cailín deas crúite na mBó."

" I beg you'll withdraw and don't tease me
  I cannot consent unto thee,
  I like to live single and airy,
  Till more of the world I do see,
  New cares they would me embarass
  Besides, sir, my fortune is low,
  Until I get rich I'll not marry,"
  Says Cailín deas crúite na mBó.

" An old maid is like an old almanack,
  Quite useless when once out of date,
  If her ware is not sold in the morning
  At noon it must fall to low rate,
  The fragrance of May is soon over,
  The rose loses its beauty you know,
  All bloom is consumed in October,
  Sweet Cailín deas crúite na mBó.

[cont. on p 213.

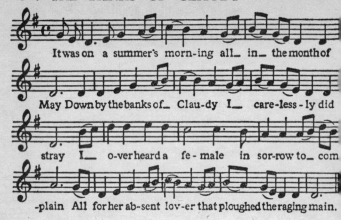

It was on a summer's morn-ing all_ in_ the month of May Down by the banks of_ Clau-dy I_ care-less-ly did stray I_ o-ver heard a fe-male in sor-row to_ com -plain All for her ab-sent lov-er that ploughed the raging main.

I stepped up unto her and gave her a surprise—
I own she did not know me, I being in disguise.
I says " My fairest creature, my joy and heart's delight,
How far do you mean to wander this dark and dreary night ? "

" It's to the banks of Claudy, if you'll be pleased to show ;
Take pity on a fair maid who knows not where to go.
I'm searching for a young man, and Johnny is his name,
And on the banks of Claudy I'm told he does remain."

" These are the banks of Claudy, fair maid, whereon you stand ;
But do not trust your Johnny, for he's a false young man,
But do not trust young Johnny, for he'll not meet you here,
But tarry with me in green woods, no danger need you fear."

" If Johnny was here this night he would keep me from
    all harm,
But he's in the field of battle, all in his uniform ;
He's in the field of battle, and his foes he does defy,
Like the royal king of honour all on the walls of Troy."

" It is six long weeks or better since Johnny left this shore
A-crossing the main ocean, where thundering billows roar ;
A-crossing the main ocean for honour and for fame,
But I am told the ship was wrecked nigh to the coast of
    Spain."

O, when she heard this dreadful news she flew in deep
    despair ;
A wringing of her hands and a tearing of her hair,
Saying : " If my Johnny's drownéd no man alive I'll take,
Through lonesome shades and valleys I'll wander for his
    sake."

When he saw her loyalty no longer could he stand :
He flew into her arms, saying, " Betsey, I'm the man,"
Saying " Betsey, I'm the young man, the cause of all your
    pain ;
Now, since we've met on Claudy banks we'll never part
    again."

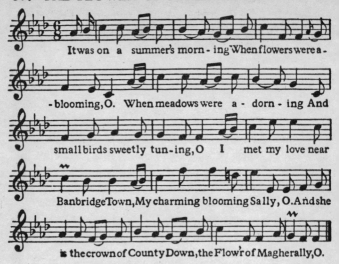

It was on a summer's morn-ing When flowers were a-blooming, O. When meadows were a-dorn-ing And small birds sweetly tun-ing, O I met my love near Banbridge Town, My charming blooming Sally, O. And she is the crown of County Down, the Flow'r of Magherally, O.

With admiration I did gaze
  Upon this blooming maiden, O;
Adam never was more struck
  When he first saw Eve in Eden, O;
Her skin was like the lily white,
  That grows in yonder valley, O;
And I think I'm blest when I am nigh
  The Flower of Magherally, O.

Her yellow hair in ringlets fell,
  Her shoes were Spanish leather, O,
Her bonnet with blue ribbons strung,
  Her scarlet scarf and feather, O.
Like Venus bright she did appear,
  My charming blooming Sally, O.
And she is the girl that I love dear,
  The Flower of Magherally, O.

An Irish lad although I be,
  With neither wealth nor treasure, O;
But yet I love my dearest dear,
  I love her beyond measure, O.
If I'd all the wealth that is possessed
  By the great Titharally, O;
I'd give it to her that I love best,
  The Flower of Magherally, O.

But I hope the time will surely come,
  When we'll join hands together, O;
It's then I'll take my darling home,
  In spite of wind and weather, O.
And let them all say what they will,
  And let them scowl and rally, O;
For I shall wed the girl I love,
  The Flower of Magherally, O.

60.—HENRY JOY McCRACKEN

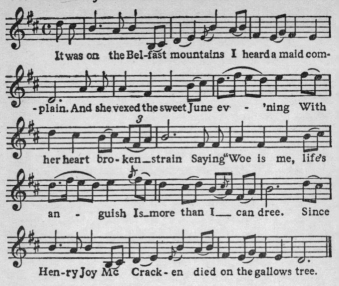

It was on the Belfast mountains I heard a maid complain. And she vexed the sweet June ev - 'ning With her heart bro-ken_strain Saying "Woe is me, life's an - guish Is_more than I__ can dree. Since Hen-ry Joy Mc Crack-en died on the gallows tree.

"At Donegore he proudly rode and he wore a suit of green
And brave though vain at Antrim his sword flashed lightning keen
And when by spies surrounded his band to Slemish fled
He came unto the Cavehill for to rest a weary head.

" I watched for him each night long as in our cot he slept
At daybreak to the heather to MacArt's fort we crept
When news came from Greencastle of a good ship anchored nigh
And down by yon wee fountain we met to say good-bye.

" He says ' My love be cheerful for tears and fears are vain.'
He says ' My love be hopeful our land shall rise again.'
He kissed me ever fondly, he kissed me three times o'er
Saying ' Death shall never part us my love for evermore.'

" That night I climbed the Cavehill and watched till morning
    blazed
And when its fires had kindled across the loch I gazed
I saw an English tender at anchor off Garmoyle
But alas ! no good ship bore him away to France's soil.

"And twice that night a tramping came from the old shore road
'Twas Ellis and his yeomen, false Niblock with them strode
My father home returning the doleful story told
'Alas,' he says, ' young Harry Joy for fifty pounds is sold.'"

"And is it true," I asked her, " yes it is true," she said.
" For to this heart that loved him I pressed his gory head,
And every night pale bleeding his ghost comes to my side,
My Harry, my dead Harry, comes for his promised bride."

Now on the Belfast mountains, this fair maid's voice is still
For in a grave they laid her on high Carnmoney hill
And the sad waves beneath her chant a requiem for the dead
The rebel wind shrieks freedom above her weary head.

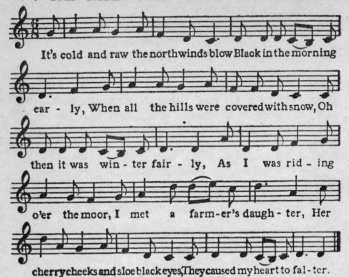

It's cold and raw the north winds blow Black in the morning ear - ly, When all the hills were covered with snow, Oh then it was win - ter fair - ly, As I was rid - ing o'er the moor, I met a farm-er's daugh - ter, Her cherry cheeks and sloe black eyes, They caused my heart to fal - ter.

I bowed my bonnet very low
   To let her know my meaning.
She answered with a courteous smile,
   Her looks they were engaging.
" Where are you bound my pretty maid,
   It's now in the morning early,"
The answer that she made to me,
   " Kind sir to sell my barley."

" Now twenty guineas I've in my purse,
   And twenty more that's yearly,
You need not go to the market town,
   For I'll buy all your barley.
If twenty guineas would gain the heart,
   Of the maid that I love so dearly,
All for to tarry with me one night,
   And go home in the morning early."

As I was riding o'er the moor,
　The very evening after,
It was my fortune for to meet
　The farmer's only daughter.
Although the weather being cold and raw
　With her I thought to parley,
This answer then she made to me,
　"Kind sir, I've sold my barley."

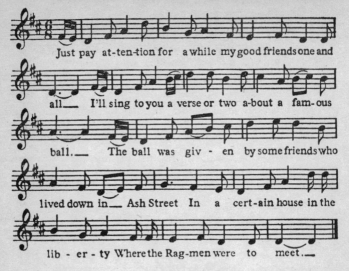

Just pay at-ten-tion for a while my good friends one and all__ I'll sing to you a verse or two a-bout a fam-ous ball.__ The ball was giv - en by some friends who lived down in__ Ash Street In a cert-ain house in the lib - er - ty Where the Rag-men were to meet.__

When the names were called at 7 o'clock, every man was on
    the spot;
And to show respect to the manager every ragman brought
    his mot;
I must say that I brought mine at twenty-five minutes to eight,
And the first to stand up was Kieran Grace to tell me I was
    too late.

Then up jumps Humpy Soodelum, and he says, " I think
    somehow,
By the way you are going on all the night, you're looking for
    a row;
But, look here, Grace, if you want your face, you'd better not
    shout or bawl,
There's a lot of hard chaws to be here to-night to respect the
    Ragman's Ball."

Then we all sat down to some fish and chips, and every man
    was there,
And as a post of honour Billy Boland took the chair;
He swiped the chair and sold it to an old one in Carmen Hall,
And danced on the face of poor Kieran Grace the night of the
    Ragman's Ball.

Says my one, "You're a quare one, and Billy, you're hard to
    beat,"
When up jumps Liza Boland, and told her to hold her prate;
But my one made a clout at her, she missed her and struck the
    wall,
And the two of them went in the ambulance the night of the
    Ragman's Ball.

Just to make the thing a swell affair, we all brought friends
    a few,
We brought up blind Gort Whelan and big Dan Kenny too;
And the gallant Jack Tar smoked his cigar, and slipped
    coming through the hall,
He lost a new bag and all his swag the night of the Ragman's
    Ball.

To keep the house alive, my boys, we brought some music, too,
We brought up Tommy Reynolds and his old tin whistle, too;
He played that night with all his might till coming on to dawn,
But we couldn't find many to dance with Dan Kenny that
    night at the Ragman's Ball.

Well, for eating we had plenty, as much as we could hold,
We drank Brady's Loop-Line porter till around the floor we
    rolled,
In the midst of the confusion someone shouted for a song,
When up jumped Dunlavin and sang, "Keep rolling your
    barrel along." [cont. on p. 213

63.—GRÁ-MO-CHROÍ, I'D LIKE TO SEE OLD IRELAND FREE ONCE MORE

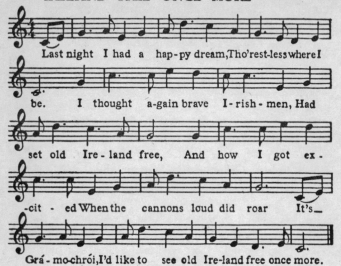

Last night I had a hap-py dream, Tho' rest-less where I be. I thought a-gain brave I-rish-men, Had set old Ire-land free, And how I got ex-cit-ed When the cannons loud did roar It's— Grá-mo-chroí, I'd like to see old Ire-land free once more.

Cold is the heart that does not love
  Its own dear native land,
When her sons are far beyond the sea
  All on a foreign strand.
By land or sea where'er they be
  They love their fertile shore,
It's Grá-mo-chroí I'd like to see
  Old Ireland free once more.

It's true we had brave Irishmen,
  As everyone must own,
The Liberator, O'Connell, true
  Lord Edward and Wolfe Tone.
And also Robert Emmet, who
  Till death did not give o'er,
It's Grá-mo-chroí I'd like to see,
  Old Ireland free once more.

Allen, Larkin and O'Brien died
　　Their country to set free,
And see to-day brave Irishmen
　　Are struggling hard for thee.
Both day and night they'll always fight,
　　Until death they'll ne'er give o'er,
It's Grá-mo-chroí I'd like to see
　　Old Ireland free once more.

Now we can't forget the former years,
　　They're kept in memory still,
Or the Wexford men of ninety-eight,
　　Who fought on Vinegar Hill;
With Father Murphy at their side
　　And his green flag waving o'er,
It's Grá-mo-chroí I'd like to see
　　Old Ireland free once more.

64.—THE REAL OLD MOUNTAIN DEW

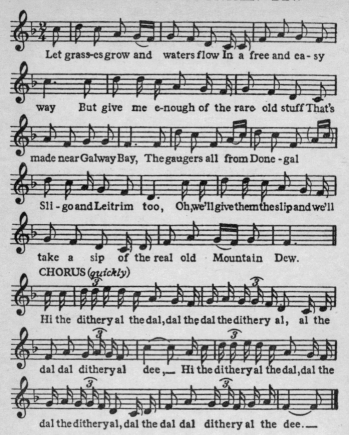

Let grass-es grow and waters flow In a free and ea-sy way But give me e-nough of the rare old stuff That's made near Galway Bay, The gaugers all from Done-gal Sli-go and Leitrim too, Oh, we'll give them the slip and we'll take a sip of the real old Mountain Dew.

CHORUS (*quickly*)

Hi the dithery al the dal, dal the dal the dithery al, al the dal dal dithery al dee,— Hi the dithery al the dal, dal the dal the dithery al, dal the dal dal dithery al the dee.—

At the foot of the hill there's a neat little still
Where the smoke curls up to the sky;
By a whiff of the smell you can plainly tell
That there's poitín, boys, close by.

For it fills the air with a perfume rare,
  And betwixt both me and you,
As home we roll, we can drink a bowl,
  Or a bucketful of mountain dew.

Now learned men who use the pen,
  Have wrote the praises high
Of the sweet poitín from Ireland green
  Distilled from wheat and rye.
Away with pills, it will cure all ills,
  Of the Pagan, Christian or Jew;
So take off your coat and grease your throat
  With the real old mountain dew.

65.—GENERAL MUNROE

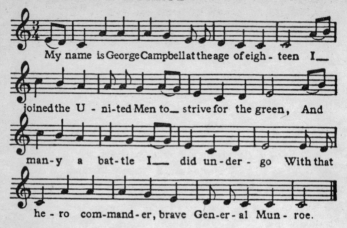

My name is George Campbell at the age of eigh-teen I joined the U-ni-ted Men to strive for the green, And man-y a bat-tle I did un-der-go With that he-ro com-mand-er, brave Gen-er-al Mun-roe.

Have you heard of the Battle of Ballinahinch
Where the people oppressed rose up in defence?
When Munroe left the mountains his men took the field,
And they fought for twelve hours and never did yield.

Munroe being tired and in want of a sleep,
Gave a woman ten guineas his secret to keep.
But when she got the money the devil tempted her so
That she sent for the soldiers and surrendered Munroe.

The army they came and surrounded the place,
And they took him to Lisburn and lodged him in jail.
And his father and mother in passing that way
Heard the very last words that their dear son did say!

" Oh, I die for my country as I fought for her .cause,
And I don't fear your soldiers nor yet heed your laws.
And let every true man who hates Ireland's foe
Fight bravely for freedom like Henry Munroe."

And 'twas early one morning when the sun was still low,
They murdered our hero brave General Munroe,
And high o'er the Courthouse stuck his head on a spear,
For to make the United men tremble and fear.

Then up came Munroe's sister, she was all dressed in green,
With a sword by her side that was well-sharped and keen.
Giving three hearty cheers, away she did go
Saying, " I'll have revenge for my brother Munroe."

All ye good men who listen, just think of the fate
Of the brave men who died in the year Ninety Eight,
For poor old Ireland would be free long ago
If her sons were all rebels like Henry Munroe.

My name it is Hugh Rey-nolds I came of hon-est par - ents, Near Cavan I was born— as you may plainly see For the lov-ing of a maid One Cath-er-ine Mc Cabe— My life has been be - trayed She's the dear maid to me— The coun-try was be-wail-ing my dole-ful sit - u - -a - tion, But still I'd ex-pec - ta - tion this maid would set me free— But O, she was un-grate-ful Her par-ents prov'd de - ceit - ful An' tho' I lov'd her faith - ful, she's the dear maid to me.—

Young men and tender maidens, throughout this Irish nation,
Who hear my lamentation, I hope you'll pray for me;
The truth I will unfold, that my precious blood she sold,
In the grave I must lie cold; she's the dear maid to me.

For now my glass is run, my last hour it is come,
And I must die for love and the height of loyalty!
I thought it was no harm to embrace her in my arms,
Or take her from her parents; but she's the dear maid to me.

Adieu, my loving father, and you, my tender mother,
Farewell, my dearest brother, who has suffered sore for me;
With irons I'm surrounded, in grief I lie confounded,
By perjury unbounded; she's the dear maid to me.

Now, I can say no more; to the Law-board I must go,
There to take my last farewell of my friends and counterie;
May the angels, shining bright, receive my soul this night,
And convey me into heaven with the blessed Trinity.

67.—NELL FLAHERTY'S DRAKE

My name it is Nell, quite can-did I tell, and I lived near Coote-hill I will nev-er de-ny. I had a large drake, the_ truth for to speak, That my grand-mo-ther left me and she goin' to die. He was wholesome and sound and he weighed twen-ty pound, And the u - ni-verse round I would rove for his sake, Bad wind to the rob-ber, both drunk-en and so-ber That mur-dered Nell Flah-er - ty's beau - ti-ful drake.

His neck it was green and most rare to be seen,
He was fit for a queen of the highest degree,
His body was white that would you delight,
He was plump, fat, and heavy, and brisk as a bee,

The dear little fellow his legs they were yellow,
He'd fly like a swallow or dive like a hake;
But some wicked savage to grease his white cabbage
Has murdered Nell Flaherty's beautiful drake.

May his pig never grunt may his cat never hunt,
That a ghost may him haunt in the dead of the night,
May his hen never lay, may his ass never bray,
May his goat fly away like an old paper kite.
That the flies and the fleas may the wretch ever tease,
And a bitter north breeze make him tremble and shake
May a four-year-old bug make a nest in the lug
Of the monster that murdered Nell Flaherty's drake.

May his pipe never smoke, and his tea-pot be broke,
And to add to the joke may his kettle ne'er boil,
May he ne'er rest in bed till the hour he is dead
May he always be fed on lobscouse and fish-oil,
May he swell with the gout till his grinders fall out,
May he roar, bawl, and shout with a horrid toothache
May his temples wear horns and all his toes corns,
The monster that murdered Nell Flaherty's drake.

May his spade never dig, may his sow never pig,
May each nit in his wig be as large as a snail,
May his door have no latch, may his house have no thatch,
May his turkey not hatch, may the rats eat his kale,
May every old fairy from Cork to Dunleary,
Dip him snug and airy in some pond or lake,
Where the eel and the trout may dine on the snout,
Of the monster that murdered Nell Flaherty's drake.

May his dog yelp and growl with hunger and cold,
May his wife always scold till his brain goes astray,
May the curse of each hag who e'er carried a bag,
Light on the wag till his beard turns grey;

[cont. on p. 214

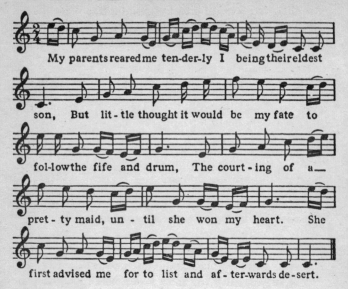

My parents reared me ten-der-ly I being their eldest son, But lit-tle thought it would be my fate to fol-low the fife and drum, The court-ing of a— pret-ty maid, un-til she won my heart. She first advised me for to list and af-ter-wards de-sert.

She being my mother's waiting maid, no fairer could be found,
Her cheeks they were all rosy red, her eyes a lovely brown,
Her skin it was a lily white, her teeth all in a row
It's for her sake I did enlist, that she with me might go.

My sword and sash, and scarlet coat, I now must lay aside,
And to some lonesome valley go, my fortunes to abide,
I bade adieu to the Light Bobs, where once I took delight
My journeys too I must pursue, and travel then by night.

'Tis beneath the shelter of a tree I am obliged to lie,
To shade me from my enemies, although my friends are nigh,
I am like the owl that hates the day, and dare not show my face,
With patience waiting for the night, to seek some distant place.

I have one brother, a sailor bold, he knows not I am here,
But all in vain I call to him, his small boats to draw near,
But alas ! the tide floats him away, his boats he can't pull to,
And here in pain I still remain, and know not what to do.

Oh, once I thought I ne'er would be in this dejected state,
A poor forlorn effigy, exposed to hardships great,
The bird that flutters on each tree with terror strikes my heart,
Each star I see alarms me—Oh, why did I desert ?

Oh, why did I desert, my boys, or from my colours fly,
No stint of pay or cowardice, those things I do deny.
It was cursed whiskey tempted me, and dread misfortune's
    stroke,
My life is in a state of woe, with grief my heart is broke.

Now to conclude and make an end to my deserting song,
I hope to shine in armour bright, and that before 'tis long,
For my sergeant and my officer have clothes for me in store,
And if they'd combine and pardon me, I would desert no more.

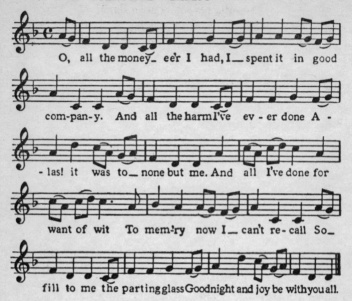

O, all the money e'er I had, I spent it in good com-pan-y. And all the harm I've ev-er done A-las! it was to none but me. And all I've done for want of wit To mem'ry now I can't re-call So fill to me the parting glass Goodnight and joy be with you all.

Oh, all the comrades e'er I had,
They're sorry for my going away,
And all the sweethearts e'er I had,
They'd wish me one day more to stay,
But since it falls unto my lot,
That I should rise and you should not,
I gently rise and softly call,
Good night and joy be with you all

If I had money enough to spend,
And leisure time to sit awhile,
There is a fair maid in this town,
That sorely has my heart beguiled.

Her rosy cheeks and ruby lips,
I own she has my heart in thrall,
Then fill to me the parting glass,
Good night and joy be with you all.

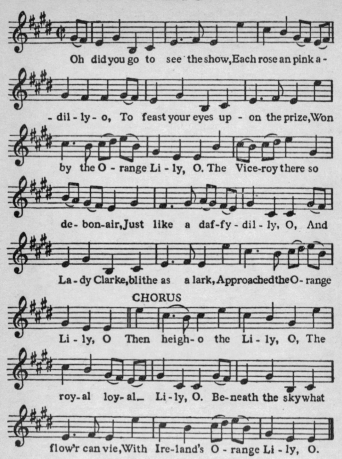

Oh did you go to see the show, Each rose an pink a-dil-ly-o, To feast your eyes up-on the prize, Won by the O-range Li-ly, O. The Vice-roy there so de-bon-air, Just like a daf-fy-dil-ly, O, And La-dy Clarke, blithe as a lark, Approached the O-range Li-ly, O

CHORUS

Then heigh-o the Li-ly, O, The roy-al loy-al— Li-ly, O. Be-neath the sky what flow'r can vie, With Ire-land's O-range Li-ly, O.

The elated muse, to hear the news,
Jumped like a Connacht filly-o,
As gossip fame did loud proclaim
The triumph of the Lily-o;

The lowland field may roses yield,
    Gay heaths the highlands hilly‚o,
But high or low, no flower can show,
    Like the glorious Orange Lily‚o.

Then heigho the lily‚o,
    The royal, loyal lily‚o,
There's not a flower in Erin's bower
    Can match the Orange Lily‚o.

71.—MRS. McGRATH

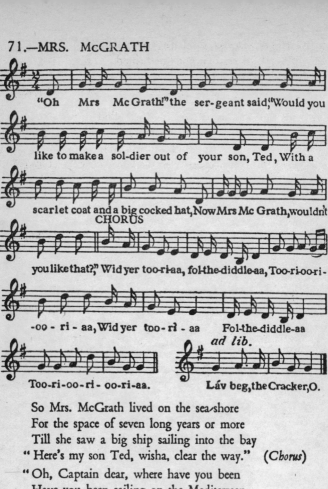

"Oh Mrs Mc Grath!" the ser-geant said, "Would you
like to make a sol-dier out of your son, Ted, With a
scarlet coat and a big cocked hat, Now Mrs Mc Grath, wouldn't
CHORUS
you like that?," Wid yer too-ri-aa, fol-the-diddle-aa, Too-ri-oo-ri-
-oo-ri-aa, Wid yer too-ri-aa   Fol-the-diddle-aa
ad lib.
Too-ri-oo-ri-oo-ri-aa.   Láv beg, the Cracker, O.

So Mrs. McGrath lived on the sea-shore
For the space of seven long years or more
Till she saw a big ship sailing into the bay
" Here's my son Ted, wisha, clear the way."   (*Chorus*)

" Oh, Captain dear, where have you been
Have you been sailing on the Mediterreen
Or have ye any tidings of my son Ted
Is the poor boy living or is he dead ? "   (*Chorus*)

Then up comes Ted without any legs
And in their place he has two wooden pegs
She kissed him a dozen times or two
Saying " Holy Moses 'tisn't you."   (*Chorus*)

"Oh then were ye drunk or were ye blind
That ye left yer two fine legs behind
Or was it walking upon the sea
Wore yer two fine legs from the knees away?" (*Chorus*)

"Oh I wasn't drunk and I wasn't blind
But I left my two fine legs behind
For a cannon ball on the fifth of May
Took my two fine legs from the knees away." (*Chorus*)

"Oh then Teddy me boy," the widow cried,
"Yer two fine legs were yer mammy's pride
Them stumps of a tree wouldn't do at all
Why didn't ye run from the big cannon ball? (*Chorus*)

All foreign wars I do proclaim
Between Don John and the King of Spain
And by herrins I'll make them rue the time
That they swept the legs from a child of mine. (*Chorus*)

Oh then, if I had you back again
I'd never let ye go to fight the King of Spain
For I'd rather my Ted as he used to be
Than the King of France and his whole Navee." (*Chorus*)

72.—LIMERICK IS BEAUTIFUL

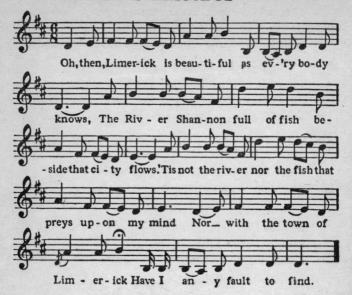

Oh, then, Limer-ick is beau-ti-ful as ev-'ry bo-dy
knows, The Riv-er Shan-non full of fish be-
-side that ci-ty flows. 'Tis not the riv-er nor the fish that
preys up-on my mind Nor— with the town of
Lim-er-ick Have I an-y fault to find.

Oh, the girl I love is beautiful and fairer than the dawn,
She lives in Garryowen and she's called the Colleen Bawn.
But proudly as the river flows beside that fair citie,
As proudly and without a word that colleen goes by me.

Oh then, if I was the Emperor of Russia to command
If I was Julius Caesar or Lord Lieutenant of the land.
I'd give my fleet, my golden store I'd give up my armie
The horse, the rifle and the foot and the Royal Artillerie.

I'd give my fleet of sailing ships that range the briny seas
I'd give the crown from off my head, my people on their knees
A beggar I would go to bed and proudly rise at dawn
If by my side, all for a bride, I found the Colleen Bawn.

144

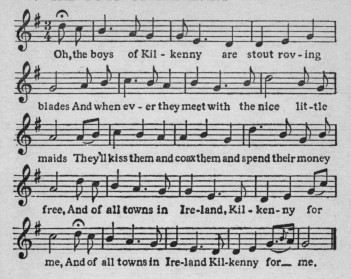

Oh, the boys of Kil-kenny are stout rov-ing blades And when ev-er they meet with the nice lit-tle maids They'll kiss them and coax them and spend their money free, And of all towns in Ire-land, Kil-ken-ny for me, And of all towns in Ire-land Kil-kenny for— me.

Through the town of Kilkenny there runs a clear stream,
In the town of Kilkenny there lives a fair dame,
Her lips are like roses, and her cheeks much the same,
Like a dish of ripe strawberries smothered in cream
Like a dish of ripe strawberries smothered in cream.

Her eyes are as black as Kilkenny's famed coal,
Which through my poor bosom have burnt a great hole.
Her mind, like its river, is mild, clear and pure,
But her heart is more hard than its marble, I'm sure
But her heart is more hard than its marble, I'm sure.

Oh, Kilkenny's a fine town, it shines where it stands
And the more I think of it, the more my heart warms,
And if I was in Kilkenny, I'd think myself at home
For 'tis there I'd have sweethearts but here I have none
For 'tis there I'd have sweethearts but here I have none.

Oh, the Ban - sha Peal - ers went
out one night on du - ty and pa - trol - ling, O,— They
met a goat up - on the road and took him for being a -
-stroll - ing, O. With bay-'nets fix'd they sal - lied forth and
caught him by the wiz - zen, O,— And then swore out a
might - y oath, they'd send him off— to pri - son, O.

"Oh, mercy, sir!" the goat replied,
"And let me tell my story O
I am no Rogue, no Ribbonman,
No Croppy, Whig, or a Tory O;
I'm guilty not of any crime
Of petty or high treason O,
And our tribe is wanted at this time,
For this is the ranting season O."

" It is in vain for to complain
  Or give your tongue such bridle O,
  You're absent from your dwellingplace,
  Disorderly and idle O.
  Your hoary locks will not prevail,
  Nor your sublime oration O,
  For Peeler's Act will you transport,
  On your own information O."

" No penal laws I did transgress
  By deeds or combination O,
  I have no certain place of rest,
  No home or habitation O.
  But Bansha is my dwellingplace,
  Where I was bred and born O,
  I'm descended from an honest race,
  That's all the trade I've learned O."

" I will chastise your insolence
  And violent behaviour O;
  Well bound to Cashel you'll be sent,
  Where you will gain no favour O
  The magistrates will all consent
  To sign your condemnation O;
  From there to Cork you will be sent
  For speedy transportation O."

" This parish an' this neighbourhood
  Are peaceable and tranquil O;
  There's no disturbance here, thank God !
  And long may it continue so.
  I don't regard your oath a pin,
  Or sign for my committal O,
  My jury will be gentlemen
  And grant me my acquittal O."

[cont. on p. 216

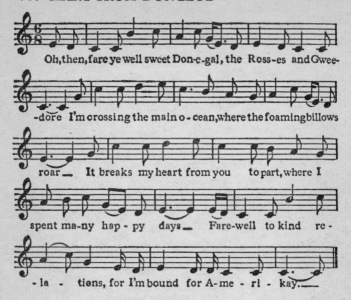

Oh, then, fare ye well sweet Don-e-gal, the Ross-es and Gwee-dore I'm crossing the main o-cean, where the foaming billows roar __ It breaks my heart from you to part, where I spent ma-ny hap-py days __ Fare-well to kind re-la-tions, for I'm bound for A-me-ri-kay. __

Oh, my love is tall and handsome and her age is scarce eighteen
She far exceeds all other fair maids when she trips over the
green
Her lovely neck and shoulders are fairer than the snow
Till the day I die I'll ne'er deny my Mary from Dungloe.

If I was at home in Sweet Dungloe a letter I would write
Kind thoughts would fill my bosom for Mary my delight
'Tis in her father's garden, the fairest violets grow
And 'twas there I came to court the maid, my Mary from
Dungloe.

Ah then, Mary you're my heart's delight my pride and only care
It was your cruel father, would not let me stray there.

But absence makes the heart grow fond and when I'm o'er the
   main
May the Lord protect my darling girl till I return again.

And I wished I was in Sweet Dungloe and seated on the grass
And by my side a bottle of wine and on my knee a lass.
I'd call for liquor of the best and I'd pay before I would go
And I'd roll my Mary in my arms in the town of Sweet
   Dungloe.

76.—THE MAID OF BUNCLODY, AND THE LAD SHE LOVES SO DEAR

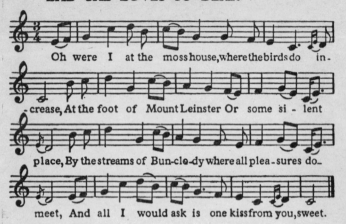

Oh were I at the moss house, where the birds do increase, At the foot of Mount Leinster Or some si - lent
place, By the streams of Bun-clo-dy where all plea-sures do
meet, And all I would ask is one kiss from you, sweet.

Oh the streams of Bunclody they flow down so free,
By the streams of Bunclody I'm longing to be,
A-drinking strong liquor in the height of my cheer,
Here's a health to Bunclody and the lass I love dear.

The cuckoo is a pretty bird, it sings as it flies,
It brings us good tidings, and tells us no lies,
It sucks the young birds' eggs to make its voice clear,
And the more it cries cuckoo the summer draws near.

If I was a clerk and could write a good hand,
I would write to my true-love that she might understand,
For I am a young fellow who is wounded in love
Once I lived in Bunclody, but now must remove.

If I was a lark and had wings I could fly
I would go to yon arbour where my love she does lie,
I'd proceed to yon arbour where my true love does lie,
And on her fond bosom contented I would die.

'Tis why my love slights me, as you may understand,
That she has a freehold and I have no land,
She has great store of riches, and a large sum of gold,
And everything fitting a house to uphold.

So fare you well father and my mother, adieu
My sister and brother farewell unto you,
I am bound for America my fortune to try,
When I think on Bunclody I'm ready to die.

77.—THE BANTRY GIRLS' LAMENT

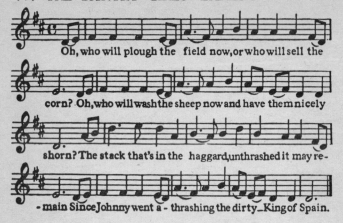

Oh, who will plough the field now, or who will sell the corn? Oh, who will wash the sheep now and have them nicely shorn? The stack that's in the haggard, unthrashed it may remain Since Johnny went a-thrashing the dirty King of Spain.

The girls from the bawnoge in sorrow may retire,
And the piper and his bellows may go home and blow the
fire;
For Johnny, lovely Johnny, is sailing o'er the main,
Along with other patriarchs, to fight the King of Spain.

The boys will sorely miss him when Moneymore comes
round,
And grieve that their bold captain is nowhere to be found
The peelers must stand idle against their will and grain,
For the valiant boy who gave them work now peels the King
of Spain.

At wakes or hurling-matches your like we'll never see,
Till you come back to us again, a stóirín óg mo chroí,
And won't you trounce the buckeens that show us much
disdain,
Because our eyes are not so bright as those you'll meet in
Spain?

If cruel fate will not permit our Johnny to return,
His heavy loss we Bantry girls will never cease to mourn,
We'll resign ourselves to our sad lot, and die in grief and pain,
Since Johnny died for Ireland's pride in the foreign land of
    Spain.

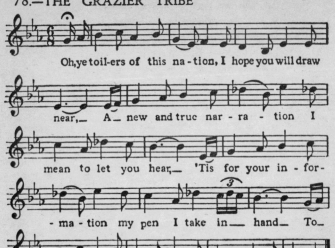

Oh, ye toil-ers of this na-tion, I hope you will draw near,— A— new and true nar - ra - tion I mean to let you hear,— 'Tis for your in - for- -ma - tion my pen I take in— hand— To— try describe a graz-ier tribe, that now infests this land.

This grazier clan has overran
　　Your country so fair,
Enough to make the angels weep
　　Or drive you to despair;
There's not a town from Cork to Down,
　　Or Dublin to Tralee.
But has a den of grazier men
　　To keep you in poverty.

Oh, ye men in name have you no shame
　　To see this beauteous land,
Turned into one vast wilderness
　　By a cursed grazier band;
This land so kind was ne'er designed
　　By providence on high,
To keep John Bull with mutton full
　　While the natives starve and die.

Oh, ye men of honest labour,
    If ever you'd be free,
Now take your stand upon the land
    And strike for liberty;
Commit no crime, now is the time,
    To burst your galling chains,
And drive this band clean off the land,
    As Brian drove the Danes.

Oh, this land of ours, of sunny showers,
    How fair 'twould be to see,
Across the plain the golden grain
    All waving like a sea;
And men so fine instead of kine
    You'd see on every hand,
To give a cheer for freedom dear
    And Faith and Fatherland.

So ye valiant sons of labour
    Wherever you are found,
To seek a home you need not roam
    But quietly look around;
There may be seen fine meadows green,
    And bullocks sleek and grand,
Just get your pole and take a stroll
    And clear them off the land.

And if Bob be there to fume and swear
    And threaten you with jail,
And for your good behaviour
    You surely must find bail;
But still you'll find true friends behind
    To cheer you in your woe,
Then you'll be so grand with house and land
    That yourself you will not know.

On Mo-ni-seed of a summer's morn-ing, Our boys they halt - ed a rest to take, When the an-cient Brit - ons, in their un - i- form,— Up- -on Sliav Beag, A great show did make. The Gor - ey cav - al - ry that day did join them, They were on blood - y— mur- der bent, But soon our boys,— they did en-gage them, They lit - tle thought that their glass was spent.

As they from Gorey set out that morning,
You'd pity the groans and the women's tears;
But on that day we made them pay,
When they came in view of our Shelmaliers.
'Twas from the watch-house into Ballyellis
To Pavy's height going towards Carnew,

It's there we had a great engagement,
Such other pikemen you never knew.

'Twas early, early on the next morning,
To Ballarahan we took our way,
To meet with Gowan and his cursed yeomen,
To them it was a woeful day.
Cowardly Gowan when he saw us coming,
Turned round and away from us did run,
Like a hunted fox he crossed over the rocks,
When he saw the flash of a croppy's gun.

We then shot Chamny and Captain Dixon,
And General Walpole got no time to run,
And long Smyth, the slater—the bloody traitor,
He fell that day by a croppy's gun.
When this engagement was all over,
And our brave boys had no more to do,
We crossed Brideswell going to Camolin,
And camped that night at Carrigrua.

Had we the wisdom to follow after,
And not have tarried in Gorey town,
We'd have saved the lives of many a martyr,
That died in Arklow—God rest their souls.
Success attend the sweet County Wexford,
They are the boys that were ne'er afraid
Of Ancient Britons nor bragging yeomen,
But on such cowards great slaughter made.

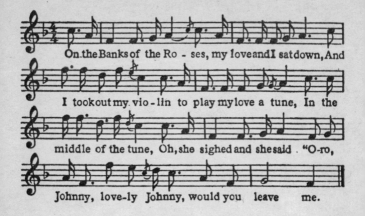

On the Banks of the Ro - ses, my love and I sat down, And
I took out my vio - lin to play my love a tune, In the
middle of the tune, Oh, she sighed and she said "O-ro,
Johnny, love-ly Johnny, would you leave me.

Oh, when I was a young man I heard my father say,
That he'd rather see me dead and buried in the clay,
Sooner than be married to any runaway,
    By the lovely sweet Banks of the Roses.

Oh, then I am no runaway and soon I'll let them
    know,
I can take a good glass or can leave it alone;
And the man that doesn't like me he can keep his
    daughter at home
    And young Johnny will go roving with another.

And if ever I get married 'twill be in the month
    of May,
When the leaves they are green and the meadows they
    are gay;
And I and my true love can sit and sport and play
    On the lovely sweet Banks of the Roses.

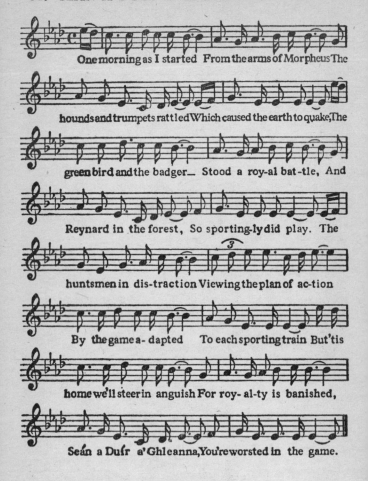

One morning as I started From the arms of Morpheus The hounds and trumpets rattled Which caused the earth to quake, The green bird and the badger— Stood a roy-al bat-tle, And Reynard in the forest, So sporting-ly did play. The huntsmen in dis-trac-tion Viewing the plan of ac-tion By the game a-dapted To each sporting train But 'tis home we'll steer in anguish For roy-al-ty is banished, Seán a Duír a' Ghleanna, You're worsted in the game.

When first I saw dear Anna, she filled my heart with rapture,
In a dewy meadow in the merry month of May,
Awhile I stood astonished, to view this charming goddess,
Her golden locks lay hanging, down to her lovely waist.

160

By the glances of this object, the greatest style demolished,
She spoke to me as follows, saying, " Lay aside all care,
So relent and take compassion, on lovely young dear Anna,"
I would think myself quite happy, if she called me her slave.

The blackbirds and the thrushes, warbling on the bushes,
The nightingale and linnet, sing sweetly in the grove.
The woodcock in the forest, the lark along the valley,
And lovely young dear Anna joined them in a choir.
How elegant do the fishes swim along the river,
The wild duck and the pigeon so merrily do rove,
But all rejoiced full hearty for none but lovely Anna,
I took her for a goddess shaded by the rose.

As I walked forth in sorrow, down by yonder valley,
I saw my lovely Anna sitting by a stream,
My eyes began to dazzle, condemned with thoughts relapsing,
I then took off my beaver and accosted this fair dame.
My joys were greatly shortened when smilingly she asked me,
" Young man, you seem a stranger, pray from whence you
        came,"
" I'm a Galway man by extraction, bred in Connamara,
And Seán a Duír a' Ghleanna they call me by name."

82.—DOBBIN'S FLOWERY VALE

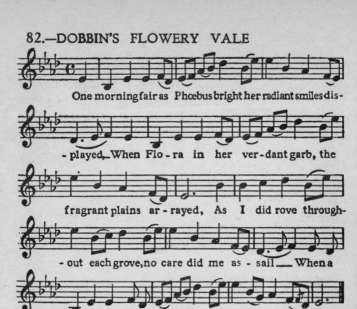

One morning fair as Phœbus bright her radiant smiles displayed When Flora in her verdant garb, the fragrant plains arrayed, As I did rove throughout each grove, no care did me assail When a pair I spied by a riverside, in Dobbin's Flow'ry Vale.

As I sat down them to behold,
  Beneath a spreading tree
The limpid streams that gently rolled
  Conveyed these words to me;
Farewell sweet maid, the youth he said
  For now I must set sail,
I'll bid adieu to Armagh, you,
  And Dobbin's Flowery Vale !

Forbear those thoughts and cruel words
  That wound a bleeding heart
For is it true that we're met here
  Alas ! so soon to part ?
Must I alone here sigh and moan,
  To none my grief reveal
But here lament my cause to vent,
  In Dobbin's Flowery Vale ?

There's many a youth has left his home
  To steer for freedom's shore
Been laid beneath the silent tomb,
  Where the foaming billows roar;
Take my advice, do not forsake
  Or leave me to bewail,
But still remain with your fond dame,
  In Dobbin's Flowery Vale.

Unwilling I am to part with you,
  No longer can I stay,
For love and freedom cries " pursue "
  Those words I must obey;
In foreign Isles where freedom smiles
  Or by the earth concealed,
I will come home no more to roam,
  From Dobbin's Flowery Vale.

It's when you reach Columbia's shore
  Some pretty maids you'll see,
You'll ne'er think on the loving vow;
  That you have made to me;
May hope content life's ending pain !
  My thoughts would oft prevail,
Of seeing no more the youth I adore
  In Dobbin's Flowery Vale.

Do not reflect that you're alone,
  Nor yet am I untrue,
If e'er I chance now for to roam
  My thoughts will be on you;
There's not a flower in shady bower,
  On verdant hill or dale,
But will remind me of the maid behind
  In Dobbin's Flowery Vale.

|cont. on p. 216

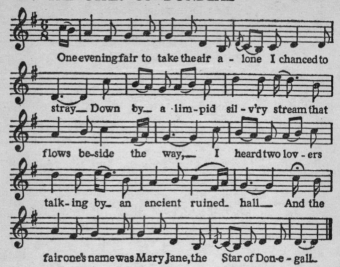

One evening fair to take the air a-lone I chanced to stray— Down by— a lim-pid sil-v'ry stream that flows be-side the way,— I heard two lov-ers talk-ing by— an ancient ruined hall— And the fair one's name was Mary Jane, the Star of Don-e-gall.

"My lovely maid" the youth he said "I'm going across the foam
Unto the land of stars and stripes where peace and plenty flows
I want your faithful promise that you'll wed with none at all
Until I do return to you and the lands of Donegal."

She blushed and sighed and then replied "It grieves my heart full sore
To think you are compelled to go and leave the Shamrock shore
Here is my faithful promise that I'll wed with none at all
But stay at home and do not roam from the lands of Donegal."

"My sweet fair maid" the youth then said, "at home I cannot stay
To California's gold fields I'm bound to cross the sea
To accumulate a fortune great, to build a splendid hall
To decorate and cultivate the lands of Donegal."

She raised her lily-white hands and said " Yon castle in its day
With all its plains and large demesnes from Lifford to the sea
Belonged to our ancestors with many a splendid hall
And if my father had his rights, I'd be heir of Donegal."

" My darling maid " the youth then said, " the day is drawing
    near
When Irishmen will return again from all their long career
Our holy land by God's command the fairest land of all
And Heaven will see old Ireland free, Bright Star of Donegal."

She blushed and sighed and then replied, " Heaven grant that
    we may see
St. Patrick's isle of Saints to shine great glorious and free.
If that be so there's none will go to New York or Montreal
But will stay at home and will not roam from the lands of
    Donegal."

He clasped her in his arms and said " My darling well you know
I love you very dearly and loth I am to go
Let us get wed without fear or dread, that puts an end to all
And then I will have my darling girl the Star of Donegal."

She gave consent and off they went to meet with Father Hugh
Who joined their hands in wedlock bands without any more
    ado
From Derry quay they sailed away and bade farewell to all
And now they're in America far away from Donegal.

One Pad-dy Doyle lived near Kil-lar-ney, And loved a maid called Bet-ty Toole, His tongue, I own, was tipped with blarney, Which seem'd to him a gold-en rule, From day to day he watched his col-leen, And oft-en to him-self would say, What need I care sure here's my droleen, ad-vanc-ing to met me on the way Tow-ri-ah, the doo-dle ad-dy Tow-ri-ah-di-the doo-dle-ay.

One heavenly night in last November,
　The moon shone gently from above,
What night it was I don't remember,
　But Paddy went to meet his love.
That day Paddy took some liquor,
　Which made his spirits light and gay,
Says he, " What use my walking quicker ?
　Sure I know she'll meet me on the way."

So he tuned his pipes and fell a-humming,
  As slowly onwards he did creep,
But fatigue and whiskey overcome him,
  So down he lay and fell asleep.
But he wasn't long without a comrade
  And one that gave him out the pay,
For a big jackass smelled out poor Pat,
  And lay down beside him on the way.

He stretched his arms out on the grass,
  A-thinking on his little dear,
He dreamt of comforts without number
  Coming on the ensuing year.
He stretched his arms out on the grass,
  His spirits felt so light and gay,
But instead of Bet, he gripped the ass,
  And he roared—" I have her any way."

He hugged and smugged his hairy messer,
  And flung his old hat at woe and care,
Says Pat, " She's mine, the heavens bless her,
  But pon my soul, she's mighty quare,
But I think," said Pat, " it's time to rise,"
  With that the ass began to bray.
Pat jumped up and opened his eyes,
  Saying " Who served me in such a way ? "

Like blazes then away he cut
  At railway speed, or as fast I'm sure,
But he never stopped a leg or foot
  Until he came to Betty's door.
By this time now 'twas dawning morning,
  So down on his knees he fell to pray,
Saying, " Let me in, och, Betty darling,
  For I'm kilt—I'm murdered on the way."

[cont. on p. 217

85.—MOORLUG MARY

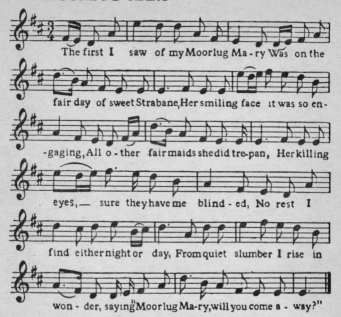

The first I saw of my Moorlug Ma-ry Was on the fair day of sweet Strabane, Her smiling face it was so en-gaging, All o-ther fair maids she did tre-pan, Her killing eyes,— sure they have me blind-ed, No rest I find either night or day, From quiet slumber I rise in won-der, saying "Moorlug Ma-ry, will you come a-way?"

From Moorlug banks I will never wander,
    Where heifers graze on yon pleasant hill;
Where lambkins sporting, fair maids resorting,
    The timorous hare and blue heather bell.
I'll press my cheese, and my wool I'll tease,
    And my ewes I'll milk by the eve of day;
The hurling moor-cock and lark allures me;
    From bonnie Moorlug I'll never stray.

I'll go down yon woodland to my situation,
    Where recreation is all in view,
On the river Mourne where the salmon sporting,
    And echoes sounding bring something new.

The thrush and goldfinch will join in chorus
  With notes melodious on Liskea Brae,
To the sweet Loch shore then I would restore you,
  Saying, " Moorlug Mary, will you come away ? "

Were I a man of great education,
  And Ireland's nation at my command.
I'd lay my head on her snowy shoulder,
  In wedlock's portion I'd take her hand,
I'd entertain her both eve and morning;
  With robes I'd deck her both rich and gay;
With kisses fragrant I would embrace her,
  Saying, " Moorlug Mary, will you come away ? "

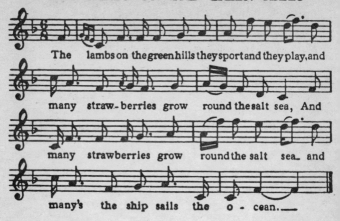

The lambs on the green hills they sport and they play, and
many straw-berries grow round the salt sea, And
many strawberries grow round the salt sea_ and
many's the ship sails the o - cean.___

The bride and bride's party to church they did go,
The bride she rode foremost, she bears the best show,
But I followed after with my heart full of woe,
To see my love wed to another.

The first place I saw her 'twas in the church stand,
Gold rings on her finger and her love by the hand,
Says I, " My wee lassie, I will be the man
Although you are wed to another."

The next place I seen her was on the way home,
I ran on before her, not knowing where to roam,
Says I, " My wee lassie, I'll be by your side
Although you are wed to another."

" Stop, stop," said the groomsman, " 'till I speak a word,
Will you venture your life on the point of my sword?
For courting so slowly you've lost this fair maid,
So begone, for you'll never enjoy her."

Oh, make now my grave both large, wide and deep,
And sprinkle it over with flowers so sweet,
And lay me down in it to take my last sleep,
For that's the best way to forget her.

The strug-gle is ov-er the boys are de-feat-ed, Old
Hung, drawn and quartered, sure that was my sentence, But

Ire-land's sur-round-ed with sadness and gloom,
soon I will show them no coward am I, My

We were de-feat-ed and shame-ful-ly treat-ed And
crime is the love of the land I was born in, A

I, Ro-bert Em-met a-wait-ing my doom.}
he-ro I lived and a he-ro I'll die.

CHORUS

Bold Robert Emmet, the darling of E-rin,

Bold Robert Emmet will die with a smile,

Farewell com-panions both loy-al and dar-ing, I'll

lay down my life for the Em-er-ald Isle.

The barque lay at anchor awaiting to bring me
Over the billows to the land of the free;
But I must see my sweetheart for I know she will cheer me,
And with her I will sail far over the sea.

But I was arrested and cast into prison,
  Tried as a traitor, a rebel, a spy;
But no one can call me a knave or a coward,
  A hero I lived and a hero I'll die.   *Chorus.*

Hark ! the bell's tolling, I well know its meaning,
  My poor heart tells me it is my death knell;
In come the clergy, the warder is leading,
  I have no friends here to bid me farewell.
Good-bye, old Ireland, my parents and sweetheart,
  Companions in arms to forget you must try;
I am proud of the honour, it was only my duty—
  A hero I lived and a hero I'll die.   *Chorus.*

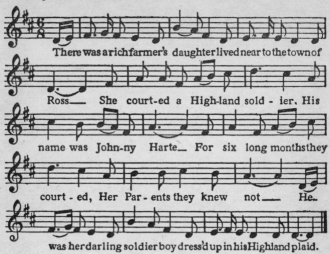

There was a rich farmer's daughter lived near to the town of Ross— She court-ed a High-land sold-ier. His name was John-ny Harte— For six long months they court-ed, Her Par-ents they knew not— He— was her darling soldier boy dress'd up in his Highland plaid.

Says the mother unto the daughter, " I'll go distracted mad,
If you marry that Highland soldier dressed up in his Highland
    plaid
To marry a private soldier for ever you're undone
You know your fortune is too great, so wed a farmer's son."

"Dear mother, do not despise my love, and do not run him
    down,
For there's many a private soldier was raised to a high renown.
And many a farmer's daughter has followed the fife and drum,
I would not part my soldier boy for any squire's son."

Next morning then her mother to the barracks did repair,
And to the colonel's quarters she straight was sent across,
And there she met the colonel, and to him a courtesy dropt,
"I want your honour in private, I have a broken heart."

The colonel being a nobleman he then began to smile,
So kindly he consented with her to step aside,
"Be quick my decent woman, to hear you I'm inclined,
If I consider your claim is fair, I'll see you justified."

"I have one only daughter, she is a foolish lass,
She is courted by one of your soldiers, his name is Johnny Harte,
To marry a private soldier is below my child's degree,
If your honour will send him out of Ross my blessing on
    you'll be."

The bugle sounded for parade, young Harte he did appear,
The Colonel he stepped up to him all in the barrack square,
"If you court this woman's daughter, and that I find it out,
I'll send you on detachment till the regiment gets the route."

"'Tis hard enough," young Harte replied, "for courting an
    Irish lass,
To send me on detachment, and leave my dear in Ross,
I love this woman's daughter and for me she's inclined
And I'd court your honour's daughter if I could gain her
    mind."

"Well done my gallant soldier, I like your courage well,
And you shall be promoted for those words you boldly tell
I'll put epaulets on your shoulders, and then you'll be a match
For the foremost farmer's daughter coming into the town of
    Ross."

To have this couple married the Colonel gave consent,
Her parents paid her portion down, it's now they are content,
Young Harte became an officer, his dear a captain's bride,
He has joined the richest family down by the Barrow side.

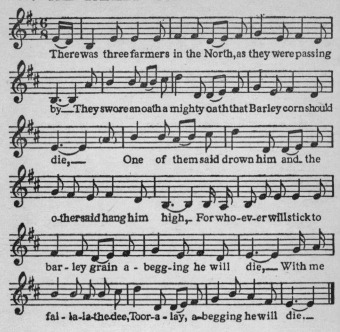

There was three farmers in the North, as they were passing by— They swore an oath a mighty oath that Barley corn should die,— One of them said drown him and the other said hang him high, For who-ev-er will stick to bar-ley grain a-begg-ing he will die,— With me fal-la-la-the-dee, Toor-a-lay, a-begging he will die,—

They put poor barley into a sack of a cold and rainy day,
And brought him off to culm fields and burned him in the clay.
Frost and snow began to melt and the dew began to fall,
When barley grain put up his head and soon surprised them all.

Being in the summer season and the harvest coming on
It's the time he stands up in the field with a beard like any man.
The reaper then came with his hook and used me barbarously,
He caught me by the middle so small and cut me above the knee.

The next came was the binder and look'd on me with a frown
But in the middle there was a thistle that pulled his courage
   down.
The farmer came with his pitchfork and pierced me to the
   heart
Like a thief, a rogue or highwayman they tied me to the cart.

The thrasher came with his big flail and soon he broke my
   bones,
'Twould grieve the heart of any man to hear my sighs and groans,
The next thing that they done to me they steep'd me in a well
They left me there for a day and a night until I began to swell.

The next thing that they done to me they dried me in a kiln
They used me ten times worse than that, they ground me in a mill
They used me in the kitchen, they used me in the hall
They used me in the parlour among the ladies all.

The barley grain is a comical grain it makes men sigh and moan,
For when they take a glass or two they forget their wife and home
The drunkard is a dirty man he used me worse than all
He drank me up in his dirty maw and tumbled against
   the wall.

They may talk of Fly-ing Chil-ders and the
speed of Hark-a-way, Till the fan-cy it be-wild-ers, as you
list to what they say, But for real bone and beau-ty, Tho'you
trav-el near and far, — The fairest mare you'll find be-longs to
Pat of Mul-lin-gar,

CHORUS

She can trot along, jog along,
Drag a jaunting car, No day's too long when sent along by
Pat of Mul-lin-gar.

She was bred in Connamara,
  And brought up at Castlemaine.
She won cups at the Curragh,
  And a charger was in Spain.
All countries and conveyances
  She has been buckled to;
She lost an eye at Limerick
  And at Aughrim lost a shoe.

If a friend you wish to find, sir,
   I'll go where'er you want;
I'll drive you out o' your mind, sir,
   Or a little way beyant.
Like an arrow through the air,
   If you'll step upon the car,
You'll ride behind the little mare
   Of Pat of Mullingar.

If Baldoyle or Killiney,
   Is the place you wish to see,
Or I'll drive you to the Strawberry Beds
   It's all the same to me;
To Donnybrook, whose ancient fair
   Was famed for love and war,
Or if you have the time to spare,
   We'll go to Mullingar.

When on the road we're going,
   The other carmen try,
Without the darling knowin',
   To pass her on the sly;
Her one ear points up to the sky,
   She tucks her haunches in,
Then shows the lads how she can fly,
   As I sit still and grin.

Then should you want a car, sirs,
   I hope you'll not forget
Poor Pat of Mullingar, sirs,
   And his darling little pet;
She's as gentle as the dove,
   And her speed you can't deny,
And there's no blind side about her,
   Tho' she only has one eye.

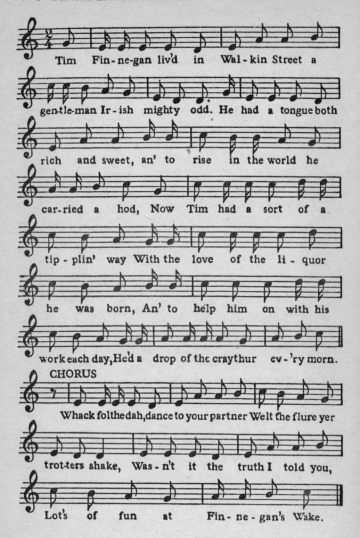

Tim Fin-ne-gan liv'd in Wal-kin Street a gen-tle-man Ir-ish mighty odd. He had a tongue both rich and sweet, an' to rise in the world he car-ried a hod, Now Tim had a sort of a tip-plin' way With the love of the li-quor he was born, An' to help him on with his work each day, He'd a drop of the craythur ev-'ry morn.

CHORUS

Whack fol the dah, dance to your partner Welt the flure yer trot-ters shake, Was-n't it the truth I told you, Lot's of fun at Fin-ne-gan's Wake.

One morning Tim was rather full,
  His head felt heavy which made him shake,
He fell from the ladder and broke his skull,
  So they carried him home his corpse to wake.
They rolled him up in a nice clean sheet,
  And laid him out upon the bed,
With a gallon of whiskey at his feet,
  And a barrel of porter at his head.

His friends assembled at the wake,
  And Mrs. Finnegan called for lunch,
First they brought in tay and cake,
  Then pipes, tobacco, and whiskey punch.
Miss Biddy O'Brien began to cry,
  'Such a neat clean corpse, did you ever see,
Arrah, Tim avourneen, why did you die?'
  'Ah, hould your gab,' said Paddy McGee.

Then Biddy O'Connor took up the job,
  'Biddy,' says she, 'you're wrong, I'm sure,
But Biddy gave her a belt in the gob,
  And left her sprawling on the floor;
Oh, then the war did soon enrage;
  'Twas woman to woman and man to man,
Shillelagh law did all engage,
  And a row and a ruction soon began.

Then Micky Maloney raised his head,
  When a noggin of whiskey flew at him,
It missed and falling on the bed,
  The liquor scattered over Tim;
Bedad he revives, see how he rises,
  And Timothy rising from the bed,
Says, 'Whirl your liquor round like blazes,
  Thanam o'n dhoul, do ye think I'm dead?'

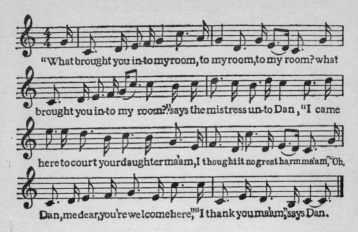

"What brought you in-to my room, to my room, to my room? what

brought you in-to my room?" says the mistress un-to Dan, "I came

here to court your daughter ma'am, I thought it no great harm ma'am," "Oh,

Dan, me dear, you're welcome here," "I thank you ma'am," says Dan.

"How come you to know my daughter, my daughter,
  my daughter?
  How came you to know my daughter?" says the mistress
    unto Dan.
"Goin' to the well for water, ma'am,
  To raise the can I taught her, ma'am."
"Oh, Dan, my dear, you're welcome here."
"I thank you ma'am," says Dan.

"Oh then, you can have my daughter, my daughter, my
    daughter,
  I'll let you take my daughter," says the mistress unto
    Dan.
"And when you take my daughter, Dan,
  Of course you'll take me also, Dan.
  Oh, Dan, my dear, you're welcome here,"
"I thank you, ma'am," says Dan.

This couple they got married, got married, got married.
This couple they got married, Miss Elizabeth and Dan,
And now he keeps her mother and her father and his
     charmer, O.
And they're known throughout the country
By the name of " Thank ye, Ma'am."

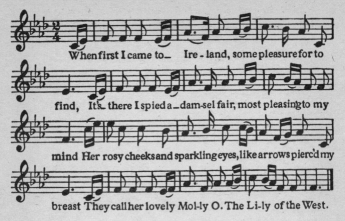

When first I came to Ireland, some pleasure for to find, It's there I spied a damsel fair, most pleasing to my mind Her rosy cheeks and sparkling eyes, like arrows pierc'd my breast They call her lovely Molly O. The Lily of the West.

Her golden hair in ringlets hung, her dress was spangled o'er,
She had rings upon her fingers brought from a foreign shore;
She'd entice both kings and princes, so costly was she dressed,
She far exceeds Diana bright—she's the Lily of the West.

One day as I was walking down by a shady grove,
I espied a lord of high degree conversing with my love,
She sang a song delightful while I was sore oppressed,
Saying "I bid adieu to Molly O, the Lily of the West."

I stepped up with my rapier and my dagger in my hand,
And dragged him from my false love and boldly bid him stand,
But being mad with desperation, I swore I'd pierce his breast,
I was then deceived by Molly O, the Lily of the West.

I then did stand my trial, and boldly I did plead,
A flaw was in my indictment found and that soon had me freed,
That beauty bright I did adore, the judge did her address,
"Now go, you faithless Molly O, the Lily of the West."

Now that I've gained my liberty, a-roving I will go,
I'll ramble through old Ireland, and travel Scotland o'er;
Tho' she thought to swear my life away, she still disturbs my
    rest,
I still must style her Molly O, the Lily of the West.

When first I came into this counterie It was to
view the sweet flowers gay, I then fell courting a pretty
fair maid, She appeared to me like the Queen of
May. I asked her kind-ly would she mar-ry Or would she
choose to be a sail-or's wife, Oh, no, kind sir, I would rather
tar-ry And I would choose a sweet sin-gle life.

Oh fairest creature, the pride of nature
Why do you differ from all female kind,
For you are youthful and fair and handsome,
For to marry you I am much inclined.
Now kind sir since I must tell you,
I am promised these five years and more,
To one O Reilly from the County Leitrim,
Which often grieves my poor heart full sore.

I wish I had you in Phoenix Island,
One hundred miles from your native home,
Or in some valley where none could find you,
You might incline then to be my own;
For there I would caress my jewel,
If along with me you'd consent to go,
I'll sail you over to Pensylvania,
And bid adieu to Reilly for evermore.

You have not me in Phoenix Island,
One hundred miles from my native home,
Or in a valley where none can find me,
So I'll not incline then to be your own,
Therefore don't teaze me nor yet dispraise me
But along with you I'm not inclined to go,
So do sail over to where you came from,
For I'll wait for Reilly for evermore.

You are like the swan that sails on the ocean
And making motions with both its wings,
Your snowy breast would be a potion,
For any Lord or an Irish King,
For you are youthful, fair and handsome
You are fitting to be a queen,
I wish I was in battle wounded,
Before your beautiful face I'd seen.

In the morning when I cannot see you,
My heart lies bleeding for you all day,
For in the evening I can't come near you
For them that's bound they must obey.
Youth and folly makes young men marry
And here no longer can I stay,
What can't be cured must be endured,
So farewell darling I must away.

95.—SWEET CARNLOCH BAY

When Win-ter was brawling, o'er high hills and mountains, And dark were the clouds o'er the deep rol-ling say, I spied a wee lass as the day-light was dawning, She was asking the road to sweet Carnloch Bay.

I said my wee lassie I canna weel tell ye
The number of miles or how far it might be
But if you'll consent I'll convoy you a wee bit,
And I'll show you the road to sweet Carnloch Bay.

You turn to the right and pass down by the churchyard
Cross over the river and down by the sea ;
We'll call in Pat Hamill's and have a wee drop there
Just to help us along to sweet Carnloch Bay.

Here's a health to Pat Hamill likewise the wee lassie
And to every laddie that's listening to me.
And ne'er turn your back on a bonny wee lassie
When she's asking the road to sweet Catnloch Bay.

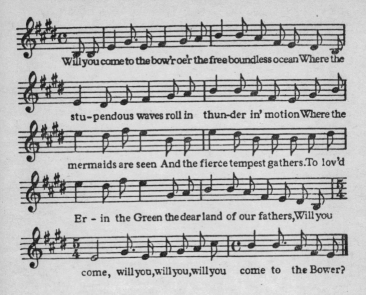

Will you come to the bow'r o'er the free boundless ocean Where the
stu-pendous waves roll in thun-der in' motion Where the
mermaids are seen And the fierce tempest gathers. To lov'd
Er - in the Green the dear land of our fathers, Will you
come, will you, will you, will you come to the Bower?

Will you come to the land of O'Neill and O'Donnell
Of Lord Lucan of old and the immortal O'Connell.
Where Brian drove the Danes and St. Patrick the vermin
And whose valleys remain still most beautiful and charming.

You can visit Benburb and the storied Black Water,
Where Owen Roe met Munroe and his chieftains did slaughter
Where the lambs skip and play on the mossey all over,
From those bright golden views to enchanting Rostrevor.

You can see Dublin City and the fine groves of Blarney,
The Bann, Boyne, the Liffey and the Lakes of Killarney;
You may ride on the tide o'er the broad majestic Shannon,
You may sail round Loch Neagh and see storied Dungannon.

You can visit New Ross, gallant Wexford and Gorey,
Where the green was last seen by proud Saxon and Tory,
Where the soil is sanctified by the blood of each true man
Where they died satisfied their enemies they would not run from.

Will you come and awake our lost land from its slumber
And her fetters we will break, links that long are encumbered,
And the air will resound with Hosanna to greet you
On the shore will be found gallant Irishmen to meet you.

Will you come, will you, will you, will you come to the
    Bower?

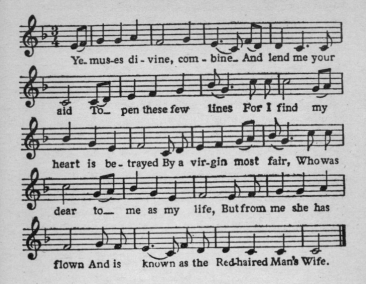

Ye mus-es di-vine, com-bine And lend me your aid To pen these few lines For I find my heart is be-trayed By a vir-gin most fair, Who was dear to me as my life, But from me she has flown And is known as the Red-haired Man's Wife.

A letter I'll send by a friend down to the sea-shore,
To let her understand I'm the man that does her adore,
And if she would but leave that slave I'd forfeit my life,
She'd live like a lady and ne'er be the red-haired man's wife.

Ah ! remember the day that I gave to you my true heart,
When you solemnly swore that no more we ever would part
But your mind's like the ocean, each notion has taken her flight
And left me bewailing the tale of the red-haired man's wife.

Your absence my dear, I fear, is the cause of my woe,
But to see you again I mean in a short time to go ;
And when I come near you I really would venture my life
That with me you would steer and ne'er be the red-haired
    man's wife.

I straight took my way next day through a shady green grove,
And crossed purling streams, where sweet birds mostly do rove
Thence I was conveyed to where nature boasts of her pride
Where I stood all amazed—and gazed on the red-haired man's
    wife.

I offered a favour and sealed it with my own hand,
She thus answered, and said—would you lead me to break
    the command
Therefore take it easy—since nature has caused so much strife
I was given away—and will stay as the red-haired man's wife.

My darling sweet Phoenix if now you will be my own,
For the Patriarch David had a number of wives 'tis well known
So yield to my embraces and straight put an end to all strife
If not I'll run crazy, or gain the red-haired man's wife.

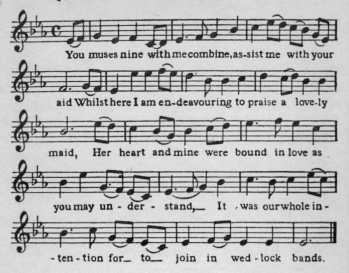

You muses nine with me combine, as-sist me with your aid Whilst here I am en-deavouring to praise a love-ly maid, Her heart and mine were bound in love as you may un-der-stand, It was our whole in-ten-tion for to join in wed-lock bands.

I hope you'll pay attention, and the truth to you I'll tell;
She was a Quaker's daughter, a maid I loved right well.
We being not of one persuasion, her father made a plan,
He done his whole endeavour to hang me in the wrong.

My name is John McGoldrick, the same I'll ne'er deny—
They swore I was a radical; condemned I was to die.
As soon as my dead letter came, my sorrows did renew,
Saying, " For to die I do deny—Brave boys, what shall I do ? "

At length my dearest jewel became servant in the jail ;
She found her opportunity and did it not conceal.
She says, " Young John McGoldrick, I hope to be your wife ;
I will do my best endeavour to save your precious life."

That night the god of Bacchus to the jailer did appear,
All with a club of gentlemen inviting him to beer.
They had the strongest liquor and the very best of wine—
The jailer and the turnkey to sleep they did incline.

She says, "Young John McGoldrick, I hope you will agree.
And bind yourself upon your oath, and come along with me;
For I have stole the jailer's keys, and I could do no more,"
That very night I took my flight out of the prison door.

It was early the next morning the hurry it begun,
The 66th pursued us without either fife or drum.
The jailer and the turnkey they quickly ran us down,
And brought us back as prisoners once more to Cavan town.

And there we lay bewailing, all in a prison bound,
With heavy bolts of iron secured unto the ground.
All for a second trial they brought us to the jail;
Their intention was to hang me, and send her to New South
    Wales.

But I may thank Lord Corry, and his father, Lord Belmore
Long may they live in splendour around Loch Erne shore!
They sent me a grand charácter, as plainly you may see,
Which caused the judge and jury that day to set us free.

You reader, now excuse me, I did refine my quill,
The praises of a lovely maid these papers for to fill.
For I have become her husband, and she my loving wife;
In spite of her old father, she saved my precious life.

You gen-tle Mu - ses, I pray ex-cuse me, Your kind in-
-fu - sion now grant once more, Till I praise a
maid - en sweet and en-gag - ing She's lovely Ve - nus I do a-
-dore Un-less you'll aid me, my art will fail me, A sketch most
pleas-ing I must have drawn And still I'm ea - ger from heart to
please her, Sweet love-ly Ka - tie of Lis-ke - haun.

One frosty morning while passing northways,
By Limerick suburbs I chanced to meet,
My darling phoenix I mean young Katie.
And she coming early up William Street,
Her blue eyes beaming their dart prevailing,
Her conversation was mild and warm
My heart was breaking for to be leaving,
Sweet lovely Katie of Liskehaun.

In the evening early when home returning
Alone by a hay-rick I did her see.
As if quite conscious her aspect fearful
That lovely fair one would shrink from me,
I would rayther than the flocks of Damer
Or the cattle grazing on O'Donnel's lawn,
That on the hay bench I could be seated,
With lovely Katie of Liskehaun.

Altho' young Katie is a rich young lady,
And far superior in wealth for me,
Yet while acquainted she is kind and faithful,
By long experience I this can see.
In the fruit season when the road seems weary
And I going early back to Drishawn,
All my consolation was seeing young Katie,
That lovely maiden of Liskehaun.

If you seen young Katie dressed out so gaily,
For pleasure facing along the street,
She appeared the sweetest most modest creature,
And was admired by all who did her meet,
Her golden fair locks in curls waving
Down on her waist her fine ringlets shone,
And in every feature the pride of nature
Was lovely Katie of Liskehaun.

If Jason famous had known young Katie,
With her he'd sail to the Persian shore,
And bold Ulysses for to release her,
The briney regions he would search o'er
And you know Paris the Trojan hero,
Who brought Queen Hélen to King Priam
He would venture greater his bride to make her
Sweet lovely Katie of Liskehaun.

[cont. on p. 217

100.—BACHELOR'S WALK: MOURNFUL LINES
ON THE MILITARY OUTRAGE IN DUBLIN

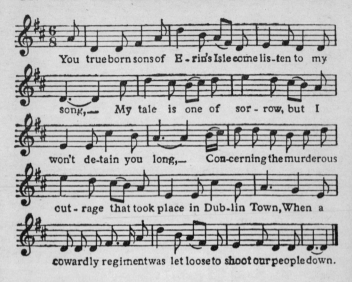

You true born sons of E-rin's Isle come lis-ten to my song,— My tale is one of sor-row, but I won't de-tain you long,— Con-cerning the murderous out-rage that took place in Dub-lin Town, When a cowardly regiment was let loose to shoot our people down.

On the 26th day of July, the truth I'll tell to you,
The Irish Volunteers all swore their enemies to subdue,
They marched straight out to Howth and soon the people
    were alarmed,
When they heard the glorious news " Our Irish Volunteers
    are armed."

The crowds they all kept cheering on as our brave defenders
    passed
But their cheers were stopped by an outrage which for some
    time did last.
Our gallant men, the Volunteers, were met in front and rear,
By the King's Own Scottish cowards who are doomed for
    everywhere.

198

God save our gallant Captain Judge, the hero of the band,
Who nearly gave his precious life for the just cause of his land
In spite of terrible injuries and weak from loss of blood,
He fondly hugged his rifle grand the prize of his brotherhood.

Next in the list of heroes is the scout so well renowned,
With the butt end of his rifle felled a Borderer to the ground,
He disarmed him of his weapons and soon made his escape,
By climbing a wall in Fairview, for his young life was at stake.

The Dublin Police were ordered the Volunteers for to subdue,
But O'Neill and Gleeson boldly replied: " Such a thing
    we decline to do.
For to fight against our countrymen would on us put a stain,
For we wish to see our native land a Nation Once Again."

On Bachelor's Walk a scene took place, which I'm sure had
    just been planned,
For the cowardly Scottish Borderers turned and fired without
    command.
With bayonets fixed they charged the crowd and left them in
    their gore,
But their deeds will be remembered in Irish hearts for evermore.

God rest the souls of those who sleep apart from earthly sin,
Including Mrs. Duffy, James Brennan, and Patrick Quinn;
But we will yet avenge them and the time will surely come,
That we'll make the Scottish Borderers pay for the cowardly
    deeds they done.

101.—THE BOYS OF OLD ERIN THE GREEN

You true heart-ed sons of Hi-ber-nia I hope you'll at-tend for a while, To a song I am go-ing to sing you In praise of old E-rin's green isle; Con--cern-ing that ter-ri-ble bat-tle, Where blood-shed and bat-ter-y was seen, With the beef-eat-ing bul-lies of Eng-land And the boys of old E-rin the Green.

CHORUS

Hur-rah for the sons of the Sham-rock, Who al-ways vic-tor-ious have been, And where is the na-tion can e-qual The boys of old E-rin the Green

To cut down the English harvest
    Some hearty gay fellows did go
From the Counties of Clare, Louth and Leitrim,
    Roscommon, Kildare and Mayo,
From Counties Tyrone, Cork and Cavan,
    The boys of Tipperary were seen;
Each man had a twig of shillelagh,
    That grew in old Erin the Green.   *Chorus.*

Being dry they went into an ale house,
    They joined to drink whiskey and beer;
Each man drank a favourite toast,
    To his wife or sweetheart so dear.
And they sang of the land of their fathers,
    Where oppression and suffering were seen,
Which caused many hundreds to wander
    Away from Old Erin the Green.   *Chorus.*

At length they all emptied their glasses,
    For that being the hiring day,
To look out for work at high wages,
    To the market-place they took their way.
The English assembled in hundreds,
    Where all sorts of weapons were seen,
Determined they were for to slaughter
    The boys of Old Erin the Green.   *Chorus.*

The town it was took and retaken,
    Three times in the course of that day;
" I'm afraid, boys, we're going to be beaten,"
    Barney Murphy to them he did say.
" Never," cried Barney McCloskey,
    McBrerty, McQuail, and O'Neill,
" Shall the English say that they conquered
    The boys of Old Erin the Green."   *Chorus.*

[cont. on p. 217

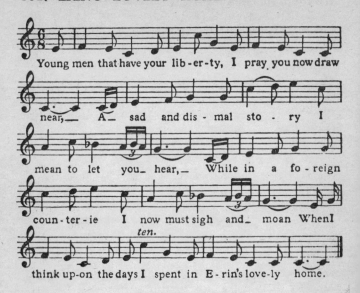

Young men that have your lib-er-ty, I pray you now draw near,— A— sad and dis-mal sto-ry I mean to let you— hear,— While in a fo-reign coun-ter-ie I now must sigh and— moan When I think up-on the days I spent in E-rin's love-ly home.

When I was young and in my prime, my age was twenty-one,
I then became a servant to a noble gentleman,
I served him, too, in honesty, and very well 'tis known,
Till with cruelty he banished me from Erin's lovely home.

The reason that he banished me I mean to let you know—
'Tis true I loved his daughter, and she loved me also;
She had a princely fortune, of riches I had none,
So that is why he banished me from Erin's lovely home.

'Twas in her father's garden, all in the month of June,
When everything was pleasant, and flowers all in bloom,
She said " My dearest Willie, if along with me you'll roam,
You need not fret for those you left in Erin's lovely home."

202

That very day I gave consent, that proved my overthrow,
Far from her father's dwelling along with her did go;
The night was bright with the moonlight as we set out alone,
We thought we had got safe away from Erin's lovely home.

When we arrived at Belfast town all by the break of day,
She said "Prepare, my jewel, our passage for to pay";
Five hundred pounds she counted down, saying "that will be
    your own
So never fret for those you left in Erin's lovely home."

Now to my great misfortune, I mean to let you hear,
It was in three days after that her father did appear,
He brought me back to Omagh Jail, in the County of Tyrone,
From that I was transported from Erin's lovely home.

When I received my sentence, it grieved my heart full sore,
The parting from my own true love it grieved me ten times more,
There are seven links upon my chain, and every link a year,
Before I can return again to the arms of my dear.

When the coach it came to the jail-yard to take us all away,
My true love she came up to me, and thus to me did say,
"Cheer up my dearest Willie, for you I'll not disown,
Until you do return again to Erin's lovely home."

In the Appendix are contained additional verses of some songs which space would not allow to appear on the double-page opening allowed for each song, and also a few more ballads sung to airs which appear under other titles.

Appendix

3A.—POOR OLD GRANUAILE

My dream to some with joy will come and comes with grief
    to more,
As it did to me, my country, that dear old Erin's shore;
I dreamt I stood upon a hill beside a lovely vale,
And it's there I spied a comely maid and her name was
    Granuaile.

Her lovely hair hung down so fair and she was dressed in
    green,
I thought she was the fairest soul that e'er my eyes had seen;
As I drew near I then could hear by the pleasant morning
    gale,
As she went along she sang her song, saying, "I'm poor old
    Granuaile."

In O'Connell's time in '29, we had no braver men,
They struggled hard both day and night to gain our rights
    again;
Still, by coercion we were bound and our sons were sent to
    jail,
"You need not fret, we'll Home Rule get," says poor old
    Granuaile.

I thought she had a splendid harp, by her side she let it fall,
She played the tunes called *Brian Boru, Garryowen,* and *Tara's
    Hall.*
Then *God Save Ireland* was the next, and *Our Martyrs who
    died in Jail,*
"You need not fret, we'll have freedom yet," says poor old
    Granuaile.

When I wakened from my slumber and excited by my fight,
I thought it was the clear daylight, and I found that it was
    night;
I looked all round and could see naught but the walls of
    a lonely jail,
And that was the last I ever saw of poor old Granuaile.

Here is a ballad which Joseph Plunkett wrote to tune No. 8

8A.—THE FOOT AND MOUTH DISEASE

As I walked over to Macharoarty
One summer morning not long ago,
I met a maiden most sadly wailing,
Her cheeks down-streaming with signs of woe.
I asked her kindly as sure became me,
In manner dacent without e'er a smile,
And says she "I'll tell you, oh youthful stranger,
What is my danger, at the present time.

"In my father's lands there were many mansions,
With horses, cattle and sheep *go leór*,
Until the stranger came over the border
With detention order that grieved him sore.
His lands they plundered and killed six hundred,
The rest they sundered north, west and south,
Saying, ' You can keep the skies and the woolly fleeces,
For the beasts have diseases of the foot and mouth.'

"Then say you'll aid me, o youthful stranger
To save the herds and my father's life,
And my marriage portion that's my only fortune
For the lad that's willing to make me his wife.
They're slaves and traitors, O friends and neighbours
Not a mouth was dropping not a hoof was sprung
But the only diseases came over from England
Were the cloven hoof and the dirty tongue."

Here is the fragment originally sung to air No. 20

20A.—THE TOWN OF ANTRIM

It being in the town of Ant(e)rim near to the River Bann
It is the finest river of any in Irelan'
It is as fine a river as ever my eyes-a did see
And I'll mind it well when far away from Paddy's green counterei.
Fare-a well unto my comrades all, that will a-meet at Drumsoo
Likewise my friends and neigh-bours to you I bid adieu
I'll miss my comrade boys and girls and my comrades they'll a-miss me
But I'll mind them all when far away from Paddy's green counterie.

27.—FATHER MURPHY (cont. from p. 55)

The streets of England were left quite naked
Of all its army both foot and horse
The Highlands of Scotland were left unguarded
Likewise the Hessians the seas they crossed.
But if the Frenchmen had reinforced us,
And landed transports in Bagenbun,
Father John Murphy would be their seconder,
And sixteen thousand with him would come.

Success attend the sweet County Wexford
Threw off its yoke and to battle run;
Let them not think we gave up our arms
For every man has a pike and gun.

39.—THE HACKLER FROM GROUSE HALL

(cont. from p. 79)

Thank God the day isn't far away when Home Rule will be
seen
And brave Parnell at home will dwell and shine in College
Green;
Our Policemen will all be then our nation's choice and all
Old Balfour's pack will get the sack and banished from
Grouse Hall.

Let old and young clear up their lungs and sing this little
song
Come join with me and let him see you all resent the
wrong;
And while I live I'll always give a prayer for his downfall
And when I die I don't deny I'll haunt him from
Grouse Hall.   *[Sequel overleaf*

Each loyal man if such there can be found about Grouse Hall
Come join with me in sympathy and pity my downfall,
I am despised and stigmatised for tyranny and wrong
Both far and near my name you'll hear re-echoed on a song.

I am belied because I tried to enforce the law
And keep the peace around the place with drunken roughs and all
Tho' my protest may be expressed in language rather strong
I think I'm bound for to confound the author of that song.

That hackling clown who can let down a tear with every smile
And all his days with perfect ease could act the crocodile
With nimble shanks he plays his pranks on peelers all along
And does aim to blast my fame by his wild rebel song.

He begs along and sings a song and has no care at all
And all around the hills resound with Jemmy of Grouse Hall;
But very soon he'll change his tune with bolts of iron strong
When Balfour's shears gets round his ears he'll sing another song.

The league 'tis true I did pursue the priest why should I spare
Who broke the laws and was the cause of bloodshed everywhere
But Martin's fall in Donegal will be avenged ere long
McFadden's crew will get their due then who will sing the song.

I do deny that ever I a naked female seen
The gentle sex I know they're vexed they feel the insult keen.
It was a shame to fix such blame upon me in the wrong
But while I live I'll not forgive the man that made the song.

In all my life to Tully's wife I never spoke a word
The crazy loon cried out too soon his jealous mind was stirred
I still maintain that he's insane tho' Lovelock says I'm wrong
That mental quack I'm told for fact 'twas he who made the song.

My poteen raid I am afraid 'twill end in failure too
Attorney Lynch won't yield an inch in what he does pursue.
The logic sound can well confound my cases right and wrong
No doubt but he might chance to be the man that made the song.

There's men of course among the force who sympathise with me
There's others, too, but not a few can well enjoy the spree.
To them I say a reckoning day will come before its long
And Cooper's fate will compensate the man that sings the song.

I'll give five pounds and jink it down to find the poet's name
Because, of course, he is the source of all my grief and shame.
And in a coach to Cecil Roche I'll march him through the throng
I know he'll be right glad to see the man that made the song.

In all my boast the hackler's ghost annoys me most of all
I'm still in dread that when he's dead he'll haunt me from Grouse Hall
In dreams at night I rave and fright in accents shrill and long
That pierce my ears I think I hear the echo of his song.

I'm well content for to be sent away this very day
To Cork or Clare or anywhere one hundred miles away.
This curst Grouse Hall caused my downfall I have been here too long
Before I'd go I'd wish to know the man that made the song.

NOTES.

" *Hackler.*"—In the days of this ballad a lot of flax was grown in
Co. Cavan. The people prepared their own flax and made it
into thread for use on the spinning wheels. The last operation
prior to the flax being made ready for spinning was called
" hackling." It was a process of fining down the flax in preparation
for the spinning wheel. Hackling was a trade and hacklers went
from house to house hackling the flax in each house.

Reference to Celebration of Mass in the "Hackler" and to
Martin and McFadden in " The Sergeant's Lamentation."—Father
McFadden of Glenties, Co. Donegal, made a seditious speech in
favour of the Land League. A special force of police was brought
to Donegal to arrest him, among them the Grouse Hall Sergeant.
The force was under D.I. Martin. On Sunday morning during
Mass the police surrounded the chapel and arrested Father
McFadden immediately after Mass. The people who were at
Mass congregated around and a melée ensued in which D.I.
Martin was killed. The affair got great publicity but it was
never discovered who was responsible for Martin's death.

Searching of Beds.—The people used to hide the poteen in the bed,
and the Sergeant always searched the beds. Attorney Lynch was
a Solicitor in Virginia who always defended the people in poteen
prosecutions.

Balfour's Shears.—Reference to the close crop given to convicts.
Cooper.—Probably a member of the R.I.C. who was dismissed.
Cecil Roche.—The local R.M.

[Words and notes supplied by John Smith, Stravicnabo, Ballyjamesduff, Co. Cavan.]

There's some says I'm foolish and more says I'm wise
But being fond of the women I think is no crime
For the son of King David had ten hundred wives
And his wisdom was highly recorded
I'll till a good garden and live at my ease
And each woman and child can partake of the same
If there's war in the cabin theirselves they may blame
    Agus fágaimid siúd mar atá se.

And now for the future I mean to be wise
And I'll send for the women that acted so kind,
And I'll marry them all on the morrow by and by
If the clergy agree to the bargain.
And when I'm on my back and my soul is at peace
These women will crowd for to cry at my wake
And their sons and their daughters will offer their prayer
To the Lord for the soul of their father.

To the same tune as No. 44 is also sung:

44A.—PAT O DONNELL

My name is Pat O Donnell and I come from Donegal
I am you know a venomous foe to traitors one and all.
For the shooting of James Carey I was tried in London town
And now upon the gallows high my life I must lay down.

I sailed on board the ship, *Melrose*, in August, eighty-three,
Before I landed in Capetown it came well-known to me;
When I saw he was James Carey we had angry words and blows,
The villain, he tried to take my life on board the ship *Melrose*.

I stood up to defend myself and fight before I'd die,
A pocket pistol I drew forth, and at him I let fly;
I gave him the second revolver, boys, which pierced him through
    the heart
And I let him have the third one, boys, before we did depart.

Carey's wife and son came to the cabin where he lay,
And seen him lying all in his gore, which filled her with dismay
" O Donnell you shot my husband," Mrs. Carey now did cry,
" Oh, yes! I did in self-defence, madam," then said I.

The captain had me handcuffed, and in irons firmly bound,
He handed me over as a Fenian when I landed in Capetown ;
I was then brought back to London until my trial came on,
And the prosecutors for the Crown was Carey's wife and son.

To all the evidence they swore, I said it was a lie,
The jury found me guilty, and the judge made this reply,
" You'll never more see Erin's shore, O Donnell, you must die ;
On the twenty-first of December, upon the gallows high."

Here's a health to old Donegal, the place where I was born,
And also the United States, to it I never showed any scorn ;
Unto the Virgin Mary on my bended knees I call,
To pray for poor O Donnell from the town of Donegal.

I wished I was a free man, and could live for another year,
I'd make all those informers fly before my eyes with fear ;
St. Patrick banished the serpents from our blessed and holy ground,
I'd make them fly before my eyes like a hare before the hound.

Good Christians all, on you I call, this is my dying day,
They say I am an Irishman, kind Christians for me pray ;
My grave is ready open, and I'm ready for to die,
May the Lord have mercy on my soul while in my grave I lie.

52.—LANIGAN'S BALL (cont. from p. 105)

Boys, oh boys, 'tis then there was ructions,
Myself got a lick from big Phelim McHugh,
But soon I replied to his kind introduction,
And kicked up a terrible hullabaloo.
Ould Casey the piper was near being strangled,
They squeezed up his pipes, bellows, chanters and all,
The girls in their ribbons they all got entangled,
And that put an end to Lanigan's ball.

53A.—THE LAMENTATIONS OF PATRICK BRADY; OR, THE HEROES OF NINETY-EIGHT.

Ye true born heroes I hope you will now lend an ear
To a few simple verses, the truth unto you I'll declare.
My name is Pat Brady, the same I will never deny
In Ross I was born, and in Naas condemned to die.

I once had a home, and a shelter from want and from woe,
But I'm now among strangers where no person does me know,
Condemned for high treason, to die on a gallows tree,
For seeking the rights of poor Erin my dear country.

My father God rest him, was taken without any crime,
And marched off a prisoner, and hanged in one hour's time,
Myself and two brothers to the wood were forced to fly
We vowed for revenge or else by the sword we'd die.

It was early next morning to Gorey we all marched away,
Where the drums they did rattle, and our fifes so sweetly did play,
Full twelve thousand heroes, nine hundred and forty three,
We took all the cannon that day from their artillery.

It was early next morning to Wicklow we all marched away,
Our hearts most glorious with liberty shining that day.
But entering of Ferns we were attacked by the Yeomanry,
We fought them for four hours till we gained a complete victory.

We fought in New Ross, and we fought upon Vinegar Hill,
And in sweet Castlecomer were the Colliers joined us with free will,
Out of fourteen engagements we received not a wound or a scar,
Till I lost my two brothers at the battle of sweet Castlebar.

To march with the Frenchmen it left me much troubled in mind,
To think I should go and leave my two brothers behind,
Through the sweet county Leitrim to Granard our way we took,
And were attacked by the army at the village of Ballinamuck.

We fought with good courage but defeated we were on that day,
We were forced to retreat, no longer our heroes could stay,
But the brave Longford heroes to fly from us they never could,
They never could yield till they'd lose the last drop of their blood.

When forced to retreat for refuge we thought for to fly,
For all that was taken was certain and sure for to die,
To the sweet County Wicklow for refuge we thought for to face,
We were taken in Rathangan and twelve were hanged in Naas.

Come all you brave heroes the truth unto you I'll relate,
From powder or ball poor Brady has ne'er met his fate,
So all you good Christians who hear of my sorrowful fate,
You'll pray for Pat Brady, the hero of '98.

57.—CAILÍN DEAS CRÚITE NA MBÓ

(cont. from p. 115)

"A young maid is like a ship sailing,
There's no knowing how long she may steer,
For with every blast she's in danger,
Oh consent love and banish all care,
For riches I care not a farthing,
Your affection I want and no more
In comfort I'd wish to enjoy you,
My Cailín deas crúite na mBó."

62.—THE NIGHT OF THE RAGMAN'S BALL

(cont. from p. 125)

So we all sat down to some ham-parings when everything was
quiet,
Well, I must say, for broken noses we had a lovely
night;
Black eyes—they were in great demand, not to mention split
heads at all,
So anyone wants to commit suicide let them come to the Ragman's Ball.

213

May monkeys still bite him and mad apes still fight him,
And everyone slight him asleep and awake,
May weasels still gnaw him and jackdaws still claw him,
The monster that murdered Nell Flaherty's drake.

The only good news that I have to diffuse,
Is that long Peter Hughes, and blind piper McPeak
That big-nosed Bob Manson and buck-toothed Bob Hanson,
Each man has a grandson of my darling drake,
My bird he had dozens of nephews and cousins
And one I must get or my poor heart would break,
To keep my mind easy or else I'll go crazy,
There ends the whole tale of Nell Flaherty's drake.

To the same tune—or one very like it, is sung:

67A.—THE OLD LEATHER BREECHES

At the Sign of the Bell on the road to Clonmel
Paddy Hegarty kept a neat shebeen,
He sold pig's meat and bread, kept a fine lodging bed
And was liked in the country he lived in.
Himself and his wife, both struggled through life
On weekdays Pat mended the ditches
But on Sundays he dressed in a suit of the best
And his pride was his old leather breeches.

For twenty-one years at least so it appears,
His father these breeches had run in,
And the morning he died, he to his bedside
Called Paddy, his own darling son, in;
His advice then he gave ere he went to his grave !
And he bade him take care of his riches,
Says he " It's no use to step into my shoes,
But I'd like you'd leap into my breeches."

Now last winter's snow left victuals so low
That Paddy was ate out completely,
With the snow coming down he could not get to town
Thoughts of hunger did bother him greatly

One night as he lay adreaming away
Of ghosts, fairies, spirits and witches,
He heard an uproar, just outside his door,
And he jumped up to pull on his breeches.

Says Brian McGurk, with a voice like a Turk,
Come, Paddy, and get us some eating,
Says Big Andy Moore, we'll burst open the door,
Sure this is no night to be waiting;
The words were scarce spoke when the door it was broke,
And they crowded round Paddy like leeches,
And they swore by the hob, if they didn't get prog,
They would eat him clean out of his breeches.

Poor Paddy in dread slipped up to the bed
That held Judy his own darling wife in;
And there 'twas agreed that they should get a feed,
So he slipped out and brought a big knife in;
He cut out the waist of his breeches, the beast,
And he ripped out the buttons and stitches,
And he cut them in stripes, the way they do tripes,
And he boiled them his old leather breeches.

The tripes they were stewed, on a dish they were strewed,
And the boys all roared out: Lord be thankit,
But Hegarty's wife was afraid of her life
And she thought it high time for to shank it;
To see how they smiled for they thought Paddy boiled
Some mutton or beef of the richest,
But little they knew it was leather burgoo
That was made out of Paddy's ould breeches.

As they messed on the stuff says Darby, it's tough,
Says Andy "you're no judge of mutton,"
When Brian McGurk, on the point of his fork,
Held up a big ivory button;
Says Paddy, what's that, sure I thought it was fat,
Brian leps to his feet and he screeches:
"Be the powers above, I was trying to shove
Me teeth through the flap of his breeches."

They all flew at Pat, but he cut out of that,
He ran when he saw them all rising;
Says Brian, make haste, and go for the priest,
Be the holy Saint Patrick, I'm poisoned;
Revenge for the joke they had, for they broke
All the chairs, bowls, and tables, and dishes,
And from that very night they'd knock out your daylight
If they'd catch you with old leather breeches.

74.—THE PEELER AND THE GOAT (cont. from p. 147)

" The consequence be what it will,
 A peeler's power I'll let you know,
I'll handcuff you, at all events,
 And march you off to Bridewell O.
And sure, you rogue, you can't deny
 Before the judge or jury O,
Intimidation with your horns,
 And threatening me with fury O."

" I make no doubt but you are drunk,
 With whiskey, rum, or brandy O,
Or you wouldn't have such gallant spunk
 To be so bold or manly O.
You readily would let me pass
 If I had money handy O,
To treat you to a poteen glass—
 ' Tis then I'd be the dandy O."

82.—DOBBIN'S FLOWERY VALE (cont. from p. 163)

It's mutual love together drew
 Both with a kind embrace,
While tears like rosy drops of dew,
 Did trickle down her face;
She strove in vain him to detain,
 But while she did bewail,
He bade adieu, and I withdrew
 From Dobbin's Flowery Vale.

84.—DORAN'S ASS (cont. from p. 167)

So he up and told her all quite civil,
   While she prepared a brimming glass,
About how he hugged and smugged the devil
   Says she, " Sure that was Doran's ass."
And " So I believe it was," says Pat,
   So they got wed on the very next day,
But she never got the new straw hat
   That the jackass ate upon the way.

99.—LOVELY KATIE OF LISKEHAUN
(cont. from p. 197)

Farewell, dear Katie, I now must leave you,
The train from Limerick is passing by,
It checks me freely and bids me stay with
The lovely maiden of Bunratty,
But summer season and times are changing
Once more I'll stray back from fair Drishawn,
And make application to my sweet young Katie
That lovely fair one of Liskehaun.

101.—THE BOYS OF OLD ERIN THE GREEN
(cont. from p. 201)

They gave a cheer for old Ireland,
   And forward once more they did go,
The town it was quickly retaken,
   And quickly they banished their foe.
The beef-eating cowardly English,
   From that day quite submissive have been,
For fear of another encounter with
   The boys of Old Erin the Green.   *Chorus.*

In the following commentary I have not attempted to give a complete list of all the published versions either of words or of music. It takes the form of a personal acknowledgment of sources, and a reference to the better-known collections, which are referred to by abbreviations, as follows :

EFS   *Journal of the Folk Song Society* (England).

IFS   *Journal of the Irish Folk Song Society.*

AMS   *Amhráin Mhuighe Seóla.* Mrs. Costello.

Ji   Joyce's *Ancient Irish Music.*

Jii   Joyce's *Irish Music and Song.*

Jiii   Joyce's *Old Irish Folk Music and Songs*

Pi   Petrie's *Ancient Music of Ireland.*

Pii   Petrie's *Ancient Music of Ireland.* (Supplement).

Piii   *The Complete Petrie Collection.*

M   Moffat's *Minstrelsy of Ireland.*

Bi   Bunting's first collection.

Bii   Bunting's second collection.

Biii   Bunting's third collection.

**   Indicates the source of the words.

BS   Printed Ballad sheets.

Many public libraries have considerable collections of broadsheet ballads. Henry Bradshaw was a pioneer collector and the most exhaustive printed list of Irish ballads is that contained in " The Catalogue of the Henry Bradshaw Collection," Cambridge. Its usefulness would have been greatly enhanced if the first lines had been given, as often we find two or more ballads under the one name, and again, the name may have different forms.

Commentary

1 Learnt in childhood from Frank Phelan of Clonmel. EFSvi, 267. *An Crimlneach Cam.* EFSviii, 146. Villikens and his Dinah. cf. No. 50 The Old Orange Flute. ** Frank Phelan and BS.

2 Learnt in Belfast from F. J. Bigger's chauffeur (Varner), about 1912. EFSv, 60. Acquittal of Thomas Halloran; id. vi, 316, *Bearta Crua*; AMS 4, *Mullach Mór*; 98, *Anach Cuain*; cf. *Coire Ceathaich.* Moffat, *Min. of Scot. Highlands*, 50. Pii, *Maidin Fhóghmhair* or *Cailín Péacach.* Piii, 2 and 1171, *Malli bán.* Jiii, The Young Man's Lamentation. ** Varner and Mrs. Reddin. New version by F. R. Higgins, " The Spanish Lady " in *A Broadside*, 1935. EFSvi, 272, The Young and Single Sailor (to a different air). BS printed by H. Disley, High St., St. Giles, London.

3 Dublin ballad singers. Piii, 790; Jiii, No. 58, The Foggy Dew. ** BS. See Appendix for another ballad.

4 Ballad singer in Galway, 1930. cf. No. 90, Pat of Mullingar. EFSviii, 96, Whiskey You're my Darling. ** BS.

5 Patrick Walsh, Clogher Valley, Tír Eóghain. Jiii, 331; EFSiv, 136, The Female Smuggler. ** P. Walsh, cf. *Old Irish Croonauns*, by H. Galway (Boosey); *Real Sailor Songs*, by John Ashton (London, 1891), p. 71, Fair Phoeby, etc.

6 From a fisherman at Ardglass, 1913. Jiii, 184, and Piii, 179-80. Levey ii, A Daughter of Daniel O'Connell. ** BS.

7 Dublin ballad singers, about 1914. ** BS.

8 Known from childhood. EFSvi, 218, *Óchal*; id. 219, *Lá dá Rausa*; IFSviii, 13, In Aghadowey or My Blooming Daisy; id. xxi, 34, *An Aisling Geal.* Piii, 1418, *Ní'r ghabh sé d'Eóchaill*; Jiii, 680, Youghal Harbour. ** BS.

9 From a ballad singer in Waterford, 1910. cf. EFSi, 25, As I walked out; id. i, 206, The Bonny Labouring Boy; id. iii, 110, The Bonny Labouring Boy. Piii, 498, The Maid of Timahoe; Piii, 657, As I roved out one morning. Jiii, 382, The Irish Girl. Also in Joyce's *Irish Peasant Songs.* ** BS.

10 Learnt in Galway from ballad singer. IFSx, 24, *Crúiscín lán*, Piii, 139; 1231-2, *An crúiscin lan*; Ji, No. 36, p. 28. M191.

11 Known from childhood as Bob and Joan. M60, Fill the Bumper Fair (Moore). *Seán a' Bhriste Leathair* often is sung with the addition of some of these verses. See *Racaireacht Ghrinn na Tuaithe* (Mac Coluim). **BS.

12 Learnt by my mother in Limerick about 1870 from Ml. Buckley, a native of Cork. cf. Jiii, 686, and H. Galway, p. 14, No. 8. ** From memory, H. Galway and Le Fanu's *Reminiscences.*

13 Air from Jiii, 209, where one verse is given. Sent to him in 1875 by W. McKimmin of Newry. cf. Piii, 1273-4 and 1290. ** BS. The last verse I learnt in childhood from my father who knew fragments of the song; cf. Kennedy: *Banks of the Boro,* 246.

14 Dublin ballad singers. cf. The Winding Banks of Erne; IFSxi, 18, Father Tom O'Neill; Jiii, 13, The River Roe. **BS.

15 Air from Bairtle O Conghaile, Carna, 1933, *Píli Cat Bán.* cf. EFSviii, 137 (with refrain). ** Known from childhood, additions from Wiseheart's *Comic Songster* (Dublin).

16 From the late Mrs. A. Gilmer (*d.* 1934, aged 96) a native of Co. Down. cf. EFSii, 276; iii, 56; and IFSxv, 31; xxvii, 41, Irish Country Songs ii. ** BS and Mrs. Gilmer.

17 From Máire, Bean Shéamuis Mhic Aonghusa, Finglas. IFSii, 33, The Airy Bachelor. To this air there is a new song by G. N. Reddin in *A Broadside* (Cuala Press). ** BS.

18 Learnt in childhood. Chappell ii, 708; Bunting, 1840, No. 57. Moore, Davis, R. D. Joyce and others have written songs to this air. ** BS, various versions.

19 Learnt in Belfast from D. Maguire, 1913. cf. EFSvii, 54, The Manchester Angel, 3rd version, and Chappell ii, 73-4. ** BS. and D. Maguire.

20 Air of 'The Town of Antrim.' Learnt in Belfast from Cathal O Byrne, given to D. J. O'S who printed it in IFSxviii, 26. ** BS. See Appendix.

21 Learnt at Dualla, near Cashel, Christmas, 1915. cf. Piii, 808, and Jiii, 208. I have also heard this ballad sung to the well-known tune which in this collection is set to 'The Lily of the West,' No. 93. ** BS.

22 From Galway ballad singer. Piii, 185, 328, 329; EFSvii, 61, The Bold Pirate; id. vii, 62. No, my love not I. ** BS.

23 Máire, bean Mhic Aonghusa, Finglas. cf. EFSii, 217, William and Phyllis; Jiii, No. 217, The Colleen Dhas; also No. 291. Jiii, 415, The Shamrock Shore. Song in Irish *Brighid Gheal Bhán*. ** BS.

24 Air from Cathal O Byrne, Belfast. ** BS and C. O B.

25 Jiii, 600, I am a real republican. ** From *A Broadside*, Cuala Press.

26 First heard in Ringsend, Dublin, about 1920. cf. EFSiii, 57, The Dockyard Gate; Piii, 316. ** BS. Dan Donnelly was born in Townsend Street, Dublin, in 1788, and died in 1820. The great fight took place in 1815.

27 Pii, 103, *Dá dtéidhinn go cóbach*; Piii, 784-5, '98 Ballad. Jiii, 226, In deepest sorrow I think of home. cf. also No. 79, Sweet Co. Wexford. ** Kennedy: *Legends of Mt. Leinster*, 133.

28 Air from Piii, 434, I am a bold defender. ** BS.

29 P. Walsh, Clogher Valley. EFSvii, 17, The Fowler (The shooting of his dear); Jiii, 409, Molly Bawn. ** P. Walsh and BS.

30 Jiii, 269. cf. EFSvi, 274, *Aryr is mé mu' anar*; IFSxi, 14, The trip we took over the mountain; id, xxi, 9, *An Tailliúir Aerach. Cnocáinín Aerach Cill Mhuire* has similar rhythm. ** BS. This is an English country song localised in Ireland. See *English Folk Song and Dance* (Iolo Williams).

31 This air was very popular for execution songs and prisoners' laments. See Jiii, 401. ** BS and *A Broadside*, Cuala Press.

32 Denis Devereux called this tune "I'm over young to marry." Words also sung to the tune of Bob and Joan. ** Wiseheart's *Comic Songster* and D. Devereux.

33 Ji, 84. Often heard in Dublin to the same tune as The game played in Erin-go-bragh; Piii, 235, 864, My blessing go with you, sweet Erin-go-bragh. Also sung to 'Villikens and his Dinah.' See No. 1.

34 The tune is a poor version of The Boys of Wexford, No. 48, q.v. ** BS.

35 Tune learnt from Dublin ballad singers; sung to various ballads. cf. Jiii, 303. ** BS. A great favourite of the late P. H. Pearse.

36 Learnt in Belfast, 1913—The Protestant Boys. Piii, 503, Lillibulero; Graves: *Irish Song Book*. Chappell ii, 572, " A New Irish Song of Lilli-burlero, to an excellent new Tune "

See *Songs that made History*, Dent, London, 1937. Said to have been written by Purcell as a harpsichord exercise. ** Sparling *Irish Minstrelsy* (Street Ballad). The popular version in Belfast of The Protestant Boys contains the stirring lines:

> Slitter, slaughter, Holy Water, scatter the Papishes (or Fenians) every one
> If that won't do we'll cut them in two and send them to Hell with the Orange and Blue.

37 IFSvi, 27, *Péurla an tsléibh bháin*; Piii, 208-9, 262, 360, 1517, 594, 1113-4, 1128. cf. The Red-haired man's wife. Jiii, 95; also Jiii, 339, 370; Pii, 36. **BS.

38 Learnt in childhood from a maid servant, E. Gilshenan of Virginia, Co. Cavan—first verse only; cf. Jiii, 168, 256. ** BS and Sparling *Irish Minstrelsy*. cf. EFSiii, 127, John McCann.

39 From John Smith, Stravicnabo, Ballyjamesduff, Co. Cavan. See Appendix for sequel " The Sergeant's Lamentation."

40 Dublin ballad singers about 1912. Piii, 565, Connemara Wedding; Piii, 844, Early in the morning (Co. Cavan); Piii, 1093, *Eirigh air maidin*; Chappell ii, 713-4, The golden days of Queen Bess. Jiii, 477, Peggy O'Hara's Wedding. ** BS. See Ji, No. 49, The Roving Jack of All Trades.

41 Learnt in Belfast from D. McCullough, 1912. IFSxiv, 31, Harvest Song. cf. Hughes: *Irish Country Songs*, ii, The Slaney Side. ** BS and D. McC.; also *A Broadside* (Cuala Press).

42 Tune learnt from my mother, a native of Limerick—odd lines of words only. cf. EFSvi, 295, *Do bugus grá cléiv ghoet*; Piii, 387, Leave that as it is; also Piii, 1130 and 1319. Jii, 13, *Fágaimid siúd mar atá sé*. ** BS. My grandfather, John Carr, Limerick (1819-90), had also a few lines in English—

> "I drink what I earn and I pay what I owe
> And what's that to any one whether or no."

43 First heard to the Gaelic words of *Saighdiúirín singil*. cf. Words and music EFSv, 55, The Elopement; words and music IFSvi, 99 (bilingual); id. vi, 102, Gaelic. Piii, 594, The Funny Taylor; Piii, 154, *Luach mo lethphíne*. *Siobhán Ní Ghuidhir* also sung to this air. See also *Londubh an Chairn* (Clandillon) " I am a young fellow." ** BS.

44 Learnt in childhood from a maidservant, E. Gilshenan, from Virginia, Co. Cavan. Afterwards heard in Conamara to song *Philibín na gCuach*, and in Waterford to Pat O Donnell. ** BS.

45 H. Galway, p. 15, No. 12. cf. Jiii, 329, Eliza; and EFSiv, 21,
    The Inconstant Lover; Lovely Willy. ** BS. The last
    verse I have known from childhood; our nurse, Mary Brennan,
    from Co. Kilkenny, used to sing it.

46 Dublin street singers about 1920; and afterwards from J. M.
    Kerrigan.

47 Learnt from Dublin ballad singers: very popular up to twenty
    years ago. The air is a version of The Black Horse, q.v. cf.
    H. Galwey, p. 14, No. 10. ** BS.

48 Known from childhood. cf. EFSvii, 160, *Yn Speiy u my
    Gheaylin* (Manx song). Piii, 45. D. Devereux said that Wm.
    Ludwig, the singer, was the first to sing these words to this fine
    version of the air; for simpler version see Rossa's Farewell,
    No 34.

49 A well-known sailor song, Rolling Home (to dear Old Ireland
    —England or Scotland) gave its tune to this ballad.

50 Learnt in Belfast about 1912; the tune is another version of
    Villikens. See No. 1. ** BS.

51 A favourite tune with fiddlers and pipers. Pi, 175; Piii, 548
    and 969. ** BS.

52 Air and fragment of words from my mother who learnt them
    in Kilkee about 1880. cf Jiii, No. 82, Hurry the Jug (set
    dance). I have seen a full music sheet of this song published
    about the 'seventies, where words were ascribed to " Mr. Gavan,
    the celebrated Galway poet." ** BS.

53 Piii, 859. Variant in Feis Ceoil Collection. ** From a MS.
    collection of ballads made about 1820, and now in the
    possession of Dr. F. S. Bourke, Dublin.

54 Learnt in Belfast, 1912, from D. Maguire. cf. EFSiii, 131,
    The Devil and the Farmer. There are two other common
    versions of this tune, with varying refrains. I gave this to D.
    J. O'S. who printed it in IFSxviii, 27. ** From D Maguire.
    I gave this ballad to my friend Bernard Duffy, who inserted
    it in his play *The Coiner.*

55 From Cathal O Byrne, Belfast. Air is a version of The Young
    Maid's Love, q.v.

56 From Varner, F. J. Bigger's Chauffeur, Belfast, 1912. cf.
    EFSii, 200, Oxford City; Piii, 317 and 765; Bunting (1840),
    No. 65, The Robber or Charley Reilly; ' The Sailor Boy '
    in *Real Sailor Songs*, London, 1891. ** Varner and BS.
    (EFSii, 292). Kennedy: *Banks of the Boro*, 62.

57 Learnt in childhood. cf. EFSii, 210, The Green Mossy Banks of the Lea; id. iv, 91; vi, 176, *Aingbir Gheas Chrúiti na Mó*; vi, 81, *Ceó drychta*; vii, 24, The Banks of the Lee: viii, 219, The Squire's Daughter. IFSxii, 19; id. xv, 28-29-30. Jiii, 398, The Dear Irish Boy. Bunting (1796) No. 54. Said to be an unlucky song because it so charmed the ear of a priest going on a sick call that he tarried and arrived too late.

58 Learnt in Belfast, 1912. cf. Bunting (1840) No. 43. EFSi, 19, The Claudy Banks. See our No. 60, The Singing Bird, a new song to this air; arr. C. Milligan Fox. ** BS.

59 Air from Cathal O Byrne, Belfast. ** BS.

60 One day in 1913, the late Francis Joseph Bigger of Belfast asked me to find the tune of this fine ballad and was greatly delighted when I turned it up in the complete Petrie Collection, Piii, 558, The Belfast Mountains. Piii,422, The Banks of Claudy is a version of the tune. The song here given was written by P. J. McCall, author of ' Boolavogue.' See EFSi, 170, The Belfast Mountains. Different words and air; also cf. Jiii, No. 97, The Girl of Knocklong; No. 154, *An Cnuicn Ruadh* (Co. Limerick singer).

61 Chappell i, 309. Cold and Raw, "to the tune of The Oyle of Barley." Joyce A.I.M. No. 55, Cold and Rough the North Wind Blows. Jiii, No. 121, I'll go home in the morning and marry a wife from Ross. ** BS, one verse omitted.

62 From ballad singer in Thomas Street, Dublin, 1913. Piii, 755. It was in Dublin City. Denis Devereux told me that Arigho who printed the ballad, was persecuted for a long time after by the various " notabilities " mentioned in it—all of whom demanded largesse. ** BS.

63 From Dublin ballad singers; very popular about 1912. George Ogle's song: ' By Banna's Banks ' is to the tune. cf. Moore's ' Harp that once,' and many variants. See footnote to ' The Harp ' in Moffat's *Irish Minstrelsy*. ** BS.

64 I first heard this song at a meeting of newly released political prisoners in December, 1916. I am told it was written by Phil O Neill of Kinsale. I have since heard it sung to the air of "Are you there Moriarity." There is a Regal record of it made by John Griffin.

65 Learnt in Belfast, 1912. IFSxiv, 35, My love wrote me a letter. ** BS and Bulmer Hobson, who wrote the last verse.

66 A Gaelic song *Doire Briain* is sung to this air. The air of *An*

Cnuicín Fraoigh is somewhat similar. Jiii, 285, is a different air to ours. ** BS.

67 Heard in various places all over the country. IFSxiii, 15, The Pooca. Jiii, 79, Connolly's Ale. Piii, 1551, *Do b'fhearr leigean dóibh.* (A spirited song by Eóghan Rua O Suileabháin, splendidly translated by Frank O'Connor in *A Broadside*, 1935.) See Appendix for *The Old Leather Breeches.* *BS.

68 Piii, 691, The Deserter, where phrases are reversed. IFSxiii, 12, The Bold Deserter and id. xix, 43 (from P. W. Joyce) ** BS

69 Learnt by my mother from my grandfather, John Carr of Limerick. cf. Jiii, 384, and Joyce *Irish Peasant Songs*, No. 2, Sweet Cootehill Town. See also A Soldier's Life in *The Spirit of the Nation.* ** My mother and BS.

70 Learnt in Belfast, 1912, when it was a very popular tune with pipe bands because of the excellent scope it offered to drummers. ** BS. I heard an older and more pungent ballad but could not find it printed. All I remember is—

"D'ye think that I would let, a —— Fenian ——
Destroy one flower of the Lily O ?"

71 Known to every true-born citizen of Dublin. In the years 1913-16 it was the most popular marching song of the Irish Volunteers. I learnt it on route marches. The late Séamus Clandillon had a better tune.

72 From my mother, a native of Limerick. EFSvii, 55, Cruise of the Calabar. cf. Bunting (1840). No. 14, Rose Connolly. A more "literary" song was composed by Ml. Scanlan. I have seen a Sheet Music Edition of this where the authorship is credited to Dion Boucicault—probably because it was introduced into one of his popular plays. 'The Wearing of the Green' has also been claimed for him for the same reason.

73 From my father (*b.* 1859, *d.* 1933) a native of S. Kilkenny, who learnt it in childhood. He always heard it sung to the tune of Moore's 'Meeting of the Waters.' cf. Bunting 1840, No. 113, The Wild Geese. Moffat, p. 192, sets the song to a different air. Crofton Croker: *Irish Popular Songs*, claims Moore as the author of these words. Moffat suggests Michael Kelly as author, and gives an interesting note on page 346.

74 Learnt in childhood from E. Gilshenan, Virginia, Co. Cavan. cf. EFSii, 259; id. vi, 299, *Aryr is mé 'r mo wogadyl.* IFSvi, 27, *An Buailteóir* (from Bunting MS.) M142, Little Celia Connellan. Written by Darby Ryan.

75 Learnt from W. Feenan, fisherman of Ardglass, 1913. He had learnt it from a Donegal girl; a variant of the air was sung to another ballad—'Donegal's the place for all, 'tis there I'd like to be.' I gave this to D. J. O'S who printed it in IFSxviii, 29

76 Learnt from my father, John O Lochlainn (d. 1933, aged 76) a native of S. Kilkenny. EFSvi, 119, *Cailin deas Rua* (2nd version). cf. Piii, 746, Willie Leonard.

77 Piii, 693; also Pi, 134.
" Oh Johnny dearest Johnny what dyed your hands and cloaths? He answered him, as he thought fit, ' by a bleeding at the nose.' "
Piii, 694, ' The dawning of the day ' is a variant. ** Sparling: *Irish Minstrelsy.*

78 Heard sung by a ballad singer in Galway to a tune very like Kickham's ' She lived beside the Anner,' to which I have here set it. ** BS.

79 Learnt in childhood to Thackeray's ' Little Billee,' a version of Eóchaill, or Youghal Harbour, q.v. ** Denis Devereux who said this was the ballad on which P. J. McCall built ' On Boolavogue as the sun was setting.' cf. No. 27, Father Murphy.

80 From my mother who learnt it from her father John Carr, of Limerick (1819-90). EFSii, 254, The Banks of the Roses. I gave this to D. J. O'S to put in IFSxviii.

81 From my mother who often heard it sung by her father John Carr of Limerick (1819-1890). She only remembers a few phrases. A good many variants with Irish words have been published. EFSvi, 282, *Seán a Duir a' Ghleanna.* ** BS with slight changes where obviously corrupt. The late Canon Sheehan wrote a fine song ' After Aughrim's great disaster ' founded on this ballad. Jii, *S. Ó D. a' Ghl.*, No. 10, p. 19.

82 Learnt in childhood from E. Gilshenan to a fragment of a ballad, *Dumb, dumb, dumb.* EFS v, 59, Kate of Arglyn. Piii, 202, 371, 648, 789, and 1070. *Cailin an Urla donn* (O Daly) is a bilingual song to this tune. Ji, No. 96.

83 Heard first in Ardglass 1912. Later learnt from P. Walsh, Clogher Valley. ** From J. Rafferty.

84 Learnt from Dublin ballad singers and pipers. Air arranged by Herbert Hughes to a ballad ' The Spanish Lady.' A variant of *Viva la* to which Davis wrote ' Clare's Dragoons. ** BS.

85 Learnt from Cathal O Byrne, Belfast, 1916. IFSii, 21, Moor-

lough Mary, and id. ix, 15. A modern version was included in *Songs of the Irish Harpers* by C. Milligan Fox.

86 Learnt from Mrs. Reddin, Dublin, 1915. Words published in Padraic Colum's *Broadsheet Ballads*, 19.

87 Learnt in childhood from Dublin ballad singers with whom it was very popular up to 1914. ** BS.

88 Learnt from E. Gilshenan, Virginia, Co. Cavan. **BS. & E.G.

89 Learnt from a ballad singer in Balbriggan, 1921. There are so many English versions of this song that we would hesitate to include it but for its fine tune and unusual chorus. cf. Jiii, 260, The Barley Malt. EFSi, 81, John Barleycorn; id. iii, 255; vi, 27; and viii, 41. ** BS.

90 A favourite tune with ballad singers; and in the North is best known as ' The South Down Militia.'
   You may talk about yer Queen's guards, Scots Greys and a'
   You may rave about yer Kilties and yer bonny Forty-twa
   And of every other regiment under the Queen's command
   But the South Down Militia is the terror of the land.
A version of this latter with many local and topical verses was popular in Irish Volunteer circles in 1913-16. ** BS.

91 Learnt by my mother in Kilkee about 1870. The late Canon Sheehan printed some of the words in one of his novels.

92 Learnt from the late Denis Devereux who had it from the late P. J. MacCall, who contributed a version of the words to *A Broadside*, Cuala Press.

93 Known from childhood as ' My Love Nell.' IFSxviii, 18, *Ar mo ghabháil tri Bl' átha Cliath dham.* id., xx, 29, *An Tailliúir is an Píobaire.* Jiii, No. 597, Up the heathery mountain and through the Rushey fields. Piii, 863, When I first left old Ireland; No. 92, *Glounthaun Araglin Eeving.* cf. also *Slán le Corcaig*, My love Nell, The Star of the Co. Down. ** BS.

94 Learnt in childhood from E. Gilshenan, Virginia, Co. Cavan. One verse only I remember, ' I wish I had you in Phoenix island,' etc. Jiii, 257 Adieu to O'Reilly is almost the same tune. I have heard *An Caisideach Bán* sung to a similar tune. ** BS.

95 Learnt in Belfast 1913, from Cathal O Byrne. ** By the Poet Mackay, well known character around the Glens of Antrim.

96 From P. Walsh, Clogher Valley, Tír Eóghain. A song for the exile's homecoming.

97 Learnt in Co. Mayo to the Gaelic song *Bean an Fhir Ruaidh*, 1910. Piii, 357-8-9, 1140. EFSvi, 119, *Cailín deas Rua* (2nd version). See also M., p. 278. A song of the same name by Katherine Tynan. Jiii, No. 105, *Cailín deas Ruadh*. Bunting 1840, Nos. 83, 89 and 118. Moore's ' At the mid hour of night' is a quite impossible version of five phrases, formed by repeating the first.

98 Piii, 840, Assist me all ye muses. ** BS and Sparling: *Irish Minstrelsy*.

99 Popular in Limerick and Clare in my mother's youth; she knows the air, but only fragments of the song. cf. O'Reilly from Co. Cavan. No. 94. Jiii, 257 and 422. ** BS.

100 Bought and learnt from ballad singer in Britain St., Sept., 1914. cf. Jiii, 303, Brave Donnelly. AMS2, *Conndae Mhuigheó*. **BS.

101 I heard the chorus of this one summer evening in 1925 from a member of St. James's Band coming home in a luggage van from Dun Laoghaire. The air is well-known as *Táim in Arréars*, from the Gaelic Song of that name. ** BS.

102 Learnt in Belfast in 1916 from a friend who had learnt it to Gaelic words *Raca breá mo chinn* in Ballingeary. I afterwards heard it sung to English words by a Waterford ballad singer; also the tune sung to Kickham's ballad of Patrick Sheehan or the Glen of Aherlow. cf EFS i, 211, a version of My Love Nell. IFSi. cf. EFSi, 117. ** BS.

Addendum

SOME DUBLIN BALLADS

(Reprinted from the Dublin Civic Week Handbook, 1929)

BALLADS OF DUBLIN, Ballads in or upon or against Dublin, Ballads by, with or from Dublin—where's a poor balladmonger to start at all?

Where do they come from? Who knows? In my own time Arigho had them, and Warren's old stock from Kilmainham was to be had, sixteen or eighteen on a sheet, all for a penny.

Before Warren was P. Brereton, in Lower Exchange Street (where there has been a printing office since Humphrey Powell's time); and before that again was W. Birmingham, 103 Thomas Street, and Nugent & Co., 35 New Row, or Harding, of Skinner's Row, publisher of *Harding's Dublin Songster*, a most popular collection.

Here they are in their hundreds before me:—" The much admired song—The True Lovers' Discussion," "A New Song called The Robber and the Carman," " Erin's Green Linnet," " The Rocks of Baun" and " Sweet Castle Hyde." "John O'Dwyer-a-Glana" beside " The Enniskillen Dragoon" and " The Boughleen Dhoun" and " The Banks of Claudy," with many doleful lamentations of murderers and patriots, of sailors' sweethearts and soldiers' wives. Of the authors nothing is known —the ballads began their career without acknowledged parents and underwent change constantly at the hands of every generation of ballad singers. One name alone has survived, Zozimus, who in life was Michael Moran, born in Faddle Alley, off Black Pitts, in the Liberties of Dublin, about the year 1794. He became blind when only a fortnight old, and hence turned to the authorship and singing of ballads. He composed a notable ballad on The Finding of Moses in the Bulrushes, which begins—

> On Egypt's plains where flows the ancient Nile,
> Where Ibix stalks and swims the Crockadile.

and follows on with many high-flown verses. It underwent many changes at the hands of Zozimus or others, and a number of versions are extant.

A fragment of one is as follows :—

THE FINDING OF MOSES

In Agypt's land, contaygious to the Nile,
Old Pharo's daughter went to bathe in style,
She tuk her dip and came unto the land,
And for to dry her royal pelt she ran along the strand.
A bull-rush tripped her, whereupon she saw
A smiling babby in a wad of straw.
She took it up and said in accents mild,
"Tare-an-ages, girls, which o' yees owns the child ? "

If the action was not located in Dublin, the dialogue certainly
was!

And next comes

MRS. MULLIGAN, THE PRIDE OF THE COOMBE

I am a scrap of a widow that lives in a place
   In Dublin that's known as the Coombe (*pron.* Cu-em,)
And my comfort and ease no king could excel
   Though my palace consists of wan rooem.
By Patrick Street corner for thirty-five years
   I've stood by me stall, that's no lie,
And while I stood there, there was no wan would dare
   To say black was the white of my eye.

Chorus :

You may travel from Clare to the County Kildare,
   And from Drogheda down to Macroom,
And where would you see a nate widow like me,
   Mrs. Mulligan, the Pride of the Coombe ?

I sell apples and oranges, nuts and split peas,
   Bulls eyes and sugar stick sweet,
On a Saturday night I sell second-hand clothes
   From my stall on the floor of the street.
I have a son they call Micky, who plays on the fife,
   He is a member of the Longford Street Band,
It would do your heart good just to see them march out
   Of a Saturday to Sandymount Strand.

Or this on the Home Rule movement:

> The Harp of Old Erin will be heard once again,
> And will twine with the Shamrock in every green glen,
> And the round tower and wolfdog in sunshine will be
> With Home Rule for Ireland and Ireland free.

Thomas Street of a Saturday Night, or better still of a Christmas Eve, when all Ireland seemed gathered there—'twas then you'd hear the ballads of half the country. "The Night of the Ragman's Ball" was one I got there. *(See page 124.)*

Another told of the Howth gun-running and its sequel on Bachelor's Walk. *(See page 198.)*

Then there are the Canal epics, "The Cruise of the Calabar" and "The Thirteenth Lock," for which they say Arthur Griffith was responsible. There isn't space to quote them, but here's a bit of "The Wreck of the Vartry," wherein the scribe was somewhat indebted to Longfellow:

> It was the good ship Vartry that sailed the sweet Liffey,
> And the skipper had taken the casks aboard, a goodly companie.
> Blue were the labels—an azure blue proclaiming Double X,
> And neither the skipper nor the crew had dreamt of storms and wrecks.

It ends with a noble admonishment:

> All ye who drink of James's Gate, no matter what your sex,
> Take warning by the Vartry's fate, through too much Double X.

Then here is a bit of old Dublin, 1850, or thereabouts:

> Come, listen to me story,
>   'Tis about a nice young man,
> When the Mileetia wasn't wantin'
>   He dealt in hawking twang.
> He loved a lovely maiden
>   As fair as any midge,
> An' she kep' a Traycle Billy depot
>   Wan side of the Carlisle Bridge
>
> Another wan came coortin' her,
>   His name was Mickey Bags,
> He was a commercial traveller,
>   An' he dealt in bones and rags

He took her out to Sandymount
    To see the waters rowl,
An' he stole the heart of the Twangman's girl
    Playin' Billy-in-the-Bowl !

Now when the twangman heard of that
    He flew into a terrible rage,
An' he swore be the contents of his twang cart
    That on him he'd have revenge.
So he lay in wait near James's gate,
    An' when poor Bags came up,
With his twang knief he tuk the lief
    Of the poor ould gather'em-up !

[*Tune No. 72*

Index of First Lines

Colm O Lochlainn
More Irish Street Ballads 80p

A second and every bit as splendid collection of ballads collected and
annotated by Colm O Lochlainn.

selected and introduced by George Speaight
Bawdy Songs of the Early Music Hall £1.25

From a treasure trove of Regency songbooks, hidden away in the
British Museum, George Speaight has assembled this magnificent
collection of the bawdy ballads of the 1830s – the good old days before
they made music hall respectable. The book is illustrated by the saucy
and scandalous prints that decorated the original songbooks.

selected and introduced by Michael Turner
Parlour Poetry £1.75

'A delightful do-it-yourself kit for neo-Victorian families wanting to
re-create the home-made entertainment of velvet-upholstered drawing
rooms. The introduction even includes tips from *The Popular
Elocutionist and Reciter* of 1902. This is also a serious and very successful
attempt to encapsulate the nineteenth-century middle-class culture.'
THE TIMES EDUCATIONAL SUPPLEMENT

edited by David Marcus
Irish Poets 1924–1974 75p

'This anthology is devoted to the works of Irish poets born since 1924.
Why, one might ask, adopt – in an anthology intended as a collection of
modern Irish poetry – a limitation which automatically excludes such
giants as Yeats, Clarke and Kavanagh . . . Quite simply, 1924 marks a
watershed in Irish history . . . only with the generation of poets born
free of the original sin of subjugation could the era of modern Irish
poetry (Mark II) really begin' *From the Introduction by David Marcus*

W. B. Yeats
Selected Poetry 80p
edited by Norman Jeffares

Professor Jeffares has contributed an introduction and notes to this volume, which contains a selection from the complete poetical work of William Butler Yeats.

'One of Yeats's great triumphs was that in his best poems the Irish scene, at the same time that it is endowed with personal passion, comes to symbolize the whole human dilemma.'
GILBERT PHELPS in *A Survey of English Literature*

edited by Norman Jeffares
Selected Plays 80p

Yeats began his career as an author – writing play after play in his teens, and his last play, 'The Death of Cuchulain', was finished shortly before his death at the age of seventy-three. In fact, throughout his life Yeats was writing plays; and this selection aims to show his range.

edited by Norman Jeffares
Selected Prose £1.00

This selection contains some of Yeats's autobiographical writings about life in the west of Ireland, in London and in Dublin; and among magicians, mediums, seers and poets. Also included are his letters – to his father, to Lady Gregory and Olivia Shakespear among others.

edited by Norman Jeffares
Selected Criticism £1.00

This selection of Yeats's criticism, which is representative of every period of his working life, contains not only critical work on poets and poetry, but also essays on occultism, politics, philosophy and drama.

Arthur Jacobs & Stanley Sadie
The Pan Book of Opera £1.25

'Opera is a complex, strange and ever-fascinating art' *The authors in their Introduction*

This ideal reference book – by two well-known music critics – describes in detail 66 operas by 31 composers, ranging from Purcell to Britten, and mentions many other operas and composers. There is a chapter on early opera and one on the opera today; many musical examples are given and there is an up-to-date bibliography.

'A potent weapon in the battle for the establishment of opera as an integral part of our musical life' COMPOSER

Leslie Ayre
The Gilbert and Sullivan Companion £1.50

'The complete reference book for the lover of these immortal operas ... it will heighten the pleasure, enhance the magic of Gilbert and Sullivan' RT HON HAROLD WILSON, EVENING STANDARD

'Brilliant ... the story of the explosive partnership, full text of the main songs and ensembles from each of the operas, and biographical details of artists who have played leading roles. This Companion should last as long as the operas, of that there is no doubt' MANCHESTER EVENING NEWS

Charles Osborne
The Complete Operas of Verdi £1.50

From *La Traviata* to the vanished *Rocester*, this penetrating and sensitive guide takes us through all Verdi's operas, introducing them through plot, music and general characteristics and linking them with a fascinating account of his life at the time of composition.

'Mr Osborne gives a true picture of an exceptionally rich nature and of an art which, like Shakespeare's, transcends all petty cavil' GUARDIAN

Antony Hopkins
Talking About Music £1.50

Looking in turn at more than thirty great masterworks of music,
Antony Hopkins explains, illustrates and elucidates the world of the
symphony, the concerto and the sonata – from Haydn to Bartok,
Schubert to Stravinsky, Mozart to Berg. *Talking About Music* is based
on the author's popular radio series, which has made him known to
millions as a persuasive and entertaining guide to the world of music.

Gervase Hughes
Fifty Famous Composers 75p

'It is quite clear that these accounts of composers . . . have been based
not only on a reading of the authorities, but also on a first-hand
acquaintance with the music' TIMES LITERARY SUPPLEMENT

'The book is admirably cross-referenced, and excellent in its provision
of historical and topographical background' MUSIC AND LETTERS

MEN

THE DARKER CONTINENT

Heather Formaini works as a broadcaster and analyst. She was a contributor to *Sex and God*. She has been awarded two UN peace prizes: one for her work in Nicaragua and at Greenham Common, and another for her programmes made in Chile. She lives in London.

HEATHER FORMAINI

MEN

THE DARKER CONTINENT

Mandarin

A Mandarin Paperback
MEN

First published in Great Britain 1990
by William Heinemann Ltd
This edition published 1991
by Mandarin Paperbacks
Michelin House, 81 Fulham Road, London SW3 6RB

Mandarin is an imprint of the Octopus Publishing Group,
a division of Reed International Books Ltd

Copyright © Heather Formaini 1990

A CIP catalogue record for this title
is available from the British Library
ISBN 0 7493 0601 7

Printed and bound in Great Britain
by Cox & Wyman Ltd, Reading

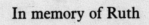

In memory of Ruth

Contents

Acknowledgements

Thanks are due to the following for permission to reprint extracts from the titles listed:

Alfred A. Knopf Incorporated for *Women and Love: A Cultural Revolution in Progress* by Shere Hite (1987); Basil Blackwell for *The Lust to Kill* by Deborah Cameron and Elizabeth Frazer (1987); Beacon Press for *Changing of the Gods* by Naomi Goldenberg (1979); Burns & Oates Ltd for *Raids on the Unspeakable* by Thomas Merton (1977); Collins Publishers for *Intimate Strangers* by Lillian Rubin (1985); Faber & Faber Ltd for *The Unbearable Lightness of Being* by Milan Kundera (1984); Harvard University Press for *In a Different Voice* by Carol Gilligan (1982); Macdonald & Co. (Publishers) Ltd for *Sexuality and Homosexuality* by Arno Karlin (1971); Michael Joseph Ltd for *A Calendar of Murder* by Dr Terence Morris and Louis Blom-Cooper (1964); Pan Books Ltd for *The Gaia Peace Atlas* edited by Frank Barnaby (1988); Penguin Books Ltd for *Parallel Lives* by Phyllis Rose (1985); *Towards a New Psychology of Women* by Jean Baker Miller (1976) and *What Is to Be Done about Violence against Women?* by Elizabeth Wilson (1983); Peters, Fraser & Dunlop for *The Right Stuff* by Tom Wolfe (1980); Quartet Books Ltd for *Bisexuality: A Study* by Charlotte Wolff (1977); Souvenir Press Ltd for *The Rocking of the Cradle and the Ruling of the World* by Dorothy Dinnerstein (1987); Zed Press for *Staying Alive* by Vandana Shiva (1989).

The author apologises for any errors or omissions in the above list and would be grateful to be notified of any additions or corrections that should be incorporated in any future editions.

Special thanks are due to Imogen Parker and Amanda Conquy for their very particular encouragement.

Introduction

All psychology is in some sense speculative, a way of searching for answers to the questions raised as a consequence of the difficulties we confront in daily life. What I am attempting to do in this book is to focus on certain issues which seem to me to be the ones that have been ignored until now. By looking at these issues we may find a way of diminishing the problems in future; at the very least, a change of focus will provide us with new topics for discussion.

Men say that they are troubled by many problems. Men's problems trouble us all, for they do not begin and end with men. Some men say that they find relationships impossible; others want to find whether it is possible to stay in a relationship; many find that trying to be a 'masculine' man, according to the definition put on masculinity in our society, is beyond them; and others wish to seek a solution to a problematic sexuality. Men also say that they experience a great deal of fear: fear of women and fear of other men; fear of responsibility and duty. They talk about loneliness and isolation, alienation, competition and rivalry with one another, and lack of friendship amongst themselves. There is often a sense of hopelessness and therefore a great sadness in men.

When women talk about men, and they often do, they sometimes feel despair, rarely delight. Women seem to be aware of the difficulties they suffer because of men's problems, whether it is through men's coldness, their lack of self-reflection, or their violence. Women speak about their need for intimacy; men talk about their fear of intimacy.

At a wider, social level there are other more complex issues: rape, sexual abuse, the murder of women, girls and children by men. Why do men abuse children and use murder as a way of seeking to solve a problem within themselves? Why can't they see that the problems which they live out are a result of structural inequalities which define women as something other, as less significant and valuable than men, in social, political, economic and psychological terms?

I belong to one of the established schools of analytic psychological thought. But my work for this book does not really fit within the category of traditional psychoanalytic theory, though my main theme, on which much else hangs, certainly originated within the context of psychoanalysis. There are problems for me with some analytic concepts and these seem to have contributed to the structural difficulties which men face. There is a sense in which men's problems are directly linked to the formulations of psychology as it has been developed. The problems are intrinsic to the foundations.

In my work as a therapist I am often confronted by the kinds of problems that men have and therefore the difficulties that men make for others, women and children particularly. So my thinking about women and men looks behind traditional psychological teaching about the nature of women and men and attempts to review its failures. Traditional psychology belongs to the patriarchal structures which underpin our society. Traditional psychology rarely attempts to critique the source of the human nature it seeks to explain. In my view, it takes too much for granted. Anyone reading a text from almost any branch of psychology will very quickly realise that the psychological models are derived from the study of boys and men. Deviations from the established models are generally women.

But what happens when, as I suggest, these models are defective? What if men are not the centre of the psychological universe? Everything must be thrown into question. Psychology has been understood as something 'natural', and psychologists

2

have charted the so-called natural course of development from infancy to old age, theorising about the various stages of life. But we know that there is very little in our lives which develops according to the intentions of nature – if nature could be understood as 'right' or 'normal' – for so much of what happens to us is the result of control or interference, for economic or cultural or political or religious reasons. And there is another problem with traditional psychology, as I perceive it: its failure to make the connection between the issues which exist on a personal level and those which stem from the structures of society. We are all creatures of our social world, but psychology often forgets, neglects or discounts this and works as though the individual is not in intimate relationship with the world. What is needed is a psychological model, or a series of models, which will serve us both as individuals and members of society.

This book is unlikely to bring me much favour. I know that some of the ideas are very controversial, particularly those about men and men's distancing from their own experience. Not all of the ideas are new nor are they necessarily mine, but many deal with the things that male society does not wish to face. One of these is the psychic split which I perceive in men. I suggest that many men live in a state of isolation from themselves and that this split lasts throughout life, unless and until it is recognised and steps are taken to deal with it personally. My observations make it clear to me that the problems men face arise very early in their lives, in infancy. This is due to the demands of 'masculinity' which are placed on a small boy. Another idea suggests that the reasons so many men have difficulty relating to others are directly associated with the 'failure' of infancy. By this I do not mean the failure of women as mothers, but the failure of us all to see that the social arrangements for child-rearing are inadequate. My feeling is that the fear and mistrust which many of us experience in relation to women is the result of being reared by women only. What we do is to see women as the ones who frustrate our need to be ourselves.

So the central question is: What happens if we turn around some psychological ideas and begin to look at men and boys not as if they were the logic by which we recognise or perceive psychological truth, but as those whose lives represent very real problems in society? When we look at the world we see that it is organised by men; when we look at what has happened to the world we have to acknowledge that it is men who have been responsible for the apparent destruction of much of the world. Why? For what purpose?

I have written about the 'typical' man – he who does not exist. But how else does one address the issues which involve every man, and therefore every woman, without conceptualising the typical man? It may appear strange that a woman and not a man is tackling these questions. A man, after all, might know things better from the inside. But I write in the knowledge that men have not been subjected to scrutiny, have not been put under the microscope from the outside. It is a pity that this hasn't been done before now, for it is a task which requires urgent attention. As it is, we have had to focus on women as though they were the only people with psychological problems. This does not mean that woman are problem-free, but rather that to deflect men's problems on to women serves no one in the long run.

What I have written is not systematic and is not intended to fit into any academic methodology. Rather, I have looked at the weaknesses in psychology so that we may begin to raise questions which formal structures often do not allow. I have not written *the* psychology of men, but have suggested that the basis for our present understanding of male psychology is both partial and unhelpful. In my account of men's issues I have also included much of the work of others whose psychological research has been invaluable but has not been widely available or accessible to the general reader. I have included it where it amplifies my observations and where it is obvious that it reinforces my arguments.

I am grateful to the 120 men who were prepared to talk so

openly with me and who gave me their permission to use the substance of their interviews. I have changed their names. Many of them said that they had not talked so intimately before about some issues and were very pleased to have had the chance to look at the questions I asked them. I hope that some of these issues will go on being raised and that the work represented in this book will foster further discussion and observation.

I also hope that the women and men who read this book will be able to bring up other subjects into the open. What is most important is that we begin to draw attention to the crisis men are in so that some understanding, and therefore change, may result. We need a great deal of change in our world if we are to preserve it and to carry out that task we need a great deal of hope and exuberance, as well as a fiery spirit.

HF
May 1989

1. Masculinity

Only with phallic psychology did aggressive manipulation
by technological inventions become possible.

Bruno Bettelheim,
Symbolic Wounds (Free Press, Glencoe, 1954)

Men sometimes make very interesting statements about themselves. Recently, when I told a young painter and decorator I was writing a book about men's psychology, he unhesitatingly responded, 'Now there's a can of worms.'

For me, the can of worms is represented by the term 'masculine'. I question whether masculinity exists as anything other than a set of constructions, the conditioning that begins very early on in life for boys – as early as the first few weeks after birth – subtly, but powerfully.

'I have given up the masculinity I grew up with,' a 35-year-old man told me. When I asked him to describe what he meant by his masculinity, he explained in some detail.

> Well, first of all it means that when the driver of another
> car begins to get tough with me because he doesn't like the
> way I am driving, I don't respond. I don't have to prove
> myself by being macho. If I bump into someone in the
> street, I don't now have to take a stand against them. It also
> means that I have begun to show real feelings to my
> children, and it means that when I make love with my wife
> I can go with my feelings instead of being cut off from
> them. It's the first time in my life I have ever really allowed
> feelings a place. I was very frightened by what I was doing.
> But I realised that it was better to be frightened because of

7

> my feelings than because men have got a death instinct –
> and that's been shown to be true by the way men are killing
> themselves. So I am prepared to take the risk of changing.

This man, Drew, a worker in the film industry, talked as if he had experienced a religious conversion, so great was the degree to which he felt liberated from the bondage of masculine behaviour. Until then, he had lived a very conventional life in Manchester with the woman to whom he is married and their three small children. But, in terms of traditional masculine behaviour, his life is anything but conventional now. He felt that he would have ruined his marriage if he had stayed a masculine man. He had been 'taught' to be masculine, he said, when he was tiny. 'But it was so hollow. It's just awful that we accept all that masculine shit without questioning where it came from.'

It seems that there is a very real conflict for men in being a masculine man or their own individual self. They get caught up in being like other men, one of the boys, and following the apparent rigid codes of masculinity which dictate every step of the way from infancy to death. And it is this process which takes them away from their potential individuality.

Of all the many men I interviewed, and of all the men I see in therapy, not one of them feels himself to be masculine. They feel as though they are failures because they don't measure up to what they believe masculine men ought to be. Yet they are prevented from talking about their feelings because to do so would not only break one of the sacred codes of masculinity, but because they might then run the risk of exposing themselves as possible unmasculine men. David, now in middle age, talked about how he has 'never felt a man among men. I have never felt like a rugger-playing man, a drinking man, one of the boys that I pretended to be.' Because he has never felt like a manly man, a masculine man, he has no male friends. Like many other men, he told me he prefers the company of women, with whom he feels much more comfortable. In this way his 'masculinity' is not constantly challenged.

David traces his masculine training back to the time when he was very small and his father took him aside and told him that he had to behave in a new way. David explains what this definition of masculinity entailed:

> If I am a little boy, I have to cut off everything that means
> being a little girl. I don't cry any more, I keep a stiff upper
> lip, and I pretend to like games even if I am terrible at
> them and I am a stoic and all that sort of stuff.

Discussed in this way, masculinity becomes a kind of 'negative': it is what being a little girl is not. As David said:

> I'm talking about all the things I had to give up. All the
> things that were considered soppy were to do with my
> feelings. It was my little boyness which actually disallowed
> me from expressing feelings.

But if his 'little boyness' was a problem, little girlness was clearly seen as an even greater problem. It was against girlness that you measured yourself and in relation to which you had to be something other, someone different. Masculinity, then, as well as being a negative, is about the abolition of sensitivity and feelings. While David feels a lack, a sense of what he should be as a 'manly man' has always dogged him in his life. As well as disallowing feelings, the imperatives of masculinity also disallow intimacy: 'I'm very bad at intimacy. I don't allow anyone ever to get at all close. Anyone. At all close.' *

When David addressed the question about the origins of his masculinity, he replied:

> I think it's largely conditioning. I remember being a very
> affectionate, rather sentimental little boy, and then my
> father, with whom I had a very good relationship, said,

---

* There is a fascinating point to be made here. If little boys are really constructed in the image of what their sisters are not – that is, they are a negative of little girls – where does this place women, who are constructed as the negative of men? Are we really dealing in double-negatives instead of two positives? It is a formidable conundrum.

'Well, you're a big boy now and that means you don't cry and you don't kiss me goodbye at the station.' And so it was really the instruction: Don't show feelings.

David's view of life is philosophical and he says that the kinds of problems that he took on as a small boy have really prepared him for the issues he has had to face in life so far. But what, I wonder, would life be like if men and women were not so burdened with the kind of conditioning they receive in infancy – conditioning which requires boys to be masculine and girls to be feminine. What would it be like if we could each be fully human from the beginning? As it is, we have to spend much of our lives in a search for what we have lost as a result of our conditioning, and many of us never find the lost part – never realise, in fact, that something is missing. David, for example, has never been able to be intimate. When I asked him how he managed in life without intimacy, he was very frank.

I ask myself that – how is it possible? – and when I was in a workshop recently I was doing an exercise as to what the blockage to intimacy was and how to solve the blockage and the solution to it was really to let myself go trustingly in a relationship.

But has David been able to let himself go?

No, I don't do it. I get prickly. Another image that came to me in that workshop was a strange crustacean creature in Hieronymus Bosch's *Garden of Earthly Delights*; and I thought that's me, a prickly crustacean.

David acknowledged to me that he lives in a 'separate world', even though he has a stable relationship to which he is committed. He also affirmed that it is the woman with whom he lives who forces him into talking about his feelings. 'She won't let me get away with anything.'

My conversation with David left me feeling that what masculinity required of him was that he give himself up – empty himself – to prepare to be something he wasn't by nature. As a child he had to relinquish his 'little boyness' in order to become what his father wanted him to be. It was not that his father told him that he had to add things to himself, but rather than he had to subtract parts of himself – in particular, any emotional expression. Giving up feelings is a very heavy price to pay for one's masculinity. Without feelings, it is very difficult to make the kind of important decisions that men need to make, whether the decision concerns personal relationships or something else.

Trouble with feelings is what brings a lot of men into therapy. When I first met Sam he told me he had a problem with the relationship he had been in for a few years. He wanted some help from a therapist. He was extremely curt and addressed me as if I were some kind of management consultant; he needed to turn over a few ideas in his head and then see how they resonated in me. He wanted plenty of feedback, he told me. He wanted directions from me: if I were the expert, he said, then all I had to do was hand out guidance and all he had to do was follow. Then his relationship would improve.

It was, I felt, a very 'masculine' approach he brought to therapy. Sam's attitude, businesslike and to the point, would not allow us to become close. No feelings would get in the way of our 'business'. And yet it was precisely because of his detachment from his feelings that he had come to be sitting opposite me in the first place.

As he explained over the following weeks and months, his problem in relationships concerned lack of intimacy, diminished sexual interest on the part of his lover, and a very great distancing between them. He was terribly sad and upset about the problems and they took up a great deal of his time and energy. He wanted the problems to go away and he didn't want to acknowledge the extent of his hurt and the damage to his feelings. If possible, he wanted to do the work of therapy without causing any more pain.

Therapy wasn't easy for Sam, as he made clear. He only came to see me when he had reached a point of desperation. One of his male friends whom he trusted had referred him to me. His friend realised that Sam needed to explore more thoroughly than friendship could allow some of the origins of his problems. Sam was unsure how he should relate to me; was I a sister, a friend, a colleague, a mother-figure? How should he deal with the silences that are part of many analytic hours?

Sam represents, in one sense, the 'typical masculine man'. He wanted order in his life. If his relationship wasn't working in the way he thought it should, then he didn't work well in his office. He was very edgy, uncertain, and put up barriers as soon as we touched a difficult area. He had a way of deflecting what was hurting him by an instantaneous reference to something else. It was a bit like being with a magician: now you see it, now you don't.

Sam was stuck in his relationship because he was stuck in his feelings. It was almost impossible for him to speak about them. He was divided from the essential part of himself which would bring about the cure, both to himself and to the relationship. Like David, as a child he had been given a very clear picture of what was demanded of him. What he had had to give up amounted to what he now needed – the missing part of himself. He described to me how his father had tried to train him, had tried to instil in him a 'fighting masculinity' based on defence skills and tactics:

> It was repulsive to me, but I couldn't let my father know
> that and so I carried on both sides of my life. One side of
> me hated what my father represented and wanted me to
> become, and the other side of me pretended that I was just
> what he wanted. And so I would play football even though
> I hated it. In fact, I was much more interested in the kind
> of values my mother showed me.

From Sam's description of what happened to him as a child, it is possible to see how the split occurred in him. He was not allowed to follow his natural inclinations and become the kind of person he wanted to be, or was naturally. He had to model himself on his father's behaviour, the traditions of masculinity, what was handed down to him through the male line.

Through his simultaneous acceptance and non-acceptance of masculine values and attitudes, he had forced a contradiction upon himself. It was that state of contradiction which we had to work with in our therapy together. It was also the problem of contradiction which prevented him from relating well to his lover.

What became clear to me in the sessions with Sam is that whatever masculinity is, it is very damaging to men. Sam's loyalty to masculine ways forced him to live by a kind of code, not a personal ethic or feeling. No one, however, can live on close intimate terms in the same way that soldiers on duty together might be bound by a code. And yet that was what it amounted to. His obedience to his father's law, learned so early on, did not give him permission to say to his lover all the things he needed to say. Although he knew what he wanted to say, the voice of his father went on echoing in his head to keep him on the masculine path. Tenderness was out: a taboo.

Eventually, he began to express his feelings and to acknowledge the sadness inside him. He began to talk to his lover about what he felt was wrong without hearing his father's tones. Sam had managed to detach himself from an imposed masculinity and make his own decisions. It became clear to him – and to me as well – that masculinity demanded that he behave like all other men, and not like himself. When he made a stand for himself he also saved what he had lost in the beginning.

Masculine behaviour seems to offer a security to men, in the way that uniforms offer security. It is like a mask which covers up what is really underneath, often an insecure man with a 'fragile sense of gender identity'.[1] Masculinity then is not just something that is learned on the outside, early on, passed down from generation to generation. It comes also from the inside. Everything we have learned, whether good or not so good, helpful or unhelpful, becomes part of us, and we must deal with it then in our internal reality. This seems to be particularly difficult for men. It demands self reflection which goes on to become self knowledge. It is not an easy process for anyone but it is essential for anyone who wishes to be their own person.

What interests me most of all is whether the demands of being a masculine man actually run counter to being a human man. My hunch is that the two states are not compatible if being masculine means to be without feeling and separate from others. My sense of what it means to be human comes from the knowledge that we all belong together, are bound somehow to each other not only by the air we breathe but by a common task. This means that we cannot be separate from each other. This does not suggest that we are not all individuals and different but rather united in our individuality.

Masculinity seems to say that separateness and uniformity go hand in hand and both seem to me to deny individuality and humanity. What Sam discovered when he allowed himself to have feelings was a sense of himself. Before then he had conducted his life according to a tradition which had no real meaning for him and which he secretly despised. It was only loyalty and a distorted love of his father which had induced him to use the cloak of masculinity at all.

Sometimes, men who come into therapy have a sense, after a time, that they have lost something; that they have had to give up the person they were before. Philip, a 45-year-old architect, told me he was

> actually trying to get my act together. It is difficult because on the one hand I am fairly solid and on the other there is a lot of flopping around. The solid bit is being confident but not having a clear direction but actually feeling that there's somebody really inside.

Philip has been looking on the inside for a number of years now. He said that being a masculine man is not easy:

> I find it very difficult. I think because of the expectations, really – that you are meant to be strong and an achiever. I

feel excluded by being a man – excluded from the human race. I realised I was carrying this terrific load.

Outwardly, Philip appears extremely successful. But he assured me that that is not how he feels:

> I resent quite a lot the need to achieve. I was conditioned by my father who said, 'Find a niche, stick to it and be a good lad and have a steady job,' and all the rest of it. And I've done it. I also have the job he wanted to have.

In Philip's world his father was clearly very powerful in the way he conveyed how Philip was to lead his life. Philip obeyed and now, in mid-life, resents and regrets that he followed his father's instructions. For him, masculinity was spelled out as representing steadfastness and success – neither of which mean much to Philip. His real concern is with sorting out his internal life because he has experienced a good deal of pain.

Aside from achievement, one of the apparent marks of successful masculinity, Philip talks about isolation. He says that the solitariness comes from conditioning and compartmentalisation. Being a masculine man means living in compartments. Philip told me that

> women find it very difficult to understand this is how men live their lives: there's a work compartment, there's a home compartment and there are other compartments – and they are not related. So when you are in one, you're not in another: your life is not a continuum; it is set up by boundaries. For instance, it is quite difficult to get a call in the office from a lover, because it's one compartment coming into another. It's seen as an intrusion and that's really difficult.

At home, Philip is not the same person he is at work:

> The person I am when I am working is quite different. For instance, I know what I have to do at work: I am being paid to do certain things, and I set out to do them. But when I am out of work I don't have that clear direction and don't

have any aims and therefore I am less intelligent. At work,
there is the strong bit; in my private life, there is the floppy
bit.

Masculinity is seen here as the performance of a role, a set of
tasks. 'At work, I am very confident,' Philip reported. In the
correct performance of this role at work he becomes confident;
in his private and domestic life, by contrast, there are no rules or
roles and he feels at sea, without boundaries – floppy, as he said.

This begs several questions about the place of boundaries in
the life of the masculine man. Why do compartments need to be
fixed so firmly in place? Flexibility is one of the marks of a well-
integrated personality and a lack of it suggests a problem in the
inner world. It suggests a degree of repression in the unconscious
when such a level of discipline is required in external reality.
When Philip speaks, as so many men do, of life not being a
continuum, it becomes necessary to ask why it is important to
break it up into parts. This raises a very interesting question for
traditional psychology. In the past it has been acceptable to see a
man's ability to cut off as a sign of maturity, to be able to leave
home in the morning and head for work without another thought
in his head about the problems he is leaving behind him. To me,
it suggests such a deep wound in the feelings that there is
nothing to link the various aspects of life. It suggests also that
masculinity has the ability to create obedience and discipline
without raising ethical or moral questions which, of necessity,
must be raised at times.

If feelings are not present to relate one part of life to another,
then feelings, when they exist, also become one compartment for
use when the requirements of masculinity make themselves
known. Some kind of feeling is needed, for example, when
marriage becomes the target of masculinity, when the codes
decree the time is right. But the commands of masculine marriage
are not necessarily the commands of love; rather, they dictate
obedience to the pattern of life laid down by traditions of

masculinity. At some point between the ages of 22 and 35 it is made clear to a man that his feelings must be brought out of their compartment and put on display for a time.

But the method by which a man chooses a wife, the female counterpart, is very often more in keeping with the conventions of his culture and background than with his real feelings. His choice of partner will be made on the basis of class, ethnicity, geography, personal appearance and religion. If, for emotional reasons, he entertains the idea of marrying a woman outside his class, his culture, or his economic group, he is very likely to be dissuaded from seeing her as a possible life companion. It would be much more likely that he would be encouraged by his peers and family to have an 'informal' relationship with her, but to marry someone more like himself. This is the way traditions are upheld and this is also the way that other structures which underpin masculinity are kept in place: class, race, religion, economics, and so on. Feelings come a long way down this list.

This does not mean that a man will not project his capacities for feeling on to a woman of his own cultural group, that he will not try very hard to push himself to have some feeling. But this kind of projection has very little to do with a real relationship. It is much more concerned with similarities than with difference, while loving another person means finding their difference engaging in the context of relationship.

But tradition, or keeping up an appearance of 'form', make masculinity a very powerful force. Richard, a lawyer in his early thirties, says that these marks are very strongly enforced at school, where the observance of masculine stereotypes is demanded:

> Men have assumed these characteristics – the hard role, no feelings – for so long, that their characters change. Probably from as early as boys start to form images of the world, they have to stifle, whether they realise it or not, those more sensitive feelings. Though they always remain, you have to pretend otherwise, and that makes it harder to reveal them.

Richard's description shows that there is a gap between the form and the experience of masculine demands. It presents an image of a wall which divides the reality of a man's inner world from the way he is expected to behave in the public domain. It gives a very clear picture of what is really happening in his internal reality. To me, it suggests a kind of void waiting to be filled. Men often want women to fill this void for them so that they can avoid confronting what is lacking in themselves.

From what men tell me about their lives, and from all that I see of the way men behave towards themselves, and other men and women, I conclude that masculinity forces upon men a split which cuts them off from dealing with their own personal experience. This convinces me that the split in men does an immense amount of psychological damage to individual men, to men as a collective group, and to men as they exist in history. This damage becomes apparent when men try to deal with their feelings. Their impulse towards love, the most human of all impulses, is somehow wounded. Having a split in their internal reality means that men have to use their energy to cover up the wound caused by the split. It would be much better if they could use their energy to deal with the split itself. This would mean confronting their own reality.

What seems clear from my personal observations, as well as the research material, is that boys are damaged very early on in life. It is almost possible to say that society requires them to be damaged so that they can carry on the tasks which society expects of them – to work and be profitable and to uphold the male systems which have been in place for what must be thousands of years. But it cannot in any way benefit society if about half of its members are damaged to the extent where they are split from their essential selves. If David and Philip and Sam and Drew are representative of men in Western society, then it is certain that they have had to work tremendously hard on themselves in order to regain what they lost in early childhood, even just a part of what was lost.

Some men seem to have no doubt at all when and how the damage of masculinity began. Once they are aware of it, they can take steps to repair the damage. But what seems to me crucial is that we begin to examine more carefully the origins of masculine stereotypes so that we may see exactly what harm is done to children. David stressed that he had to give up his 'little boyness'. Society forces sex roles on children because of false views of what biology means. Women's biological function disqualifies them from full participation in ordinary human enterprise, a possibility that is commonplace for men. Women's role as mothers has been adjudged as their primary role. This is a very unhappy equation in my view. Its consequence is that women and men have become half-human: women have been designated the feminine part and men the masculine. But neither role allows a full humanity. I see it as a distorted view of the theory of complementarity which is by no means a theory of equal complements. By labelling some people 'feminine' and others 'masculine' we are forced to divide up human qualities into two categories. Inevitably, some qualities have been labelled 'good' and others 'bad'. We fall into a trap which prevents us becoming individual persons with real human qualities. Instead, we have to become either feminine or masculine beings and stand or fall according to whether we succeed or fail to measure up to our labels. And we have to stick very firmly within the boundaries of our designated categories.

It seems to me, then, that little boys get a very raw deal. If they are forced to become what little girls are not, and if they have to reject simultaneously their 'little boyness', they are left with a deep question over who it is they once were, who they are now, and who they have to become. They are also left with a sense of wrongness about themselves, since what they ought to be is subject to such change and disapproval. My sense of a boy's dilemma is that, in having to reject so precious a part of himself, he is left with a permanent sense of insecurity as well as the knowledge that he has had to give himself up.

Masculinity seems to carve up little boys for its own purposes. It is disrespectful of the natural state and order that exists, and it denies that reality in favour of formal codes and traditions which men have created for themselves but which turn out to be death-dealing, as we shall see later on.

Given that masculinity – that is, the behaviour of boys and men – is a set of constructions and conditionings, can we possibly accept masculine psychology as the criterion by which we measure psychological development? The textbooks would have us answer 'yes'. Surely, however, such a basis suggests that our knowledge of psychological development is little more than acceptable codes of masculine behaviour, nothing truly to do with real human development.

Human development would mean transcending the conventions of tradition, going beyond the stereotypes constructed to inhibit personal and therefore individual development. Real human growth depends essentially upon the integration of personal experience. In this way it becomes possible to develop in relation to one's past experience so that there is a continuity of development. What so often happens to men, through their denial of self-reflection, leads them to conform to the rules of convention and live according to collective values which demand no real consciousness. But unless we are conscious, we are not really human; we are simply one of the herd.

2. Sexuality: a problematic zone

The male–female collaboration to keep history mad has
become impossible to sustain in the light of . . . our changed
perspective on 'progress', on the sources of what we have
always thought of as 'evil', and on the nature of what we are
responsible for.

Dorothy Dinnerstein,
The Rocking of the Cradle and the Ruling of the World
(Women's Press, London, 1987)

The demands of male sexuality have a good deal in common
with the demands of masculinity. They are both constructed
according to the acceptable standards of long established traditions and codes of the socially dominant group: that is, white,
heterosexual men. Simply because they are the socially dominant
group, these men are also the most powerful and the most
influential. It is their version of sexuality which is the most
obvious and, for that reason, the most difficult to decode.

Thomas is an academic, a man in his late fifties. He is an
exciting person to be with and when I interviewed him he talked
openly and expansively about his sexuality. Thomas is exclusively homosexual, as are between 4 and 10 per cent of the
male population in Western society. When he was younger he
says he tried to be heterosexual, for reasons which were 'largely
social'. Today, Thomas lives in a stable relationship with a
younger man. In his adult life he has had just a few very
important relationships. He told me that he had very deep
feelings for his lovers and he still maintains close friendships
with them.

When discussing his sexuality Thomas told me, 'I cut my sexuality off into a separate compartment from the rest of me.' Thomas recognises the connection between masculinity and sexuality. It is very strong in him, he said. When he was a very small boy at his prep school – he was about 7, he thinks – Thomas developed what he calls his strategy for dealing with his 'lack' of masculinity. He imagined, though he did not know, that the other boys at school felt differently from him and did not feel the lack as he did. So, to make himself acceptable to the other boys, he decided to

> become their lieutenant, and I've always done it since. It
> means that you attach yourself to them (boys or men you
> believe to be masculine) and you interpret for them their
> relationship to the world and you establish yourself by this
> relationship to someone who is more active, more positive,
> more butch, and you work through them, in a way, to
> achieve what you want to do. So it's a kind of influencing,
> but it's also a kind of supplying for oneself the aspects of
> one's character that one feels are missing.

What surprised me was that most of the men I talked to felt very much like Thomas. It was irrelevant that their sexual identity was so apparently different: heterosexual, bisexual or homosexual. Most men seem to feel that a part of themselves is missing, in exile. What is also very clear is that none of them talks about it with other men and exposes what it is they feel to be their lack. So men go on seeking for what they have had to lose, or give up, and very often look for it in other people, generally other men; after all, their masculinity is based upon what girls and women are not, so the lack is usually sought after in other men.

This desire to be reconnected with the missing part is very powerful in men. But they seem inhibited by the difficulty they have in defining what it is they lack and so they search for the lost part by engaging in sexual relationships with other men. Since Kinsey's research in 1948, which showed that between

30–40 per cent of heterosexual men had at least one sexual experience to orgasm with another man, other studies have continued. The most recent research[1] shows that between 50 and 70 per cent of men in Western society who claim to be heterosexual do in fact have ongoing relationships – sexual relationships, that is – with other men. The figure is very surprising to many people and points up the degree of secrecy in which men engage in relation to their sexuality. Indeed, it appears that while they may describe themselves as exclusively heterosexual, many men – who are very likely to be married – live as bisexual men. They live in conventional relationships with women, who rarely know anything about the sexual behaviour of their partners, but engage with men in 'low-emotion, high-sensation sex'.[2] These sexual encounters tend to take place in public places, wherever groups of men gather informally. This kind of sex demands a high degree of risk and is generally impersonal. What seems most important is the excitement and the physical pleasure it brings.

While it is widely agreed that most of us are bisexual by nature, women do not live out their sexuality in the same way as men whether they are heterosexual or lesbian women. Women tend not to be nearly as promiscuous as bisexual men. This is not to say that many women do not experience at least one major sexual encounter with another woman, but generally women tend more towards fidelity. One explanation for this stems from the greater seriousness with which most women view their relationships – whether lovers, husbands or friends. Clearly another is the way their sexuality develops; in my view it is much more integrated in their lives. Few women I have encountered in therapy have had the same difficulties with compartmentalisation.

Bruce, 36, emphasises the pleasure aspect of sex. He told me quite candidly that

> one learns in one's life to be able to inflict physical
> sensations of a pleasing nature – a sexual, erotic nature –
> upon bodies, and learn to get a sexual response to it.

Bruce sees sex as physical sensation which can be either man-to-man or man-to-woman – he doesn't mind which. He says that it is about one body with another body. 'I think,' he told me, 'that men are opportunistic, generally speaking, when it comes to sexuality.' His description of the way his sexual nature is lived fits with other men's feelings about the way they separate their sexuality and its expression. Although Bruce speaks about sexuality as pleasure, it seems clear to me that he is searching not just for sensations but for a missing part of himself.

What does this mean, the lack that men obviously feel, in sexuality and masculinity? My understanding of this lack has developed by observing in men the split from which they seem to function. It is as though a man is always trying to bring himself together, to unite himself with what he takes to be lacking. But instead of looking on the inside, through self reflection, men tend to act as if they might find their missing part in the external world rather than in the internal. And it is fascinating how this occurs in men, often resulting in a kind of obsessiveness with sexual experience. Men act out their desire to find what is missing in themselves by having sexual experiences, sometimes with women, sometimes with men. But in 'acting out' their relentless search they miss the meaning of their sexuality, and become further separated from themselves. For a man will only ever find himself, and whatever it is he thinks is missing, when he looks at himself.

It interests me very much that men seem to know at some level of themselves who it is they are looking for in another man. For Thomas, it is someone who will fill in the missing macho bits, the active one who will be the partner to his sensitive, artistic nature. But how did Thomas know that it wasn't enough to be a sensitive, artistic child? Was there some way in which 'demands' were made upon him to make him feel incomplete? Thomas does not feel that any explicit demands were made upon him by his family. His memories of this early period are very clear and he remembers the names of the boys he recognised as those who were necessary to him. It seems that, somehow or other, little boys know how and why they are incomplete in themselves.

While women and men get divided into 'feminine' and 'masculine' roles, yet another set of divisions seems to function in the definitions applied to masculinity. When boys perceive what it is that is missing, they then set out to find it. Thomas believes that it is his British background, the culture in which he grew up, which denies a full expression of sexuality and therefore insists upon a split between the body and the spirit, as he expressed it. This is true not just of British culture, but of all Western societies, predicated as they are on the attitudes and functions of the socially dominant group. All Western societies, in my view, perpetuate the same problem because the culture is founded on a basis of masculinity, which therefore brings about a split. When a society demands a division between body and spirit there is almost no way of escaping it; if such a schism is built in to the culture then it becomes even harder to detect, let alone defy. More significantly, it comes to be seen as natural.

As David remarked (see Chapter 1) the need to give up his 'little boyness' fitted him for the society he had to live in later on. But that he had to be so constructed is, in my view, a tragedy and a sad reflection on the requirements of convention. I question whether we have ever been aware of the damage that this kind of social conditioning does to individuals and societies: it is a psychological fact that whatever it is we have to reject in ourselves gets buried in the unconscious and therefore goes on to play a significant, though irrational, part in our behaviour. We may not be aware that we are reacting in relation to whatever it is that is buried, so, in that sense, our behaviour becomes autonomous and we are denied our full capacity for choice. In other words, it is simply not possible, psychologically speaking, to deny or repress parts of ourselves: they will always try to have some outlet. Sometimes a repressed or denied part will get acted out at a time when it is possible to observe its destructive force and do something about it; at other times it may return as a pathological issue needing urgent attention. The worst part of this is that we often repress our very best qualities, believing them to be worthless.

When, for example, a man cuts off his sexuality and denies it – the demand of Western society is categorical in this respect – the insistence with which it may return could overwhelm him. If every man in a society is busily denying his full sexuality, then it means that a whole underground life is being conducted – but at a level and in a place where it cannot be seen. And the more it is hidden, the more men will come to feel guilty and wrong about it and so suffer the consequence of an even more distorted sexuality. This seems to be what is happening now, even though it appears that men in Western society are obsessed by sex. My observations of male sexuality in its distorted aspect lead me to conclude that all the acting-out of sexuality – that is, the kind of low-emotion, high-sensation sexual expression – has very little to do with real sexuality. For so long, sexuality has been a split-off and misunderstood part and has, in a collective sense, become the repressed part of male society. It links men in a hidden way and gives them a common underground cause for as long as it remains hidden. So it is an undercover existence which some men lead.

The real psychological issue here is that men are forced to live double lives because of the demands of a fractured culture. They believe also that they have to keep their bisexual relationships hidden from the women they live with and therefore they enter a life of deceit. They believe, because of their own sense of contradiction, that they are forced to live a lie. In fact, they live a lie at a number of levels, for not only do they deceive their female partners, they also deceive themselves. When such men discuss their bisexuality they insist that they are heterosexual. Many are as homophobic as the most prejudiced members of society.

Bruce has relations with women and men, though he too

insists that his primary attraction is to women and he has no doubts about his heterosexuality. When he goes to bed with men, though, he is unwilling to get involved in anal sex – one of the reasons for which other men like man-to-man sex. 'I don't indulge in it,' he told me, 'but I am quite happy to indulge in oral sex both ways with other men. I see it as an expression of affection and I don't consider it to be homosexuality.'

Although some of the heterosexual men I talked to about their views on bisexuality said they were not aware of the high proportion of bisexual men, others were well aware of it and had some experience of it. Most of the homosexual men I interviewed (one-quarter of the 120 men) knew because most of them had been sexually involved with married 'heterosexual' men. A number of women said that they had rarely any involvement with a man they knew to be heterosexual who had not also had sexual relationships with other men.

Why is it that so many men who claim to be heterosexual get so involved, to the point, often, of compulsion, in man-to-man sex? It is certainly true that male fear of women may be one of the reasons. Steve, a bisexual man, is a builder in his late thirties. He has had a number of relationships with heterosexual married men, and he confirms that fear is a strong motive:

> Well, it is observed experience at one level, but I think men are frightened of women and don't want intimacy with women and somehow a quick bash with a man isn't as frightening. I think men find it very difficult to talk to women about the kinds of things they would talk about to men and that seems to me to be one of the major problems. And I also think when married men have sexual experience with other men it's a performance. I don't mean that they don't enjoy it, but it is as though they can be somebody else.

Men say that they fear women are going to make demands on them. Men also say that women want intimacy with sex, a desire which makes them nervous. Men want physical pleasure without any strings attached. Their bodies and their feelings are discrete.

What I perceive in bisexuality is the deeper self-evasion it allows men. For the more men go in the direction of isolated physical pleasure, the more they flee from self-knowledge – and the more they are able to put aside the reasons for the lack of intimacy in their life. But the most significant reason of all, in my view, is that self-evasion allows men to live according to the demands of the split; the more they put aside self-reflection, however, the less they will be able to deal with the real problem.

Adam, a journalist of 40, was quite shocked to learn that so many heterosexual men – his friends and colleagues – sought out other men for fast sex. Why? I asked him. 'I don't know. I think it's because so many of my married friends have affairs with women, but not with other men.' He seemed to take man-to-man sex as a personal insult. So why, I put it to him, did his married friends have affairs with women? 'Oh, that's something else. It's about some kind of security because, basically, they feel alone.'

When Adam was married he experienced a profound loneliness and this was one of the reasons he divorced. But my feeling is that men are not lonely simply because they are married; rather, loneliness or isolation is one of the offshoots of masculinity. It becomes a condition that men experience without recognising it for what it is. So they put it down to the fact that they are married or insecure, instead of examining the source of the feeling.

Bisexuality may in fact be seeking to address a number of problems, amongst which loneliness seems very important. Brief physical encounters may be all some men can manage in order to keep loneliness at bay. It satisfies a sexual longing and allows them to maintain a psychological distance at the same time. Charlie, a marketing man, told me that he was not at all intolerant of men seeking out other men for sex:

I am surprised at the percentage because I know that the
majority of men pride themselves on being wildly
heterosexual and so this shows a schism in their personality
to allow themselves to admit that they are attracted to men
and actually go and seek their company. It must cause quite
a feat in mental/sexual gymnastics to do that.

Whether bisexual men are in fact attracted to other men is a
very interesting point. My feeling is that the bisexual man does
not so much feel the attraction as the desire for gratification, as
if sexual gratification is a substitute for something much more
real and lasting, but too dangerous because of the implications in
having to dredge up repressed contents bubbling away beneath
the surface of his life.

It appears to me that there is a collusion amongst men which
allows them to go on denying the split in themselves, while at the
same time turning a blind eye to their real actions. In the study of
bisexuality undertaken by Charlotte Wolff, it was found that half
of her subjects – women and men – were married, and the men
claimed to be married happily. But the most revealing aspect of
her study showed 'the greater sexual restlessness' amongst the
men. The homosexual experiences of some of the bisexual men
ranged from 80 (for 16 men), to 300 (for 7 men) and over (for 3
men). Wolff adds: 'Several respondents mentioned that it was
impossible to count them all, as they came to many hundreds,
and two declared that they had been involved in such acts over
three thousand times.'[3]

For me, one of the most fascinating accounts, written in an
autobiographical paragraph, comes from a man who looked at
the reasons for his need to go to bed with another man:

The problem was that I was looking for a mirror-image of
myself – a manly man to go to bed with which is a paradox.
I sometimes am the passive and sometimes the dominant
partner with a man – either with different men or the same
man on different occasions.[4]

He was searching for the mirror-image of what he felt was
lacking in himself.

Many psychologists, sociologists and medical people believe that we are all bisexual, whether or not we express physically our sexual nature. But what the research shows, over and over, is that there is a compulsive, repetitive quality to male bisexuality – and this perhaps points up the compulsive attitude in many men, whether they be bisexual, heterosexual or homosexual. The important question is what it means to have so many sexual contacts – for contacts is all it is possible to label them. It suggests to me a deep psychological wound which is seeking to be acknowledged and healed. The means being used – wrongly, in my view – is sexual activity. The most appropriate way to deal with a wound so powerful is to open up the subject for discussion and reflection. To act out sexuality in a compulsive way, even though it may be very exciting and enjoyable at times, suggests that sex is an escape route taken by men to prevent them having to face themselves. And it appears to mean that men go on searching for their missing bit, the 'manly man'.

In my work with men, particularly in the area of sexuality, I see a terrifying fragility, as though men will do almost anything to prevent themselves from having to look on the inside. Men are much more comfortable with the outside world and in discussing ideas about themselves, rather than their real feelings and behaviour.

I see what happens to male sexuality when men are forced to reject so much in themselves from so early on. In having to become 'all that little girls are not', men are forced to suppress and reject the feelings which later turn into compulsions. The man's need to become a 'masculine' person is directly connected to the classic stereotypes of little girls and mothers: nurturing and supporting. His identity is formed by rejecting what girls and women are. But in denying what is really desperately import-ant to him, he is very seriously hurt. He is forced to live out, in some way, the rejected part.

With the part of him that is left, he does his work in the world; he creates culture and seeks to make history. These acts become, I feel, the substitute for the missing bit of himself. What this does is to create a strong barrier against the pull towards deep, rather than shallow, sexual experience. Jean Baker Miller says that men's desire for sexual expression is stronger than women's and 'in a more total sense'. But the problem which works against desire shows 'they have also erected strong barriers,' because they fear that 'the pull will reduce them to some undifferentiated mass or state ruled by weakness, emotional attachment, and/or passion and that they will thereby lose the long-sought and long-fought for status of manhood.'[5] This is true, and it points to the kind of war which exists inside a man, having to erect barriers in order to prevent intimacy. So what a man does when he is asked to reject intimacy is make sure that someone else carries it for him, and generally the someone else is a woman. He is saved again from looking for the missing bit and finding the essential part of himself.

Intimacy brings up all kinds of terrors in men. It seems to be one of their greatest fears. (There are very clear reasons for this, which I shall dwell on later on.) Intimacy and love are obviously closely connected, so a man will need to avoid both. In a piece of American research, undertaken with undergraduates at university, female and male students were asked to state how they felt about 'loveless sex'. Eighty per cent of the women felt that they wanted sex with someone who loved them. But less than 20 per cent of the men wanted love. Russell Vannoy, the researcher, noted that 'this raises grave implications for the viability of heterosexual love if the two sexes really do have such divergent views on sex.' He suggested that 'one or other of the sexes is suppressing his or her own views to please the other in order to have sex or love at all. And in a sexist society there is little doubt which sex is suppressing its views.'[6] The men in this study wanted 'quick, hard, direct sex whose primary goal is ejaculation'. Whatever sexual orientation a man has, it appears to me that high-sensation, low-emotion sex is what he prefers. In other words, men separate physical pleasure from emotional attachment and commitment. And that, in my view, is how many men would wish it to stay.

But why should that be the preference of the typical man? One explanation might be that the physical pleasure is so great that it is irresistible and that the degree of pleasure outweighs the other, perhaps more human, considerations. Another is that male desire has been so constructed as to take no account of the relationship between sexual desire and love, men's desire being constructed according to their split and to ensure that men stay separate even after being sexually involved with another person. It is an attempt, in my view, to take away the power of sexuality, and therefore love, and to diminish both.

Tim and Carla had been lovers for two years when he announced to her one night that he never 'had sex' with anyone he loved. Carla froze when she heard Tim say this to her, for she had understood their sexual relationship to be based on the love relationship between them. Her understanding of what had been going on between them over two years turned out to be completely different from his. She was shattered by this. What did it mean to him that he had been treating her like this? How could she allow herself to be involved with someone who was so cavalier about her and her body? He had been using her to satisfy his needs without any regard for hers. In a way, she didn't exist, except in relation to his needs and his expectations.

This created very severe problems for Carla. She left the relationship after another year, during which time she had, she felt, fully understood their different motivations and perceptions. What Tim wanted was high-sensation, low-emotion sex. The psychological condition brought on by this kind of attitude to sex keeps men, as it kept Tim, in a state of infancy, and does not allow real development or maturity. Psychological development is the result of engagement with one's own integrated experience and an acknowledgement and relationship to the different identities of others. A mature person is one whose internal reality has been finely wrought and made stronger through intimate contact with difference. Maturity is not threatened by the difference of others but is excited by it and engages with it from the stable relationship with the self. But no person can happily engage with difference if they themselves are not sure of who they are – if their sense of themselves needs to come from an identification with other people who are like themselves, or whom they perceive to be like themselves.

So what happens to people like Tim – and to many men, I believe – is that they try to control their relationships by exercising power over their partners; they see things in terms of ownership. But what is really happening when someone tries to dominate a partner? Essentially, the person in control feels that they are not in control of themselves, and to gain some control over their own lives they project their inner reality on to the partner and control themselves from that safe distance, or what appears to be a safe distance. This is an unconscious process and the person being controlled often gets very caught up in the whole event, as treacherous as it is. Women, who often feel very powerless in the patriarchal societies of the Western world, often get involved in trying to exercise power over men because it is the only way they feel they can have any power in relation to themselves. But it never works because no one can have power over anyone else and expect to be in relationship with them. Power denies relationship and the intimacy involved in important relationships.

When I look at men I often see that in order to maintain a sense of themselves as individuals they have to reject any possible intimacy with another person – particularly with a woman, whose difference they perceive to be nothing less than monumental. Many men feel that to get close to someone could confuse their sense of themselves. This is because they do not have flexible psychological boundaries in their internal reality, and thus to maintain their personal identity they must keep others at a distance. This underlines the rigid conventions to which men must adhere for the sake of their outward appearance as 'masculine' men. Psychological boundaries in men either don't exist or are extremely rigid, owing to the fact that their gender identity – their maleness – is based upon their difference from women, and not the capacity to be themselves.

This is a very complex issue and one which needs careful attention. For men's lives, from infancy, are built on the foundation of their dissimilarity from women. To be like a woman is to be inferior. But to be a woman is to be human. And the first model for what it is to be human comes from a woman. Men have to be different from that. It is an almost impossible task and it is little wonder that men come across such profound psychological difficulties in their lives. They have to try to be what they are not in order to conform to a convention based upon notions of the inequality of women.

So intimacy and closeness are rejected for negative reasons that have little to do with what a man really wants. He may very much desire to have an intimate connection with someone but his internal reality is threatened by that and so he has to deny himself for the sake of safety.

This means that male sexuality has at its very centre a pathological issue to deal with. But because male sexuality has been identified with 'natural' sexuality it is very difficult to deal with the problem – which is, in fact, a universal pathology. Men's sexual behaviour has been 'excused' on the basis that men 'cannot help themselves', that their physical urges are so great that to deny or control them would be tantamount to forcing a man to damage himself physically. This shows how fundamental is the connection between the way a man sees himself as a person and the way he sees himself as a sexual being. His gender identity, as fragile as it often is, is intimately attached to his sexuality. If his sexuality is denied, then he is denied. It is both as simple and as complex as that.

By accepting that their sexuality is natural rather than the product of social and psychological conditioning, men have been brutalised and damaged on the inside and outside. Because men have been forced to be harsh, their capacities for 'love and tenderness' have been damaged. It is a psychological fact that whatever is damaged gets pushed into the unconscious and remains there as a kind of blockage until it is recognised and rescued and returned to consciousness. The very real difficulty that men face has come about because they have all been required to be harsh and cold and have been 'trapped in Western macho nonsense', thereby making it appear that this is the nature of their biological forces. It seems to me to be all the more difficult because it is now a collective problem with roots deep in history and tradition: it is, therefore, less easy to isolate. Male sexual behaviour is so deeply embedded in tradition that it is hard to tell how much derives from biology and how much from social conditioning.

What is certain, though, from the discussions I have had with men, is the degree to which they themselves are unhappy about their sexuality and the way they have been taught to express it. According to Ken,

> I've been trying to find out what my sexuality is and do I
> accept it? No, not really. Because there's a whole dichotomy
> of being a male stud as opposed to some other way of being
> sexual. One is conditioned to think that one should make
> the moves – you know, should go around screwing – and
> actually it's not terribly nice. But it's not really screwing, it
> is actually looking for somebody to relate to – it is trying to
> get the other half of you filled in. And the only way one
> can express that is through screwing.

Here is an image of emptiness looking for a way of being 'filled in'. Ken is heterosexual and keenly interested in studying his own psychological behaviour. Like the homosexual and bisexual men described above, he is also looking for his other half. Part of him has also gone missing. Where is the missing part? How did it get lost? Will 'screwing' make a difference? Ken felt this was a very inadequate way of looking for himself. He acknowledged to me that he had not got very far by being sexually active with a number of women. But something of him was caught between the desire for self-knowledge and the conditioning which had taught him that he would find himself, his other part, when he found the right woman. Ken's story shows the power of child-hood conditioning over what he now feels to be 'not terribly nice'. He found that what was expected of him was distasteful, but he was confused by the social expectations because his identity was so bound up in them. Ken is divorced and lives in a settled relationship with another woman, though he had a time when he was very taken up with acting out his sexual desires. Nowadays, he is more concerned with self-reflection and sees that his real identity will only be found that way. He is also very relieved to have discovered that he is not required to go around screwing.

Male sexuality, like 'masculinity', opens up another can of worms, from what I observe. It is not a natural form of ex-pression but one which is contrived by the demands of ma-sculinity in order to prove something, though exactly what is hard to define. According to the rules of heterosexual men, every new woman is seen as a conquest – though in the problem-atic sense which Ken described. For if heterosexual men are seeking their lost part in a woman, what their 'screwing around' actually does is further separate them from their lost part. The more a man invades a woman, the more he damages himself and his own self-perception (as well as violating the woman). Even though he may be performing the prescribed rituals of mas-culinity and accruing male rewards as a result, he is nevertheless working against himself and against the development of his human capacity. His internal reality, from my observations, is set further apart from his daily life and consequently becomes harder to reach.

Men's emotions and men's bodies are separated by a gulf as deep as the split in their internal reality. It is as though the penis is detached from the body and lives a life of its own, reacting to each physical prompting with the compulsions which originated long before, in childhood, and which have gone on getting stronger and stronger. But when compulsion is at the root of a problem it is very hard to see the root. All the psychic energy becomes displaced and is used in living out the compulsion.

Because men – regardless of their sexual orientation – are trained to be harsh, they are divided from the natural human connection of love and the physical expression of that love, whether or not there is a sexual component. The love and tenderness that are naturally present in early childhood turn all too easily to hatred and harshness through the distortions forced upon men. They become an ambivalence which threatens every-thing men care about and undermines the natural human process of emotional development. This is one of the reasons that men often marry women they don't quite love. They often reserve love for moments outside marriage because to live with love would demand of them more than their resources can allow.

When we look at male sexuality, what we see is a compulsion born of social construction as well as a dissociation from real human feeling. Male sexuality tends towards the impersonal physical act and is high in risk and physical pleasure, though low in emotion. It carries fears of dependency and poor performance and is ultimately connected with men's separation from their real selves and women.

For men, genital sexuality has come to represent the total sexual experience. Genital sexuality, however, is just a tiny part of sexual experience, as the penis is just a small part of the male body. What integration of male sexuality into the total psychological development of men would mean, I think, is a unity of the sum of the parts that are presently disparate or lost – gone missing. In its essence, it would signify a union of sex and love.

3. The split in men

If this feeling of emptiness, of something 'without form, and void', can be deliberately accepted, not denied, then the sequel can be an intense richness and fullness of perception, a sense of the world reborn.

Marian Milner, in *Psychoanalysis and Art*
from *Psychoanalysis and Contemporary Thought*,
ed. J. D. Sutherland (New York, 1959).

Men, I believe, are divided against themselves. Their inner world is very often separate from their experience of external reality. This is not in any sense a natural state of development for men, but one which arises as a result of two separate issues, both of which are intimately connected to the social arrangements which prevail over early infancy and childhood. In being divided against themselves, men face many personal and collective difficulties. Most important of all, men get cut off from direct contact with the 'essential self' and this then means that great problems arise which inhibit the kind of psychological development leading to maturity.

'When you think of a man,' Colin said, 'imagine a 6-year-old boy in shorts. That will get it about right. Anything more is a bonus.' Colin's view of himself, and most other men, conforms in psychological terms to this image of the 6-year-old boy. He puts himself somewhere between early childhood and primary school, even though he is a professional man in his early fifties. But on the inside he feels very young. He also feels he is as vulnerable as a young child and has a young child's needs. Colin's description of himself fits with what many men say about the way they feel about themselves: on the outside they are grown men, though they remain quivering children on the inside, endlessly seeking to protect their fragility.

Men's sense of themselves also belies their appearance. For men rarely come across as vulnerable children. More often they appear confident and in control, particularly in control of their feelings. But it is here that it is possible to see the split for what it really is – a division between inner and outer reality. At some point in the developmental process a blockage is created and a barrier gets erected between the inner and outer world; for how else does it occur that a young child – or aspects of a young child – goes on living inside the body and soul of a grown and sophisticated man who seems very much at home in the professional world of men? Where did the child get stuck? Does the child wish to be somewhere else? How does the child manifest its presence?

Many of these questions can be answered by examining the way child-rearing and sex roles are organised in Western society. By saying that women should be in charge of child-rearing, we set up one of the most fundamentally difficult psychological problems, and one which, because of its very ubiquity, has become very hard to see for what it really is. Alongside the problem created by woman-centred child-rearing, there is another significant problem established by the training given to boys in infancy: the training implies that a great difference exists between them and girls. The outcome of these two complex issues leave us with a psychological inheritance which takes years of unravelling for those who undertake it. If, on the other hand, there were a clear account of the difficulties, we could make the necessary arrangements for change and in consequence alter the problematic structures of society as we know it.

All of us suffer psychologically and therefore developmentally in infancy through being reared by women alone. The ideal situation would be if men and women equally shared childcare. As it stands, we all are damaged to some degree – and boys, I believe, more than girls, for reasons which will become clear. The core of my argument focuses on the fear and resentment which get built in to our psychological structures and which become set in concrete through the traditions of child-rearing. (This is as true for children of women who work full time as it is for children whose mothers are at home with them. With rare exceptions, it is women who work in childcare, whether in public or private nurseries, day-care centres, or as nannies at home.) Fear and resentment of women develop as naturally as the spontaneous love infants have for their mothers, and alongside the love relationship. This brings a confusion to the feeling of love and undermines it, setting up in a child contradictory feelings towards the individual mother and all women; later on, these feelings are extremely difficult to resolve simply because they developed so early on. They then form part of an unconscious attitude to women which is carried along with the other feelings.

Interestingly, children of single parents often do not correspond psychologically to children who live with two parents. This may be because of an absence of conflict between the parents. Single mothers I have spoken with tend to say that they find it much easier being on their own with their children, especially if they have had a partner earlier on. They say that they find it much easier to manage things without a man present making demands. The real difficulty is financial. Psychologically speaking, children with one parent at home often do extremely well at school and professionally for reasons which I believe spring from the attention they often receive from that single parent. Nor do children of single mothers sense the so-called inferiority of their mothers – a sense which can come directly from the father.

Growing up is a very difficult process. It can be wonderful and it often is; but it is also terrible. For a time an infant feels that it is one with its mother. There seem to be no boundaries between them. Then, at some point between 18 and 24 months, a child begins to distinguish the differences between itself and the mother. Terrible and difficult moments occur; there are tantrums. The will of the mother is not the will of the infant. Her will sometimes conforms to the child's, but sometimes it does not. The mother's power over the child seems overwhelming when they are in conflict; at other times she is the same wonderful mother of past experience.

The confrontation with the parent's will is natural and necessary; but the problem that occurs here is that the child confronts only the mother's will (or the woman's, if the power-struggles take place at the nursery) and not the father's. She begins to represent all that is dangerous and powerful, someone to be conquered, while the father comes to be seen as a kind of refuge from her. It is in this manner that the split which develops in boys is established. All children see the woman as the enemy, even though she is also the best-loved one. So a boy now loves, fears, resents and sometimes hates his mother. Since he does not come into conflict with his father – his father only rarely appears – he projects the positive aspects of being human on to his father.

Girls too come into conflict at this point in their development, though the consequences of the difficulty for them are not nearly as serious as they are for boys. Although they too internalise the conflicts with their mother, they do not have to separate from her in the same way as boys. Neither do they have to become different from her. Boys have to become 'unlike' women, even though women are their first model for what it is to be human.

As well as making obvious problems for women, keeping men out of child-rearing forces children to remain infantile. This happens as a direct consequence of the projections a child makes on to its mother. The child does not have to deal with his own problems in his inner reality, but keeps the projections fastened on to the mother. In one sense, she then takes on his inner world and has to grapple with his feelings as well as her own. He is now divided from his essential self, since he has put his problems on to her. His experience, which in ideal conditions he would integrate into himself, becomes attached to his mother.

If women and men had an equal share in child-rearing this particular problem would be avoided. Women and men would both represent humanity and both would present difficulties for the child. The child would be forced to deal with the day-to-day power-struggles and frustrations with a man as well as with a woman and would thus be forced to deal with his own experience and not project it on to the woman alone. The child would then need to accept the fact that the feelings he has belong to him and are not the responsibility of his mother. He could begin in infancy to understand that being human is difficult as well as wonderful, that being human means to take responsibility for one's own desires and feelings, and to live with them on the inside.

Under the present child-rearing conditions, a state of neurosis develops in young boys. (I shall discuss what happens to girls on p. 49.) They get stuck with a whole set of feelings about women and men which are unrealistic and damaging. Since we never have to resolve the difficulties of dealing with a father and a mother, all our negative feelings – and our love – are focused on to the woman, generally the mother, the one who is primarily responsible for our care. So in our times of frustration and rage, and especially when we get older, the father becomes a solid refuge from her, because we do not have to grapple with his power over us. This is where the difficulty occurs, and it sets up, I believe, a split in all of us, though with much more serious repercussions for the male of the species. He has not only this problem to contend with, but a good few others which increase the tendency for him to become more and more divided against himself.

That we are cared for by women alone is partly the responsibility of history, as well as of mistaken beliefs about the dictates of female biology and maternal instinct. It is clear that at some moment in our past, divisions were made about 'female' and 'male' tasks in life. Some say that this division probably took place when men became interested in cultivating crops, though this can only partly explain its origins since women have always been active participants in agricultural pursuits. It is much more likely that women were given the task of bringing up the children for economic purposes which masqueraded under the guise of biology. Putting women in charge of childcare ensured that women would not interfere in what had been designated (by men) the affairs of men; neither would women then have access to financial power.

The unhappy result of giving women sole charge of childcare is our residual fear and resentment of them for the power they exert over us when we are infants and unable to have any say. The legacy of woman-centred child-rearing is more sinister than that, though, for boys are left with a distorted view of women and a neurotic attitude which holds them in a state of infancy. A part of men – in my view, the essential part – lingers on in infancy until some kind of resolution is found, though this is by no means a general outcome. Few men therefore resolve their conflicts with women or themselves.

It is this ambivalence towards women which is the central feature of the pathological feeling which lies close to the heart of Western society. Arising out of woman-centred childcare, the equivocal attitude persists because we never have to confront our feelings of ambivalence as we would if we were reared equally by women and men. Our need in future is to experience an equal input from fathers, the equivalent experience of his male body, and the equivalent experience of male love and power.

Some men do, it is true, spend time with their babies and young children. But it is rare for men to have much intimate contact with them on a day-to-day basis, for long periods, except for purposes of play. Even men who believe that they are excellent fathers rarely spend more than half-an-hour a day caring for their children, though they generally believe that they are very generous with their time. Men not only spend minimal time with their children, they also see them at their best – when they have eaten, are bathed and sweet-smelling at the end of the day. They do not have to ask their children to do unpleasant physical tasks like hair-washing or change smelly pants. Women become associated with unpleasant tasks; men with happy times before bed.

So it is the mother who becomes as familiar to us as we are to her. She seems to have no separate identity from us for the first couple of years; there appear to be no boundaries between her body and ours, her ego or will and ours. She bears the brunt of all our childlike love and anger and terror and vulnerability. She takes on, in our mind, the responsibility for the feelings that begin in our experience of infancy. Under the present social arrangements it is not just that we have only one kind of experience – the woman experience – but that we make her responsible for that experience. It is difficult for infants – and it is difficult for her. It is also just possible, if not highly probable, that she also resents the fact that she holds so much responsibility. Very likely she would prefer to be out in the public domain, living her own life and enjoying her creativity – freedoms she can't enjoy without the social censure that tells her she is not a good mother or, worse, that she is a bad mother. She will question whether she possesses the divine gift of maternal instinct and probably find herself lacking!

This creates a hidden conflict between child and mother. The woman is not free to express her resentment without bringing down upon her head the feelings that she is unnatural and selfish. The child holds on to its feelings until, at some point, it manages to learn to live with them; few ever resolve them because they are unable to think through the reasons for the disability. It seems bad enough to have to live with the problem.

There are a number of reasons why I believe that men are more damaged than women by woman-only child-rearing. My observations, and those research studies made by analysts of diverse persuasions,[1] lead me to conclude that the ambivalence established in the inner worlds of young boys becomes, as it were, the cornerstone of their psychological foundations. This is where the basis of male contradiction lies. Arising out of the experience he has of mother-centred infancy, the contradiction leads a man to turn in two different directions later in life: towards a woman (who, as mother, he loves with a deep passion); and away from a woman (who, as mother, he fears and resents). His life axis is thus constructed.

He not only has his own personal experience to go by, but he also learns very early through his observations of the social world that women are thought to be inferior to men. This adds a good deal of weight to one side of his contradiction, and suggests to him that he was right to fear and resent her. Even though he loves his mother, he begins to feel that this is not an appropriate emotion. He loves someone who is inferior to him. He begins to hate the part of himself that loves her. In this way the split that began as an ambivalent feeling becomes hardened.

How is it that a small child recognises the so-called inferiority of women? He first knows it because his mother tells him she is inferior; this doesn't happen directly, of course, but in a whole range of subtle ways that imply he holds the social power and therefore must be raised accordingly. He is aware also that his mother does not hold the same power and authority as his father.[2] He sees the way women are treated at home; outside the home, his awareness is heightened by the more obvious statements about women's inferiority. Thus his feelings of ambivalence are sharpened even further. None of this happens at a conscious level, though, but at a deeper and therefore more persuasive level.

These feelings of contradiction establish a kind of psychic gap inside a man, so that he is always facing in two different, not to say opposing, directions. This is part of the nature of contradiction. While it is true that we all face issues of contradiction in our lives which we must somehow resolve, the particular difficulty with the contradiction established in infancy stems from the fact that it is unconscious. A small child has no powers of self-reflection and cannot locate for himself the source of his feelings. But these feelings certainly inform his actions, particularly in later life. Moreover, when difficult feelings are established so early in life they take a great hold and become more and more powerful the longer they are not interpreted for what they really are – that is, false feelings brought about through false and contrived social arrangements which give women the responsibility for what is really the mutual task of women and men together.[3]

The ambivalent nature of a young boy's feelings are further confused by the process of separation, which takes place for all infants sometime between 18 and 24 months. According to the general process of separation – what should be a natural development of movement away from the state where there seem to be no boundaries – a child begins to sense its own identity and his difference from his mother. What should be, or could be, a natural step becomes a deep wrench and a source of insecurity. So destructive is the process of separation, as it is experienced in the West, that it forms a wound in the infant's unconscious. The love to which he has always had access seems now to be lost to him and his response to love in future will be made very difficult. This is the point at which he has been deeply hurt and he will not forget it.

Unlike a girl, a young boy has a dual task to perform. He not only has to separate from his mother, but because of the demands of masculinity he has to repress his feelings of love for her. He experiences a terrible sense of loss and deprivation at this point in his development. The reasons for his sense of loss stem from the necessity to separate from one parent in order to move towards the other parent, the masculine one. But he does not understand that the reasons for this move are socially constructed, organised by the needs of Western society to make him a man. Lillian Rubin explains this as another set of ambivalent feelings which develop towards the mother:

With the repression of the identification with mother,
therefore, the attachment to her becomes ambivalent. He
still needs her, but he can't be sure that she can be trusted.[4]

Rubin continues with this point:

This mother, who has until then been the loved adult on
whom he could count, with whom he could identify,
abandoned him to the shadowy and alien world of men.[5]

Not only does a young boy possess a twofold set of feelings for
his mother (and therefore all women), then; he also learns at this
point that she cannot be trusted and that he cannot rely upon
her. This is because he interprets his need to separate from her
as her movement away from him. In fact, she is just as present as
she ever was, although that is not how it appears to him. If the
one to whom he has been most attached cannot be trusted, is
there anyone in the world who can be relied upon? The identity
of mother and son has been so bound up that he blames her for
separating from him. He cannot blame his father because he
does not have the same experience of closeness with him; the
father has been a rather peripheral figure until now. Along with
all this, the boy now has the task of becoming like this unknown
figure: a man.

How, then [Rubin wisely questions] could she – or any
woman – ever be wholly trusted again? In the circumstances
it is quite understandable that he should try to cut himself
off. The tragedy is that in doing so he also blocks off the
essential part of himself. It is an unconscious act brought
about through unworkable and ineffectual parenting.[6]

A young boy cannot see what is happening to him. He had
projected his experiences on to his mother and made her responsible for them; now he is separating from her but she, it appears,
still holds on to his feelings. In this way, the essential part of
himself is lost to him. If he had been reared equally by his father
and his mother, he would have projected his experience on to both
of them and would have been forced at some point to withdraw

those projections and make the experiences his own again. It is in this way that all unconscious projections are finally resolved – by withdrawing them and integrating them into the personality.

A boy's feelings of love and fear and resentment of his mother remain with him so that when he, as an adult, meets a woman he feels he might love, he is filled with terror and confusion as well as a powerful sense of attraction. Because of his need he is magnetically drawn towards her; but his ambivalence pushes him away in case he is once again abandoned. This 'sense of abandonment' becomes a key in his psychology, even though it never *really* happened. Since he is unconscious of that first deep wound he will react to it all the more strongly. Furthermore, he will go on reacting until the time when he has learned what is really at issue. In my experience, not many men learn about the source of their problem. They tend to continue to blame the woman, as they first blamed their mother. This is one of the reasons why men learn to live in such a separated and isolated state. They feel they are not safe with women, but neither do they feel safe in the world of men.

The underlying ambivalence towards women, which began as the child's ambivalence towards his mother, goes on to become an ambivalence towards life itself, driving a wedge between a man and his essential self. It cuts off his natural human and psychological development. The 'natural' process of development implies a process of integration of all the component parts of life. What I think happens to the 'typical man' is that he gets cut off from his feelings and is therefore unable to relate easily to others, women or men. He learns to act towards others in an unsmiling, hesitant way; he holds on to himself as if he were at risk of falling apart. His manner often becomes harsh and direct, governed by the fear of being caught in a relationship which might show the same signs of betrayal which he thought he once experienced with his mother. Because it was an unconscious experience, he comes to anticipate it and so the natural process of his development is thwarted by his fear and anxiety. He

engages himself in relationships which can never be really important to him and consequently cannot hurt him.

Although the natural process of psychological development is
denied through the social conditioning that takes place, setting
up a dilemma in the child's inner world, he is nevertheless being
'prepared' for his social role in life. That is, he is being made to
adapt to the kind of world in which he is to take his place.

Girls are also forced into a social mould. Although their
conditioning seems to be much less damaging, they are nevertheless also divided from their essential wholeness through the kind
of training they receive in infancy. Where boys learn very early
that they are superior, girls receive the opposite message: that
they are inferior to boys. They learn that they must serve men,
or at least take care of them. They learn how to look for gaps
in the kind of care men receive and how to fill those gaps. Where
separation for boys is predicated on becoming different from
their mothers, girls must become like their mothers. This is a
saving grace for them, for they do not have to become like
someone they have not experienced. Their sense of being human
comes from the relationship they have with the mother, even
though they sense it is an inferior kind of humanity. They are
not required to be different from other women. So they do not
experience the same feelings of abandonment or betrayal. They
retain a continuity of experience rather than a break from it.

Girls and boys are both separated, to one degree or another,
from their natural development as human beings. As it is, boys
become set against their internal world and girls are made to feel
they do not belong in the external world. But of course this is to
assume that the two worlds are divided and it is here that the
fatal flaw in social construction occurs. The inner and outer
worlds both impinge upon each other; each forms the other,
whether for good or ill. The handicap comes in being separated
from one or the other.

The whole system of social adaptation would break down if
men were given, and took, equal responsibility for child-rearing.

Contact with children, with real human needs, has a profound impact on us as persons. We become more human when we are in touch with the vulnerability of children, when we converse with them. It also touches that still vulnerable part of ourselves and allows that part of us to be healed. But most men are cut off from that aspect of themselves and so remain in their isolated containers, separate from real human encounters and their own weakness.

For as long as men remain in their separated state they remain at war with themselves, trying to deal with the fundamental contradiction at their centre, unable to contact others at an immediate level, unable to reach into their inner world to make contact with their own lost part.

It is true to say that boys get a raw deal in infancy. Because men have such little part in child-rearing they do not develop lively enough relationships with their sons. Fathers often talk to their infant boys in clipped, authoritarian tones, as though they were addressing the managing director, or at least preparing a small child for that position. Little boys are kept on the outside of human interaction in the way that they are excluded. Boys are not often encouraged to participate fully in conversations in the same way that girls are. Boys have to keep their feelings and their words tucked in, like their shirts. All of this behaviour reinforces their feelings of ambivalence.

I believe that it is because boys are so cut off from their feelings and the expression of those feelings that they then begin to use their physical force to exert dominance. Because they get isolated so early on in life they do not learn to use verbal skills to deal with issues that are always better dealt with in this way. Boys use violence as a way of expressing themselves, but this is a degraded and often sordid means to express distress or unhappiness, and it doesn't help little boys feel better about themselves.

Infancy would be, in its natural state, a period of settling into the world, into a happy and creative environment which could lead then to self-creation and enterprise. As it is, infancy seems to set the pattern for many of the problems that continue during the rest of life. For a man, it means the start of a process whereby 'merging' and 'separating' will be the two key aspects of his relationships with women. When he falls in love (is it real love or a rerun of a neurotic pattern acquired in infancy?) he will merge with his new love in the way he was once merged with his mother. Later, he will begin the process of separation, as once he separated from his mother. He will find the state of intimacy – the merged condition – too hard to take after a time. He wants it, but he cannot 'suffer' it. So he begins to move away from the woman and the closeness that she desires.

What appears to me to be the legacy of infancy is the never-ending story of mergers and separations. In his effort, albeit unconscious, to deal with the first wound, a man will return over and over to a scene which closely simulates that original scene. He will re-create the place and the characters. That is the way the psychological process takes shape. Until we deal with an issue we must return to it until healing takes place, or else suffer the consequences, which may be a neurotic symptom or two.

My observations of infancy and the kinds of problems men have in their love relations lead me to conclude that there is an intimate connection between the infancy-to-separation period and the length of most love affairs. Love affairs tend to last between 18 months and three years. So I ask why it should be that infancy and love affairs are related to each other? Is it nothing more than coincidence? Does this coincidence have a particular meaning?

My experience with men in therapy leads me to suggest that it is indeed a meaningful coincidence, the nature of which is to reconnect a man with his wound. The tragedy of it all seems to be that many men need to go on revisiting their mothers so much. For often, as soon as a man has separated from his old love (or mother?), he quickly establishes a new merger. In repeating this pattern over and over again, he gets no closer to resolving his conflict but only seems to increase its intensity. Love affairs may be, I suggest, a reworking of the unresolved state of infancy. The memory of that first love will always remain for him a dominant force in his life and he will be caught for ever between the pull towards and the one against it, unless he makes a conscious effort to see what it is he is involved in. That requires quite a deal of self-reflection.

As we know it, infancy cannot lead to healthy development and maturity; rather, it blocks us and does not allow us to move on to the next stage unimpaired. Clearly, we do move on but we have to take with us a great deal of psychological baggage, a load that will only get heavier as we move through life. The only way we can hope to be able to deal with the natural process of development – and that is a great enough advance as far as I can see – is to have equally shared parenting. Until that happens, all of our problems will be focused on women and all of our hopes will be placed on men. Only when women and men are equally represented in infancy and childhood will we be able to go beyond that first stage of development. And only then will men, as fathers, have the opportunity to be fully human. The only viable way for men to be in touch with their essential selves is to undertake the work their own fathers didn't do. Or, if they don't have their own children, they must undertake the task of self-reflection.

4. Sex and gender

Writing against the masculine bias of psychoanalytic theory, Chodorow argues that the existence of sex difference in the early experience of individuation and relationship 'does not mean that women have "weaker ego" boundaries than men or are more prone to psychosis.' It means instead that 'girls emerge from this period with a basis for "empathy" built into their primary definition of self in a way that boys do not.'

Carol Gilligan, *In a Different Voice*
(Harvard University Press, Cambridge, Mass., 1982)

It is a sad fact that small boys become conditioned very early on and are taught in infancy to be 'little men'. They become 'products' of traditional male society and are taught all the things that will be important to them later on, when they 'take their place in the world'. Throughout their infancy their future is brought before them. 'You can see he'll be the leader of the team!' 'Make a great train driver!' 'He'll be the prime minister, you know!' 'Could make the Senate with a bit of time!'

While these comments are being made by well-wishers, the infant may still be at the breast, on his father's knee, in his cradle. But already there are plans afoot to place him somewhere else, where his importance as a man will be gratifyingly apparent to all who know him.

No one takes these comments seriously of course, but it is important to explore why we are so quick to locate tiny babies in roles which are defined according to sex and gender. Why do we talk about baby girls being 'able to twist a man around her little finger' and boys having the ability to 'go for a six'? The little girl is placed in relation to man – that is clear. The boy's definition is closely aligned with sport or work. The patterns are set before them for all to see. That is the way the world has gone on; and that is how it shall continue.

Defining children in accordance with the demands of culture is the nature of social conditioning. It creates a division between the natural process of development and the contrived process which is the outcome of conditioning learned over hundreds of years of 'masculine' training. Conditioning is really teaching a child to be what it would not otherwise be: conditioning cuts across natural development. Western society thinks it is important to teach boys very early on that they are different from girls and that they have a gender-specific task in life. My view of this is that it does untold damage psychologically as well as socially and culturally.

There is no evidence to suggest how girls and boys would be different from each other if they were not subjected to severe social conditioning and made to feel, almost from the time they are born, that they have certain roles to perform in life. As it is, children become functionaries of society's demands. There is almost no way a child can escape from the tasks set before it. If that child is a girl, she knows her function partly from observations she makes about her mother and her mother's behaviour. She sees how her mother behaves at home and outside the home and she models herself on her. Thus, she learns very early that hers is a lesser part, especially when it is compared to her brother's. She directs herself according to her mother's role and learns that women serve people and take care of others' needs. She observes the way others may need to be served and she sets about looking after them. All of this she learns even though she is given no written rules of instruction at her birth.[1]

A boy models himself on his father and his brothers. He sees how well they are taken care of by the women and the girls at home. He watches closely outside the home and notices that the same rules apply. Women look after men and their needs. Social and cultural traditions such as these are imbibed not at a conscious level, but unconsciously. They are therefore much more difficult to become aware of and, as such, harder to change. We take them in at such an early age that they are impossible to resist.

There is a difference of just one chromosome between girls and boys, but there is a world of difference in the learned and conditioned behaviour of both sexes. What makes a good little boy good is quite different from the way we define a good little girl. The boy will be allowed a whole range of freedoms to which a girl is not entitled. In keeping with his superior status, his 'spirited' behaviour will be a sign of something on which he is to be congratulated. A girl's high spirits may be something else altogether, something verging perhaps on bad manners. She will be expected to be demure and sweet and graceful and passive; he may be boisterous and unruly but still acceptable. Inequality is built in to gender construction and it continues until the end of our lives.

From the moment a child is born it is treated according to whether it is a girl or a boy. The experiments where boys are dressed in pink and girls in blue show just how much even colour signals the appropriate reaction from the outsider. A number of studies, most of them conducted in the United States, point out how powerful gender 'construction' is. It makes clear the manner in which boys and girls are to behave and it goes even further than that and specifies which is the superior manner. Between 18 months and 3 years, children know their gender and they know its meaning. Carl told me that when he was a 'tiny boy' he knew 'that women were somehow inferior, although they were dominant and powerful'. The world was divided into two: the world of women, at home, and the world of men, outside: 'I have to say that the dominant tradition was that it was somehow better to be a man. Qualitatively speaking, men were more important.'

Robert Stoller's study cuts across a good deal of accepted psychological theory. Like so much other research on sex and gender, Stoller's shows that

> those aspects of sexuality that are called gender are primarily culturally determined; that is, learned postnatally. This learning process starts at birth, though only with gradually increasing ego development are its effects made manifest in the infant. The cultural process springs from one's society, but a sense of this is funnelled through the mother, so that what actually impinges upon her infant is her own idiosyncratic version of society's attitudes. Later, the infant's father, siblings, friends, and then gradually the whole of society present upon his developing identity.[2]

Even when anatomy and genitalia do not fit with the gender construction (that is, when a female or male child is reared as if it belonged to the opposite sex) it is the gender conditioning which is the more powerful. A girl reared to be a boy will prefer to have a sex-change operation than to become a girl, and vice versa. In other words, we hold fast to the conditioning we receive in infancy and childhood.

What Stoller shows very clearly is what many women psychologists have been saying in other ways for a long time – that 'femininity' and 'masculinity' are culturally determined. They are not biological conditions which are innate. Other pieces of research show just how difficult it is to differentiate the biological from the learned aspects of behaviour. For example, a study of infant girls and boys showed that 'boys are more restless before feeding and become more tranquil or fall asleep more readily after feeding, whereas the reverse is true for girls.'[3] But Stoller points out that another study shows that the 'amount of activity in boys in the first few months of life is directly dependent on the way their mothers deal with them.'[4] Surprisingly, perhaps, this same study also shows that the activity of baby girls continues to develop irrespective of the mother's treatment of them.[5]

What does it mean, then, that our conditioning has greater

effects on us than our biological make-up? What are we to make of the notion of 'complementarity' that is said to exist between women and men? Might it mean that the behaviour of little boys and girls is the result not of innate traits (boys are so active and girls passive), but conditioning?

We all have been put into categories which fix us in a position which lasts the whole of our lives. Girls are called 'feminine' beings and are taught the appropriate feminine behaviour; boys are labelled 'masculine' and have their behaviour defined for them too. No one escapes. Failure to conform to our assigned behaviour means that we feel wrong and bad about ourselves. We are not encouraged to break the laws of sex and gender; and certainly no one questions whether the demands of society are contrary to the demands of being human. There ought to be questions asked, though. For what society does is not in our best interest as persons. Society's interest is concerned with how effective we will be as economic and political and cultural supports, not how human we will be.

Complementarity exists between women and men in one sense only. Physically, women and men go together. But that is where complementarity ends. The real mistake has been to assume that physical complementarity is replicated in other areas of life.[6] Because we read into physical complementarity so much more than really exists we fall into terrible traps and keep ourselves sub-human.[7]

The notion of complementarity rests on the 'doctrine' of masculinity and femininity – that is, depends for its existence on cultural construction. Only if we believe that women and men are half-human can we fall into the error of seeing complementarity as a goal. But the whole idea of masculinity and femininity separates men and women into a dualism of opposite principles, each with different valuations placed upon them.[8] Until we see such principles for what they really are, we are faced with an impossible problem – one determined by power relations rather than nature.[9] Women and men each have the potential to become fully human, whether or not they have a partner of the other sex.

Dorothy Dinnerstein writes that

> bodily complementarity is for us something much more than
> a source of agreeable sensation. It can be (and is, under
> favourable conditions, which have so far, to be sure,
> remained proverbially elusive) a central manifestation of the
> human delight in existence, a focal part, symbolizing and
> providing expressive release for the whole of our erotic
> connectedness to the world.[10]

Somehow, by locating complementarity in many aspects of male/female behaviours, we have managed to reduce the power of the only area in which real complementarity exists. Instead of seeking the delight where it exists we have sought for it where it cannot exist. We have split ourselves into halves and go on seeking the other half, the lost half. But all the time we ourselves may be complete in and to ourselves, provided we look on the inside for the rest of us.

Masculinity and femininity fit into a hierarchical scale: a one-up, one-down scale. Men are up; women are down. Men have the opportunities; women stay at home and take care of children. Men deal with the money; women are given a share of the money earned by men. In practical terms this is what complementarity means, though it is dressed up to look like something else entirely.

One other aspect of the doctrine suggests that unless the 'feminine' member of the duality is true to her femininity she will turn out to be something distasteful. She will run the risk of becoming a masculine woman, it is said, and that is indeed a terrible thing! What we must all be aware of is that the doctrine of complementarity, for all its apparent charm, makes one sex subordinate to the other. 'It follows that sub-ordinates are described in terms of, and encouraged to develop, personal psychological characteristics that are pleasing to the dominant group – characteristics such as submissiveness, passivity, docility, dependency, lack of initiative, inability to act, to decide, to think, and the like.'[11] Particularly is this true in psychological thought.

The categories of behaviour are so carefully defined and guarded that they become commonplace. We hardly see them. For instance little Daniel plays rough in the nursery. His mother laughs when he bashes Tess. She doesn't stop him, even though Tess's mother is quite desperate about the way Daniel's aggression is directed towards her little daughter. Daniel's mother explains that Tess will have to get used to being bashed. It is, after all, a man's world and she will have to learn her place in it. And Daniel has to learn what it is to be a man. He has to realise that he is going to need defence skills to look after himself. So Daniel's behaviour is not curbed. He is not chastened for being rough and aggressive. He continues in this behaviour. Tess recognises that she will have to conform to something in Daniel, something she will come to recognise in most boys and men. She will have to carve herself out to fit their behaviour. As she is, she is not acceptable. Therefore she cannot be her real self. Daniel thinks that he is being his real self, though in fact he is conforming to patterns of gender behaviour, constructed hundreds, if not thousands of years ago and perpetuated as a sign of masculinity in the West. Both Tess and Daniel learn from this experience that women are powerless. Even at three Daniel holds all the power, albeit in his fists.

So the problem is how to retrieve our human capacities given the degree of conditioning to which we are all subject. If we were brought up in the Tuareg culture in Africa we would have learned entirely different gender behaviour. Men in that culture wear the veils and wait until a woman proposes marriage. They are passive and receptive where women are active and assertive: the bread-winners!

For in the performance of our roles as either masculine or feminine persons we have learned to assert one side of our personality and hide and distort others. If we are masculine we will have forgotten what it is to be weak and vulnerable, because we have identified ourselves with a role that says we are strong, even if we have no real strength. We will be alienated from our weakness. This does not mean, however, that we are not weak; rather, it simply means that we keep our weakness on the inside so that we are still children in our internal reality. It also means that we will project our unconscious weakness on to others and make them carry it for us. So we will be assertive, even when passivity or another behaviour would be more appropriate to the occasion. We will speak when silence might be better. And so on. Our learned behaviour – the result of our social conditioning – has turned us into people wearing masks which perform roles. In following the demands of gender, we have become even more separated from our real selves.

What about girls and women? What does femininity do to them? How far does it distort their true nature? My observations about these issues lead me to conclude that femininity is not only a terrible bind for women, it prevents them from being 'born' in a world owned by men. It keeps them down; it keeps them submissive; they spend their lives (I cannot say *live* their lives) in relation to men. Since femininity has been defined as gentle and full of grace, as sweet and passive, it prevents women from saying what needs to be said, doing what has to be done, and stops them challenging the status quo, even when they can see quite clearly that things endlessly work against them because of the way they have been defined.

A male theatre director recently asked me for some theoretical advice about a play he was directing. What is it, he asked me, that makes women grieve? My view is that women grieve for their lost lives, for never being allowed to take their real place in the world, for not being able to be self-defining people. Women grieve also for being made to carry the guilt of the world; having to be responsible for what they have not done. Women's lives are based on a set of negatives, like femininity itself.

Femininity also means that directives have been laid down in relation to girls' and women's bodies, generally about how small (and insignificant?) they should be. Masculinity is much more generous in relation to male bodies and male codes of dress.

Femininity and masculinity, then, are not the two halves which eternally belong together. They are cultural constructions which have as their aim political and economic ends, giving more power and money to men, thereby keeping it out of the hands of women. Ruskin said, in his nineteenth-century tones, that

> each has what the other has not; each completes the other.
> They are in nothing alike, and the happiness and perfection
> of both depends on each asking and receiving from the other
> what the other only can give.[12]

We are in some way 'other', we women and men, but not in the way Ruskin described. His view was as unsatisfactory – and as untrue – for the last century as it is for us now. Although it is true that women and men are different, or 'other', we shall have no possibility of being able to see those differences for what they really are until we put aside the cultural conditioning. Perhaps one chromosome will be seen to make profound dissimilarities between us; on the other hand, we may discover wonderful new attributes which have never been allowed to emerge.

What gender construction does to us all is reduce us to the level of the sub-human.[13] What it does to men in particular is confirm them in their split. The damage that was first established in infancy is now hardened and set by culture. In my view, the seeds of destruction are sown very thoroughly and men are further removed from their capacity for love and tenderness. The boy who becomes a man goes on defining himself in opposition to the girl and woman. She is the loving and tender one; he must resist those qualities, as well as the one who owns them, because he thinks that since she possesses them he is forbidden access to them. Therein lies the danger of gender construction.

Gender construction not only defines the boundaries of the roles for women and men but it goes on to establish the literal territory where they may tread. Their lives may be conducted only on this basis unless they wish to be seen as perverted or disturbed. Cultural rigidity is the name of this game. Psychological distortion is its end-product.

5. Men and friendship

And so I ask myself: what is the meaning of a concept of
sanity that excludes love, considers it irrelevant, and destroys
our capacity to love other human beings, to respond to their
needs and their sufferings, to recognize them also as persons,
to apprehend their pain as one's own?

Thomas Merton, *Raids on the Unspeakable*
(Burns & Oates, Kent, 1977)

Men appear to see danger in close affiliation, and safety in
isolation. This means that friendship is a very difficult area for
them.

My conversations with men in and out of therapy lead me to
believe that the kind of closeness that comes with friendship
threatens them. They prefer separation and compartmentalisation, even though a part of them longs for intimate friendship.
But don't we all need friends? Surely it is impossible to live
without friendships? Men are not as sure of this fact as women.
When he talks about friendship Robin hesitates a good deal. 'I
think I prefer women friends,' he says. 'I find men friends too
tricky – men are so difficult to be friendly with because they are
so insecure.' Men are insecure, I suggest, for precisely the
reason that they reject intimacy: separation makes for insecurity.
Friendship brings with it confidence and the secure knowledge
that one is loved.

With his women friends Robin will talk over most things. He
really likes them and enjoys their company. This doesn't mean,
though, that he doesn't withdraw when the conversation touches
a difficult area for him:

> Yes, I will also hold things back, the closest things. I tend
> to hold back from men because I don't feel I can trust
> them. The difficulty about talking to men is this
> competitiveness which you can't get away from.

Robin's experience shows him that men are insecure, un-
trustworthy and competitive. Several years ago, when he had
just separated from his wife, he tried very hard to develop
friendships with men. At that time he recognised that his sense
of isolation and loneliness stemmed from something inside himself. He had felt very lonely in his marriage. Because of this
recognition he set up a men's group, of eight men, in the hope
that they could raise and discuss their feelings with one another.
The group didn't last very long. Most of the men found it too
difficult and too threatening. They were unaccustomed to being
open with one another. On the whole, they were not used to
cooking for one another. Robin had hoped that having meals in
group members' homes would create the appropriate setting.
What the failure of the group showed Robin was the inability of
men to come out of their sex roles. Men, he felt, seem to assume
that they will be taken care of rather than do the caring.

At 35 Dave says that he has few friends, although he has
many, many acquaintances:

> I will talk with anybody about some things. It's the social
> intercourse that is important. But I don't discuss my
> intimate feelings. I tend to have cages and walls to hide
> behind. As far as my emotional content is concerned, I want
> to protect myself.

So Dave keeps himself safely isolated in the midst of his many
acquaintances. By doing that he does not run the risk of having
anyone break through the cages and walls he has built around
himself. He is perfectly open about finding safety in separation
and fear in intimacy and can easily talk about the cages and
walls: what he can't do, though, is remove them. Neither does he
want to.

Philip, in his late fifties now, gives every appearance of being a very sociable man. He loves dinner parties and social events. But when I asked him about friendship with men he said he felt he had been 'conditioned' to feel more comfortable with women. So does he have male friends?

> No, I have a smallish number of women friends, but no male friends. I think this is largely due to being very much the youngest in the family – I was largely brought up in the company of my mother and her friends who were women, so I learned in a way to feel easier with women than with men.

But this is a curious point because Philip went to a prep school where there were only boys and male teachers. Later on, he went to a single-sex school and then a male college at Oxford University. So what happened in his school and university life really made little or no impact on his ability to make friends with men. He is no longer in touch with his friends from university and school. He has acquaintances – many of them – and is a popular guest. But because he cannot let anyone get close to him he limits his conversations, even with his women friends. 'I talk about myself, I talk about events, news, and what they are doing in their life, nothing very intimate.' Philip longs for a kind of interdependency: 'I would like to be able to achieve this. But I louse it up all the time.' He goes on being independent.

Philip goes so far as to say that although he can see that some people treat their feelings as though they were reality, he can't. 'I can't completely believe in my feelings for others.' As well as not trusting in closeness, Philip does not trust any feeling which has the possibility of leading to closeness.

When Mark makes comparisons between the kinds of friendship he has with women and men he says:

> I have never felt there has been any restriction with women and it never seems particularly difficult to talk about 'those things' with women – it seems natural, whereas if you spoke

to a man about some of those things you'd be kind of
telegraphing 'now we are getting serious' so we'll put on
different hats or we'll change channel. It doesn't seem the
case with the women I know. I don't go out to talk about
heavy or depressing or in-depth subjects but they just seem
to arise more naturally without any trouble and then
disappear from conversation in the same way.

Subjects which are appropriate for conversations seem to be
divided into certain 'safe' subject areas for and by men. It
appears that 'heavy' subjects are inappropriate. Men seem to
prefer bar talk: sport, finance matters, housing policy – anything
that is 'out there' in the world. Lightness is what men seem to
prefer with other men.

Larry, who is a teacher of dance, has an equal number of
women and men friends. One might have thought that being gay
would make him prefer men to women.

I would say there are about five or six friends who are
important to me and by friends I mean those I would call
'family' and I could say anything to them in a family
situation. Half women, half men. I talk about everything.

Although he is happy to talk about everything in his family of
friends, Larry also says that

I think the women I talk to are much more sympathetic and
understanding with emotional issues and it depends on the
kind of man too – whether he is gay or straight.

Larry emphasises that he has never had any problems in his
relationships with 'straight' men.

Why is it, I wonder, that men find women much more sympathetic than other men, even when they might expect men to have
a far greater knowledge and experience of their inner lives? I suggest
that this is precisely the reason that men cannot tell their male
friends about the experiences which need sympathy: because they
cannot expose what appears to them to be their weaknesses. To do
so would be to let down the drawbridge on their island of safety.

Of the many men I talked to, Larry stands out as one of the most free and unselfconscious. For this reason, his perceptions seem to me very interesting. For example, how easy is it for men to open up and talk about their feelings?

> I don't really find in my relationships, friends or otherwise,
> that it is easy to talk directly about feelings in any great
> depth. There's a tendency I've noticed in people which is
> that if they don't actually shy away they feel uncomfortable.
> So I don't often get to that kind of level.

As a woman I find it at once fascinating and sad to listen to what men say about their feelings. There is also a sense in which it is incomprehensible, although clearly not at a rational level of understanding. Women are so much at home with their feelings, with their sense of experience of feelings, that they cannot understand why men draw back at that level. But from what men say it seems that they prefer women as friends because that is the level at which women function – though not the only level – so easily and comfortably. The barrier created by men's unwillingness to enter this area means that a gulf is fixed between women and men and when, as sometimes happens, it slips, it is quickly reinstated by the man.

Joseph has a lot to say about friendship, including his own attitudes. 'I have a few friends. Both women and men. Yes, close friends.' And what does he talk about with his friends? 'About myself, a lot. All kinds of things – everything that we're mutually interested in.' Joseph talked about the way in which he chooses friends:

> There are two ways of becoming friends. One is because
> one has a great deal in common at some fundamental
> spiritual level; and you can become friends because you share
> particular interests. I have had quite a lot of friends because
> we h'ad shared interests but those friends tend to disappear
> when the common ground disappears and I don't think
> there's anything wrong in that though I sometimes think
> I'm a bit cavalier about it – that I do rather drop people.

Joseph says he finds it almost impossible to talk about everything, even with his close friends:

> There are certain things about my sexuality I certainly
> would only talk about to a very few friends. I wouldn't keep
> it secret from my closest friends – I would allude to it. I
> mean the kind of things one does in order to get sexual
> pleasure.

This suggests to me that men make a secret of the areas where they believe they are most at risk. If it is not possible to talk openly about one's sexuality it makes the subject that much more secret. What men could learn from women is that opening up supposed areas of weakness or secrecy can lead to the feeling that defences really are not as necessary as they appear to be. Sometimes they are appropriate, but a good deal of the time they just get in the way and spoil what might otherwise be a good relationship.

Most of the men I interviewed said that they preferred their friendships with women over those with men. Tony, a 38-year-old nurse, could point out three close women friends he valued and saw often. That's the way it had been for a long time, he said. But nowadays a real change was taking place and he was beginning to make friends with men:

> It's beginning to be possible to be able to talk about some
> personal things. In the last couple of years I realised I didn't
> have men friends or was out of touch with men, so this has
> actually been quite important to me.

Tony went on to say that as well as having a few men friends he was beginning to be able to talk about intimate subjects:

> I don't think there's anything that is completely blocked off
> but there are subjects that I will only talk about with certain
> people. It doesn't mean to say that there aren't subjects that
> aren't blocked off – I probably just don't know about them.

Tony also has some experience of working in groups with men.

'In groups men talk more, feel in a different way. It's more about ideas, sort of intellectual ideas, that men talk about.'

Ideas for men can be like the cages and walls Dave sets up around himself. Ideas, as exciting as they often are, can be the very medium through which men learn to deny their feelings, as Tony explained:

> Men don't actually talk about their feelings, and I actually think that's the way they are made up. And they also think feelings are dangerous. But it's despair, loneliness, impotence and inadequacy that are very dangerous for most men.

Tony presents a very bleak image of men sitting together but desperately trying to defend themselves against any possible closeness. What would happen if someone let the barriers down? It seems an almost impossible question for men. They would then be exposed to themselves and to one another, dissociated from their particular male role and confronted with a truth they do not, for whatever reason, wish to face. When I asked Ian if he ever lets the barriers down he replied, straightforwardly, 'No. I mean I talk about a lot that is deeply personal but there are whole areas I keep to myself.' This means that Ian has a kind of hierarchy of friends; with some, he'll talk about some aspects of his life while he'll hide some other bits of himself from view. So I supposed that his partner would be the only one with whom he could be completely open. 'No, I'm not completely open with my partner. There are some things that I keep to myself because they are difficult to share. They are very personal.'

In the need to keep things so well guarded there is very likely an element of shame. It is the repressed parts of the personality which work, as it were, against the truth. And very often it is the repressed parts of the personality which can, in the long run, be the most valuable – but only after they have been exposed, at least to the conscious self. Repression also means that a person is not free to act as he truly is; repression demands the need always to be on guard in case anyone comes close to discovering the secret.

More seriously, unless there is personal openness, here is a denial of the self. A person is clearly unhappy about himself if he cannot bring himself to own a repressed part. There is a gap between the person he pretends to be and the person he really is, or might become. This creates an obvious and difficult tension in the internal reality and such a tension takes a lot of energy away from external life.

Friendship not only allows us to function humanly but it brings us a great many possibilities for self-development and self-knowledge. The crises we experience in close and deep friendships, the rifts we suffer, show us where our personal complexes and psychological issues can be located. They point us in the direction where we need to work on ourselves.

So men miss out on many of the good and important aspects of what are otherwise ordinary moments of human development. Men get stuck in quite rigid social habits and depend heavily on being rescued. One of the most obvious ways men perform the task of self-rescue is through man-to-man sex. Bisexual sex allows men to have a kind of intimacy with other men without any risk of getting involved in opening themselves up on an emotional level. Provided the encounter with another man is conducted on a physical level and is quick and emotion-free, it relieves a good deal of the tension created by feelings of lack of intimacy. The man is able to sublimate the need for close friendship through fast sex, though only temporarily.

War has also, like sex, been the means of bringing men together and creating bonds which might otherwise not have been formed. It is probably the only time that men address the issue of friendship in the way women do. Some psychologists suggest that war is a necessary event in human life – a theory I reject – but it does seem to bring men together in a way that no other life-experience ever does. If war is the only way that some men can make friends, then it is a very great tragedy; however, it is also possible to understand it on a psychological level as a way of acting out an unlived aspect of life which is almost totally neglected under normal circumstances.

Men, especially Australian men, have mates. Mateship, though, is rarely friendship. It is, rather, a collective code of behaviour which demands a macho image and a denial of women. It is typified by a kind of fearlessness in the face of danger, and the image of the warrior comes to mind. It is an ethos which is concerned with external appearances and a language which denotes certain underlying attitudes. Mateship is a substitute for friendship. Mates drink together and play football together, talk in corners with one another, pat one another on the back from time to time; but mates don't have heart-to-hearts or give the kind of emotional support that typifies real friendship.

This is because the fear of self-revelation is very great and could bring ridicule to a man. So mates learn about the life of another mate through innuendo, clipped or snide statements about problems at home, or the expression on his face, his attitude of hostility or silence or sadness – not what he tells them.

While mateship is the name of the Australian game which masquerades as friendship, it is easily recognised in other Western countries in the familiar brotherhoods: Rotary clubs, Masonic lodges, the endless old boys' societies, and so on. These exist not so much to offer friendship as to keep life safe from friendship as well as to keep the male system intact and women as far away as possible from that system. Within the male system men can behave traditionally: they can compete with one another and search for the achievement they seem so much to desire.

Brotherhoods keep life safe for men.[1] Their established codes, their language and their gestures all fall within formal structures and present no threat of emotional entanglement or intimacy. Their methods, like their manners, are fixed to disallow any spontaneity; the hallowed name of tradition takes care of that. Whilst the economic and political justifications for the brotherhoods are very apparent, what are the psychological motivations that operate here? They stem from the very real fear men have of women's power, and the corresponding need to keep separate from women in case women invade that fragile area of men's power. Certainly men's power structures don't *appear* fragile from the outside, but that doesn't mean that men don't feel them to be powerless. Monolithic and immensely wealthy such institutions certainly are, but that doesn't mean they couldn't be toppled by women – at least in the minds of men. Women's lack of tolerance for men's coded behaviour would put an end to male monopolies as they exist. Women's directness would want to ask the kind of questions that could not be sustained by all-male groups.

So it is that men defend themselves from the kind of contact that could allow any possible analysis of their psychological or emotional state. And this brings up a very interesing point about the relation of violence to men's feelings of separation, the feeling that some harm will come to them if they are implicated in intimacy. In an American study by Carol Gilligan and Susan Pollak,[2] the close relation of fear to intimacy was noted in a way that the researchers found 'bizarre'. A group of men and women was asked to write stories appropriate to a picture of a couple sitting tranquilly by a river. Twenty-one per cent of the 88 men involved in the study introduced violence into the scene: 'homicide, suicide, stabbing, kidnapping, or rape'.[3] None of the 50 women participants made any connections of violence to the scene.

Continuing their study, the researchers found that

> the men . . . projected more violence into situations of
> personal affiliation than they did into impersonal situations
> of achievement. Twenty-five per cent of men wrote violent
> stories only to the pictures of affiliation, nineteen per cent
> to pictures of both affiliation and achievement, and seven
> per cent only to pictures of achievement.

In their conclusions, Gilligan and Pollak wrote that

> if aggression is conceived as a response to the perception of
> danger, the findings of the . . . study suggest that men and
> women may perceive danger in different social situations
> and construe danger in different ways – men seeing more
> danger in close personal affiliation than in achievement and
> construing danger to arise from intimacy.[4]

This study leads to an endless stream of questions as to why
men should feel like this. Is their fear the result of years of
training to isolate men? Does it explain why men talk so much
about the need for defence, and about protecting oneself from
'enemies'? – enemies, one suspects, who do not exist except in
the minds of men.

The stories written for Gilligan and Pollak show how dangerous men perceive intimacy to be. It can lead to 'entrapment', or
'betrayal', or 'smothering'; the men used words such as 'humiliation', 'rejection' and 'deceit' to describe their feelings about such
situations. Intimacy, for men, seems to connect sex, women,
betrayal, humiliation, smothering, and so on. And these connections show that women and men inhabit entirely different
worlds, show that women and men perceive the world differently. But the difference is so great that it is sometimes difficult to see where the common links occur. If men need to
interpose violence in order to protect themselves from closeness
and personal connections, then the threat which they see suggests that men live in a kind of war zone, always on the look-
out for a potential enemy. Moreover, since personal affiliation
is an aspect of every human life, then it suggests that men must
spend a great deal of time being fearful. Is this, perhaps, the
reason for such bravado?

Men seek achievement in the external world. This seems to be
where they are most comfortable. Women, as well as feeling at
home in the public domain, seek relationship. But men see
danger in relationship, while women do not often seek achievement for its own sake: the danger they see in such a pursuit is

that it may lead them away from their real goal of relationship. It is here that the real danger of sex-role stereotyping, which leads women and men to have entirely different perceptions about life and its meaning and the place of love and friendship, can be located.

Yet even though men see danger and possibilities of betrayal in close relationships, it doesn't mean that they are not often jealous of the friendships that exist between women. Indeed, men often complain about the time their female partners or wives spend with friends. Men sometimes see women's friendships as a kind of denial of the love for a man. When a woman and a man live together this can be one of the most difficult sources of conflict between them. For it is the woman – she is the one with the friends – who tends to take responsibility for the social arrangements of the couple.

At the beginning of a relationship this is often an agreeable part of their social exchange. It adds richness to a relationship; it brings continuity and a sense of community. But it is also one of the reasons why many relationships break down, for a man may begin to feel inadequate and resentful of his partner's ability to make friends and sustain other relationships. He will then project hostility on to his partner's friends instead of realising that he has neglected both friendship and his part in making the social arrangements. This comes as something of a blow to such men, for they tend to see masculinity as 'superior' and believe that women are 'unable to do many of the things defined as socially important'.[5] Men's lack of ability in making and sustaining good and successful friendships reinforces them in their isolation.

There are several ways to look at this. The first and most obvious stems from the fact that since men have so clearly defined themselves as isolated people, they tend to be very awkward when it comes to making social gestures and arrangements. Men aren't explicit in conveying what they mean, so things fall through because of lack of clarity. Men also seem to have the knack of appearing so socially inept that women take pity on them and automatically take control of the social organisation of their lives. As well as evoking resentment in men, women then tend to appear bossy and over-organised and this obviously works against them in the long run – for, as usual, the focus is on women.

In friendship, as in so many other areas of life, women and men are poles apart. Women share every aspect of their lives with their friends and put a great deal of time and energy into maintaining their friendships. Men appear to spend the equivalent time in avoiding the closeness friendship requires. How much of this is due to implicit homophobia is impossible to calculate. But it is certain that many men fear to be seen in close relationship with other men in case they are suspected of being homosexual. Women do not have this fear and are therefore allowed to be free in their physical gestures to their friends. Men have to keep a tight rein on their gestures as well as on their feelings: they cannot be too open in case a homophobic reaction is aroused. However, it goes deeper than this, I think. For if, as the research conducted by a number of clinics and by various psychologists at universities in Australia and Britain[6] shows, 60 per cent of self-defined heterosexual men are really bisexual, then the fear must be something that is perceived *in* themselves, not outside. Perhaps it is true that men really do fear that if they got close to another man they would discover the real depth of their feelings. They fear they might be homosexual. Rather than run the risk of society's disapprobation, they hold back.

My hunch is that if men did take the risk they would discover not so much their sexual feelings for other men as their feelings of friendship. While no friendship is without some form of sexual love, it does not mean that it is necessary to express it physically. Women have no difficulty in touching one another, for their relationships do not result from fear, but from love. If men could discover friendship, my feeling is that they would discover that they have no need to express themselves sexually in quick, emotionless sex. For quick, emotionless sex would be seen in its reality, as the substitute for friendship.

Social approval seems to stand in the way of men's good relations with one another. So men need to reassess their apparent need of approbation and break through the false codes which dictate and inhibit male behaviour. If men could make friends with other men this would not only give them the opportunity of loving and supporting one another, it would also take away the pressure from women. Women would not be the objects of resentment they presently are. Men's social networks could help to support social arrangements in the way that women's networks currently do. More importantly, men might be able to drop their competitive edge with other men and open themselves up to sharing their hopes and fears. Between women and men a measure of equality would be achieved.

Men see danger in affiliation and safety in isolation. They fear women as they fear self-knowledge. The only conclusion to be drawn from this is that men fear love. That may seem to be a simplistic equation but it is nevertheless true.

In holding themselves aloof from women, other men, and anyone who might have the possibility of getting close, men deny themselves the opportunity of self-knowledge. It is not enough – and this is supposing that it sometimes happens – to reflect on oneself and one's actions in isolation. Each of us needs close relationships in order to be self-reflected and self-reflective. We each need to be self-reflective in order to know ourselves and to stay in touch with ourselves. Without the self-knowledge that comes through our encounters with others, we cannot develop our human capacities for love and tenderness.

By this I do not mean that it is our capacity for love and tenderness solely towards others that is so crucial: it is also essential that we have the power to love and be tender in relation to ourselves. Only when we have achieved a measure of self-knowledge can we be true to ourselves. It follows from this that we can only be friends once we have achieved some knowledge and understanding of ourselves. The love and compassion which we show towards ourselves will also be the kind of love and compassion we are able to show towards our friends. Men do not enjoy the kind of friendship that is available to them because they neither know nor trust themselves; they cannot know and trust themselves as long as they remain the isolated people they are. Isolation leads only to violation and destruction. Friendship means health.

6. Men and love

'What's love? It isn't an emotion I have ever experienced. I know about being "in love", but love is too difficult. I really don't know what it is.' In response to my question about how important love is to him, Alex is quite clear: he has never experienced it.

Dougal was as certain as Alex: 'I'd like to think it is important but don't believe it is. I'm not sure that I've actually found out what love is.'

Curiously, perhaps, both of these men call themselves well experienced. They have both been married; they both have children; they both had other relationships. They both like women and Alex has lived with a woman for the last few years. He claims to be happy even though he also claims never to have experienced love.

Mike says that love is a word he doesn't use much: 'I suspect it is enormously important but if I get into my feelings all I can do is to cry and that's not very satisfactory, it seems.' Mike went on to discuss with me how he sees that there are a number of kinds of love. He says there are about six different ways of looking at love:

Love is just a fancy word for attraction: physical attraction
between two people; and we gift-wrap it and call it love.
And then there is the love that is really 'need' and I don't
like the idea of me being 'needful', or other people being
needful of me all that much, and so that's a love I don't like
very much. Then there is something – which I regard as an
ideal – which would be 'conscious love', which for most of
us is that kind of love for an animal or a young child or
baby where one can will them to be themselves as much as
possible and take joy in their being totally cat or totally
baby at the moment. That I think of as being rather a good
kind of love, even between adults who are having a
relationship – not wishing them to be different. That is my
ideal. And then there is the love that is shared intimacy that
I am very bad at, though attracted to, but I always think
that, well, the mermaids will not sing for me; that I could
never let myself go enough, just as I could never manage to
be hypnotised, so I could never let myself go in that kind of
love unless I was dying or something.

Mike is highly articulate in his analysis of love and able to see
how he fails in relation to his own desire. For him, loving in the
way he wants to love would mean 'letting go of himself', giving
himself up to something greater than himself. It is also something
that he can imagine doing when *in extremis*, like when he is
dying. So he knows what love is (unlike Alex and Dougal), but
there is a gap between himself and the object of his desire.

Joseph hesitated a while before he responded to my question
about love.

I don't know how to answer that question. I would suppose
that love is very important to me but I don't think I always
recognise it for what it is. I think that the kind of distancing
that I do tends to make me try and keep my cool about
things and therefore in a way almost to resist love – or to
keep its manifestations very carefully under hatches, and
only in one relationship in my life would I say that it had,
however momentarily, completely over-spilled and worked
as a whole.

For Joseph and Mike, love is deliberately kept at bay. They know about it, are aware of it, but it scares them. When I asked Joseph how he would describe how love had 'over-spilled' in his life, the conversation took a slight turn: 'I think what I am talking about is that – for a time, anyway – the body and the spirit were working together.' This is what was frightening, then. The aspects of his life which were usually separated into definite compartments came together for a while. Joseph puts the body/spirit split down to his British upbringing:

> It's Puritanism, I suppose – a neo-Platonic feeling and the
> ideas about shedding the body, about disciplining the body,
> about not allowing the body to control, about feeling that
> the spirit·is more important than the body, about the
> dichotomy between body and spirit.

Joseph closely relates his experience of love with his sexuality. But it is clear that he also relates love to fear – so he keeps its manifestations under hatches.

Love is central to the lives of women; but men relegate it to the periphery of their lives, replacing its importance generally with work or scholarship or sport. But this does not seem to mean that men do not often feel very deeply; rather, they get so overwhelmed by feeling that it terrifies them. They seem to have no way of mediating it through one part of themselves to another; so it stays separate. Joseph was very clear about the depth of his feelings, yet fearful at the same time. So although men can and do feel deeply, can experience love, they also have a powerful resistance to it – so much so that they claim not to know what it is.

So the question is easily formulated: how do men come to have this fear? What are its origins and its pattern of development? Why does the fear of love linger alongside them throughout their lives? The answers to these questions lie in the problematic arrangements of child-rearing, however remote they may seem to be from the problems of love and loving. Dorothy

Dinnerstein, Professor of Psychology at Rutgers University in New Jersey, began writing about the problems of gender arrangements early in the 1970s with a view to analysing the pull between society and the individual. She speaks about our 'maiming and mutual imprisonment' which stem from childhood.[1] Locked into the love the infant child has for his mother is the seed of ambiguity – what I have called the 'split' in men. The mother is not only his first love, she is his 'first boss', as she is the 'first representative of the flesh'.[2] The conflict that is thus set up in the infant's inner world revolves around power. (The conflict affects girls as well as boys.) The issue becomes one of how to go beyond the mother's power, the mother's will. Though a male child loves his mother with a total infant passion, he becomes aware with time that he needs to go beyond her; when he begins to separate from her he feels that she is pushing him away, and another seed of mistrust is sown. This time it is the seed of mistrust which is not focused on his mother alone, but on all women.

Woman-centred child-rearing keeps us all, to some degree, in infancy because it allows us to continue to focus our difficulties on women. For a boy, the ambiguity which, in a more desirable circumstance (that is, the circumstance of being reared by both parents equally), would be central to life is allowed to rest on the woman. All the problems the infant boy has in becoming himself get projected on to his mother. They are not resolved.

This is the way a boy gets separated from his experience. He pushes it on to his mother, or the woman who raises him, and keeps it focused upon her, as though it had been her experience rather than his. On to his father he projects an image of the hero. Thus he undervalues his mother and overvalues his father. The ambiguity he feels in relation to both parents he sees as belonging to his mother. What should belong in his inner world he makes the woman carry for him. She now holds not just the love which she first commanded, but all the problems which arise from the unequal child care arrangements.

For girls the issues are less difficult although girls see their mothers ambiguously and their fathers as hero-figures. The experience of their mothers (amongst many other experiences) often leads them in later life to adopt patriarchal value systems; sometimes, when they understand what was really going on in infancy, they take back the difficult feelings they had cast on to their mothers. Some women recognise in themselves the feelings of distaste of, sometimes fear for, other women which began with the distaste and fear of their mother. Although I believe it is generally easier for women to live with the problematic feelings left over from woman-centred child care, women's relationships are often tinged with fear and dread, echoing the powerlessness they experienced in childhood. Fortunately though, their relationships with each other, their open discussion of their experiences, can free them from many otherwise difficult issues, particularly fear.

Nevertheless, fear of women is present in us all. When Tom talks about his fear of women there is a note of terror in his voice. He is very serious when he says, 'Oh, they might eat me, devour me, might get angry. When I think of it, I see myself as very small and pathetic.' Peter says that fear often inhibits friendships between women and men, even though he recognises that most men prefer women friends over men. Friendship, though, requires a different kind of intimacy from that demanded by love. Joseph, who is gay, told me how frightened he is by love. 'And then it's actually pathological how frightened I am of sex with women.' We come back to the love/sex/flesh axis.

Men are deprived of the love that might otherwise be available to them by projecting fear on to women. This is the fear of the power that women had over them when they were babies. So to rid themselves of this uncomfortable feeling, men tend to say that love is the prerogative of women: it is women's work. They separate the emotional and the physical side of love and convince themselves that they really cannot 'believe in and rely on affiliation'.[3] That tiny seed unconsciously sown has grown into a permanent state of ambivalence, carrying with it a whole division of life-expectations and sex roles with women holding the love and men the work.

But what is work without the love of work? What is work without the attitude of love behind it? Is it possible to create culture unless it comes from love? The malaise which began in infancy continues its divisive role throughout a man's life.

In their state of separation, men see love as the job or duty of women. Because men see women as inferior, they tend to see love as inferior. The male part in life, without the binds of love, is the higher part. This is not, however, what another part of a man says. His 'higher knowledge' does not prevent him from falling passionately in love, even if his passion is tinged with a whole range of other feelings. Lillian Rubin describes the process:

> He moves close, wanting to share some part of himself with
> her, trying to do so, perhaps even yearning to experience
> again the bliss of the infant's connection with a woman. She
> responds – woman style – wanting to touch him just a little
> more deeply, to know what he's thinking, feeling, fearing,
> wanting. And the fear closes in – the fear of finding himself
> again in the grip of a powerful woman, of allowing her
> admittance only to be betrayed and abandoned once again,
> of being overwhelmed by denied desires.[4]

This experience of getting close and then becoming fearful is so common in men that I am tempted to believe it is a dynamic which underpins the personality. The feeling is so gripping, so compulsive, that it threatens to tear the man apart. But why should something so potentially good and exciting push him to abandon it? It is the fear of being betrayed and then abandoned that cautions him to leave and return to his separated state.

This is almost impossible for a woman to understand. If love is what the man feels for her, why should it also be the very reason for leaving her? She could never leave him for this reason. And yet his feelings of love may be precisely why he will leave, or get involved with someone else as well, to protect himself from too close an attachment. Because his need to stay separate is so great he will muster all his defences to maintain his position of safety. He may try to 'cool' things, to make meetings less frequent, to come home later, to involve himself if not with another lover then with some idea or group or sport.

This drive towards separation derives from the simple fact that his sense of self – his separate sense of self – is built on so fragile a foundation that love would threaten his entire existence. His whole life as a masculine man is predicated not on the basis of his humanity, but on a set of social and cultural constructions. It is for reasons of social convention that he must turn away from love in the direction of autonomy. His natural potential to love and respond to love is thwarted by his need to function in society, as well as by his original fear of love.

Many women complain that the men in their lives vanish for a time and then return. More often than not, women say that men disappear after an occasion when they have become particularly close, when it appears the relationship has achieved a new kind of intimacy. It may be that a man will stay away for a couple of weeks after such an occasion, returning to the relationship but not in quite the same way. Sometimes the departure comes after a year or so, when it seems the relationship has become more or less permanent. Some men want to establish a zone of safety for themselves and so they look for a way of keeping a potential love relationship safe. This means, in the words of novelist Milan Kundera, the rules of threes: 'Either you see a woman three times in quick succession and never again, or you maintain relations over the years but make sure that the rendezvous are at least three weeks apart.'[5] The rule of threes is practised by many men I have met and talked to. They appear to want to stay on the outside of an event, to remain an observer of it rather than become a participant in it.

So a man tries to tame love, to put a space between his feelings and what he sees as his responsibility to social demands.

This is how he tries to deal with it on a rational level. But there is the other – the hidden – level, which necessarily must work against him and threaten his safety. For although he carries inside him a fear of the flesh, he cannot repress for ever the irrepressible interest that is also there.

To try to cope with convention and the need to have some kind of affective bond, a man often reverts to a time-honoured system of marrying a woman he does not quite love, and loving a woman he cannot marry. In this way he can maintain a state of idealism about love – for men do idealise it – and yet never face the reality of it. He then turns the woman he has married into a mother-figure and he projects his other love on to the other woman in a region of safety outside the marriage. By behaving in this manner, he never has to confront his real feelings for any length of time. He works within the context of his own fragility. The real lives of women, however, have to be abandoned to fit in with the limited capacities of men in relation to love.

Because of the nature of social construction, many women start out believing what is said about them: that their part in life is to love and be content with what love calls out of them. Another way of seeing this would be to say that women are asked by men to belong to a servant class and, as such, to take care of men in the name of love. But women have been getting wise to this, and over the last 15 to 20 years have begun to discover for themselves the real joy of work outside the home,* as well as the absence of love in their relationships. They have begun to substitute work where they were once told love was the only thing. Claire, a 40-year-old woman with two young children, said that

> When I asked myself how I was feeling about my marriage,
> my children and my work, I realised that I loved my

* This is not to suggest that women have been working outside the home only for this time; but over the last 20 years or so the choices for women have been much greater than those in the past.

children and my job but that my marriage was impossible.
Then I asked myself where I wanted to put my energy and
I decided to put it where my love was: with my children
and my job.

Many women seem to feel like Claire and, like her, when they
take their place in the public domain they do not leave their
feelings locked away but bring them to their work.

In the United States 50 per cent of married women now seek a
divorce from their husbands. Often, it is because they are dis-
satisfied with the way their husbands express their 'love': 'I
believe my partner is afraid to love – that requires a commitment
he can't give. His wall gets higher and higher – but he clings
tighter and tighter.'[6] Another woman said that

> Most men are afraid to let go in love, because love is a form
> of expression and men have been raised to not show their
> emotions. Many want the kind of love that is there when
> they need it, no matter whether they work to keep it alive
> or not. It depends on the man and how deep his
> understanding of himself is.[7]

These contributions were made to a study by the American
researcher into sexuality, Shere Hite, whose study on female
sexuality focuses on men's inability to keep love alive. The
attitude of so many men to love seems to be that once they have
captured it, they are content to leave it alone. Another way of
looking at it might be that once they have captured a woman,
they are content to leave her alone – as long as she does what
women are supposed to do, why should he worry? Men can be
satisfied by the love women show them in terms of 'service'
(cooking, cleaning, taking care of children) but women cannot be
satisfied by what men offer, since it is so little. Women are now
much more likely to be satisfied by a good job and the close
relationships they have with other women and with their children, if they have any.

Richard was very keen to marry Kate. And she believed him.

From all appearances, it looked as though this was a relationship of equality – they were both professionals – with love as the central concern. But several years on, appearances can be seen to belie the reality. When Kate has problems she turns to her women friends to discuss them. Richard doesn't really have the time to listen to her. He told me that the real point in being married was to have a place to be able to operate from. What it came down to was his need for a settled existence to allow him to get on with his real life – that is, his work. How will love go on living in this relationship, I wonder, when only one of the couple retains an interest? In Kate, Richard found his intellectual equal but what he wanted, besides intellectual companionship, was a mother and a maid – perhaps, in time, a babysitter.

Kate feels miffed. She knows that she has kept her part of the 'contract', but doesn't know how best to approach Richard about the issues that concern her. 'Is this all there is?' she asks herself, not at all content with what there is. But he does not see it that way, for he has what he wanted. They are both playing the game of 'Mothers and Fathers', according to the traditional rites in their middle-class house and the middle-class suburb. But the rites of tradition no longer have much bearing on the life of an educated, professional woman. Tradition, especially the tradition of love, has always favoured the male of the species. It is possible that Kate will leave this relationship in time, since it takes so much from her while giving her little in return. Or she may possibly opt to have a child in the hope that the intimacy which characterised the early part of their relationship will return.

Intimacy is part of the problem of love for men. While women seek for greater intimacy, men flee from it. A man finds it tolerable – even enjoyable – at the beginning of a relationship, but if it continues there is the fear that it will consume him and so he must stand aside from it. What was the mutual aim for many couples like Richard and Kate becomes the single goal of the woman of the couple. He feels it will stifle him. She knows what it is that will keep love not just alive, but always in a state of delight and development. What began as a psychological dilemma in the infant male can now be seen as a fully developed psychological complex, taking him away from his human connections and in the direction of further separation. Love is like a beautiful wild bird which he can allow out to fly around. But for most of the time, it needs to be behind bars.

At the point of separation Richard had to take on an identity which was foreign to him; he had to enter the alien world of men. This meant the rejection of all that he had formerly known and loved in his mother's world. By 'merging' with Kate, he re-entered his mother's world for a time but he knew he could not stay there and be a man. He has swallowed the convention which states that men and women inhabit different worlds and have different tasks to perform in their separate worlds. He can hear the other voice of humanity calling him to put convention behind him, but how can he be sure about it? It would mean, possibly, giving up his ideas of success (and he *is* successful) and giving up his ambitions for the sake of love. Will he, or won't he? Only time will tell.

If Richard stays in his separated, masculine world there is the possibility that Kate will leave. If that happens, he will be devastated – as men are when women leave them. For women are meant to be powerless in the face of love; instead, they are often very realistic. In truth, it is men who suffer more when a relationship breaks down; it is men who often take much longer to recover from the emotional damage that has been done in the relationship.

As well as perceiving the fundamental psychological issue which is central to this, there is also a problem of communication. Women's ability to articulate their feelings often gives them an advantage in dealing with relationships; the male mode of separation tends to make men internalise the problem and elicits only a state of silence. The more a woman can discuss her feelings, the less a man seems to be able to locate his. He feels done for.

Because men feel more comfortable in their separated world they give much less attention to nurturing their good relationships; they feel that it is dangerous to depend upon love, for love will take away separation. When a man's relationship breaks down the point is reinforced and elaborated. He feels he must not fall into the trap of love again, though he generally does, if only to discover his own ambivalence.

Men's separation effectively means separation from love. This means that the model of development for men, based on separation, is contrary both to the development of women and, in my estimation, to the development of human potential. Men's capacities get repressed further and further and are locked away – as Joseph described it – 'under hatches'.

At Harvard University during the 1970s, Carol Gilligan conducted a study of the place of morality in women's and men's lives.[8] She found that when men describe themselves they do so in terms of achievement, not affiliation. When women describe themselves, regardless of their positions of power or status, they associate themselves with those they love.

Gilligan quotes a number of men whose marital and professional status is the same as the women. One man describes himself as

> Logical, compromising, outwardly calm. If it seems like my statements are short and abrupt, it is because of my background and training. Architectural statements have to be very short and concise.

Another man said:

> I would describe myself as an enthusiastic, passionate person who is slightly arrogant.

And another:

> I would describe myself as a person who is well developed intellectually and emotionally. Relatively narrow circle of friends, acquaintances, persons with whom I have real

contacts as opposed to professional contacts or community contacts. And relatively proud of the intellectual skills and development, content with the emotional development as such, as a not very actively pursued goal.

The three female counterparts of these men, asked exactly the same question, replied:

> This sounds sort of strange, but I think maternal, with all its connotations. I see myself in a nurturing role, maybe not right now, but whenever that might be, as a physician, as a mother.

The second woman answered:

> I am fairly hard-working and fairly thorough and fairly responsible, and in terms of weaknesses, I am sometimes hesitant about making decisions and unsure of myself and afraid of doing things and taking responsibility, and I think maybe that is one of the biggest conflicts I have had . . . The other very important aspect of my life is my husband and trying to make his life easier and trying to help him out.

Another woman told the researcher:

> I have sort of changed a lot. At the point of the last interview I felt like I was the kind of person who was interested in growth and trying hard, and it seems to me that the last couple of years, the not trying [part] is someone who is not growing, and I think that is the thing that bothers me the most, the thing that I keep thinking about, that I am not growing.[9]

Whereas all the women see themselves in terms of attachment and psychological development, the men's preoccupation is with personal achievement, regardless of personal attachments to others. What Gilligan concludes is that women and men follow two separate kinds of development: 'When women construct the adult domain, the world of relationships emerges and becomes the focus of attention and concern.' This is a very different world from the one described by men. Gilligan goes on to say that her research 'suggests that men and women may speak different languages that they assume are the same, using similar words to encode disparate experiences of self and social relationships.'[10] In my view, it is precisely these different languages tnat bring the conflicts in love relationships: women and men are in fact not only speaking different languages, but each is living in a world that is alien to the other.

So when a man loves it is certain that he means something very different from what a woman means. When love enters a woman's life everything changes and she knows that it will go on changing: that, for her, is the nature of love. She knows that love will demand of her a greater commitment; she also hopes that the love itself will grow with time and attention: that is also in the nature of love. What a man means when he speaks of love is a pleasant addition to his life. He does not see it in terms of a demand upon him, but rather something that will make his life easier – and it does.

Because a woman's life has always been about her connection to others – and therefore about love for others – she does not quibble about love's demands: she expects them, and she knows that her tie to this new person will grow stronger. But the man's life, based on separation, cannot tolerate many demands. Like all the Richards in the world, the man will make some small sacrifices – provided they are justified by the ends: that is, if love will allow him to have a settled life the better from which to work or operate. They speak different languages; and they have different expectations. In the past, women had no choice but to accept the other language as the superior one, and to learn to adjust their expectations to something meagre. But economic independence means that women do not have to tolerate any longer the other voice or the other expectations. They are free now to live according to the nature of love, as *they* perceive it – not as it best suits men.

Women have learned that to be loving sometimes means to

give up what they thought of as love. Women have also learned that the language spoken by men does not suit the womanly tongue. What women have also noted about men is that separation does not lead to a better form of psychological development but to a kind of violence and destruction of the inner and outer worlds. This has made them stand back from the love of men and ask themselves whether there isn't a higher kind of love which need not take them away from their own development. Loving a man has often meant that a woman has had to deny her own life; that kind of male reciprocation is rare indeed.

Men, I observe, marry not only women; they seem also to marry the organisation, the trade union, the factory for which they work. Who can say whether men have a more perfect kind of love for their organisation? What is certain, though, is that they offer their workmates or colleagues and organisations a loyalty and devotion which is rare amongst husbands for wives. This loyalty may be the overwhelming success of the claims of masculinity – or it may be a perverted diversionary tactic which is a hangover from infancy.

In the lives of men, the organisation often behaves as the tyrant. Yet men continue to obey this tyrannical master with the same love-inspired blindness for which women are often criticised. What is happening, I believe, results from the man's having been mother-reared. What he cannot offer to the woman at home, he now offers to the organisation – which is a kind of father-substitute. If, as a child, he had had to face the problem of being human by confronting both his father and his mother he would not have had the problem of projecting the central concern of his life on to women. As it is, he has never had to confront the difficulty in men. He would have had to do so if his father had had an equal share in his upbringing. So he, a man, remains a child with all his infantilism alive in him, for he has never had to overcome it.

In relation to his workplace, too, he is an infant still – sometimes adoring, sometimes kicking, blind in his inability to see what is really going on. Between his selves – at home and the organisation – he is caught in the dilemma that he should have had the opportunity to resolve when he was a small child. Woman-centred child-rearing not only prevents him from growing up, but it keeps him from seeing what is really happening to him.

Can men love, then, seeing that a part of them is still located in infancy? My observations lead me to conclude that it is a difficult task, one which few men satisfactorily succeed in. This does not mean, however, that they cannot peel away the scales from their eyes and begin to see what has happened to them – how they have been duped by the system which claims them as its own and prevents them from becoming free individual persons with human lives to develop. Contrary to some psychological theories which have been perpetuated through the generations, love is the central axis of the developed person, whether woman or man. But as long as men go on being fearful of love, they cannot function with love at their centre. As long as this holds true, it will be possible to say that men have not taken up their human calling.

7. Men and marriage

The thread of dependency runs through all human
relationships – modern marriage is itself a complex mix of
dependency, sexuality, autonomy. While popular myth tells
us that women are dependent and men independent, a turn
of the axis puts a radically different light on women's and
men's dependency needs and gratifications.

Susie Orbach and Luise Eichenbaum, *What do Women
Want?* (Fontana, London, 1984)

Problems with marriage or long-term live-in relationships very
often bring people into therapy in my experience. Such problems
are generally the reason men go to see a therapist or a counsellor,
often when it is too late to begin to deal with the kind of issues
that have brought on the problems. Men have to deal not only
with their personal suffering, but also with a challenge to their
experience and perceptions.

Talking to men about marriage has shown me how wide a gap
there is between the value women and men place on the relationships which are understood to be central to their lives. It is a
subject of utmost complexity and very difficult to try to unravel.

Chris has been married twice. He describes his first marriage,
which lasted for just a few months, as a power-struggle. He has
taken a long time to separate from the next woman to whom he
was married for seven years and with whom he has a child. Why
does he think men get married in the first place?

> I think men are opportunistic, generally speaking, and
> marriage itself is a form of opportunism. It just happens to
> be the time when they wish to get married; I think that if

you put that to men they would say that their marriages are anti-climactic – they don't fulfil their expectations, which are romantic with a capital 'R'.

He went on to tell me that he views marriage 'fairly cynically'.

I do not believe in love and marriage. You only have to look around at the amount of repressed prostitution in marriage, and I am not talking only from the female side. I am talking from the male side.

By 'repressed prostitution' I understand Chris to mean that men feel there are expectations about sexual performance which they don't or can't measure up to. He told me about the kind of conversations that go on in the pub amongst married men who feel dread at the prospect of having to go home and 'perform' sexually. It is as though they have an image to keep up: the virile man.

Many modern marriages are little more than form though they sometimes convey the image or appearance of happiness. The truth is that they contain a great deal of tension and even anguish. Sometimes, though, one sees a couple who have achieved a relationship based on mutal acceptance and friendship; these relationships are generally the result not only of love but respect and personal integrity.

But it seems that good and happy and satisfying marriages are the exception. My experience suggests that the reason for this lies in the fact that men fear love and therefore do not marry the women they love. Many men do say, however, that they didn't marry for love but to establish a household and a sense of order in their lives. They want to be able to keep life under control. As Chris says, opportunism plays a major role: when a man feels that convention demands marriage he will look around and find a woman to marry. Whereas women see love and marriage going hand in hand, men tend to see a marriage as a social adjunct – a state that will be advantageous to them as they move through their lives: it bolsters their status, their job, their political life, whatever they are involved in. It gives them a good background from which to operate, no matter what social group men come from. Tom Wolfe puts it quite directly in his book *The Right Stuff*, his analysis of the training of fighter pilots and astronauts in the United States: 'Of course, it was well known that a gracious, well-spoken small-talking, competent, sophisticated wife was a great asset to her husband's career, precisely because they were a team and both were in the service.'[1] These wives are commodities, like supermarket products which can be bought or even exchanged if they don't do the job for which they are intended!

When I asked Ed if he felt men married the women they love, he replied:

> This begs so many questions. I think they think they're
> marrying the woman they love at the time, but they may
> have persuaded themselves for all sorts of reasons that this
> is the woman they love.

Ray said he felt that he was very disillusioned about the motivations men had for marriage.

> In my opinion, a smaller proportion actually marry for love.
> The others marry, sadly, unfortunately, for various reasons,
> sex being the obvious one. But they want security, home,
> the whole thing that goes with status. And I think that it is
> sad in any sort of relationship because there is so much that
> is special that can happen between two people, whether over
> two years, five years, 20 years or 60 years. But I would say
> in my experience a very small proportion of men marry for
> love.

The demands of convention made on the external lives of men, whatever social group they come from, determine the pattern of their lives. They are required to conform very specifically to their defined sex roles. A certain kind of education is followed by a certain kind of job; and according to the social group, a certain kind of wife – the appropriate woman – goes with these conventions. There is little real flexibility, little real choice.

Jake was sent to do some work in a country where he did not speak the language and where he felt alien. When he met Annie there he felt he had found a companion with whom he could at least have a conversation. She was in a similar position. They married within six months of meeting, even though, they both now say, Jake hardly liked her. But his sense of social convention, like his need to be in control, was very strong. Annie fitted his external requirements: class, age, religion were all right. Both of them have lived to regret the part social convention played in the few years they lived together. They are both scarred as a result of their destructive relationship. They both regret the part played by opportunism. The discrepancy between the image and the reality of the ideal partner has convinced Jake that there is no such thing as a good relationship. Jake is embittered and finds it almost impossible not to blame Annie for his lack of self-awareness and self-reflection. He has not been able to see that they both entered into a relationship simply for the sake of convention. He expected to get things from this marriage; rather as though he were doing Annie a favour by marrying her. He had no sense of equality in marriage but saw the relationship as one which should serve him. Since that is his view of marriage, Jake runs the risk of never mastering his experiences; consequently, he is in danger of making the same mistake again. Interestingly, Jake fell in love some time after his marriage had ended but felt totally out of control: he could not take this new relationship up. He loves Barbara, but is terrified by his fear of love.

Joseph, who is gay, has observed the way his heterosexual friends have married:

> Men marry women for very many different reasons. I would
> say that men marry for love about half the time. I can think
> of two friends who definitely married for love and I can
> think of two other friends in whom there was quite a large
> element of the eye for the main chance – somebody marrying
> a woman because she would be a good wife under the
> circumstances.

In Joseph's view, heterosexual couples get things wrong a lot of the time:

> I think heterosexual couples have been unreal about what
> marriage is about. They think marriage is about
> consummating a love relationship. But it is also about
> creating a bond which, within society, will create a
> sufficiently well-established bond even if the love
> relationship disappears, whereas I don't think homosexuals
> are subject to these pressures so I think that homosexual
> relationships are intrinsically less permanent.

This may be a very good description of the expectations of marriage in society: creating an appropriate, even essential, framework from which good society can develop. But it can deny the need that we all have to live in a loving relationship, even a loving relationship with oneself. Living without love, or in a relationship where the love has died or been destroyed, diminishes the persons involved and further separates them from themselves. This clearly has repercussions for society at large.

There is another reason why I query traditional marriage and this stems from the burden I believe it places upon women. Women seem to me to be the ones whose responsibility it is to keep the relationship going, to tend it on a day-to-day basis. This was Jake's expectation and it seems to be the expectation of many of the men I have worked with. They seem to feel it is the duty of women to sustain a relationship rather as they feel it is men's place to cut the grass. But this also begs the question of whether men see love as necessary to the whole of their lives, or as a possibly momentary lapse from their real concerns – be their real concerns football, the production-line, politics or the stock exchange. This separation between the different parts of a man's life is, I suggest, why men marry women they don't or cannot love, and keep the person who inspires them to love outside their marriage. They can only be in control of their lives if the demands of real love are kept at bay. This is the direction in which the split in men takes them.

Some men who settle into marriage tend to turn the women they marry into mothers. A colleague recently remarked to me that she felt men need to marry their mothers because they could then always be sure that the soup was there at home, simmering for them whenever they returned. Another colleague, a man, qualified this remark by saying that although he believed that men like to marry their mothers, he felt that they wanted to have sexy mothers. In formal psychological terms he was talking about a kind of incest, though that wasn't the way he put it to me.

Even though men marry women they don't love, or women they subsequently turn into mothers, most men (around 88 per cent)[2] marry sometime between the ages of 22 and 35. If they divorce, they tend to marry again very quickly;[3] and if they divorce a second time they still, very often, marry again.[4] Men are tied to marriage in a way that women no longer are; perhaps because the benefits of marriage are so much greater for a man; perhaps, also, because men are much more tied to convention than women.[5]

How is it that men can turn women they marry into mothers? The answer to this is very complex. A man first encounters a woman as his mother; she is at once his first love and his mother. His relationship with his mother is always an unresolved relationship since it contains the seeds of ambivalence and because it is unconscious. Every woman a man meets when he is adult is a potential lover, and since his experience of woman is as both lover and mother, he sees every potential lover as mother also. But just as the ambivalence towards his 'first' mother derived from the degree to which she was responsible for his development, so ambivalence characterises his relationship to the adult woman lover. He has never had to resolve, through confrontation with his father, the issues which hold him in this state.

He remains, in his relationship to women, an infant, with the same overwhelming feelings of love, the same sense of her power over him, the same dread of that power: in other words the same ambivalence. But just as he never could see or understand the will of his mother, so he cannot understand the will of this other woman. In order that she will not control him, as his mother did, he determines to control her. Their relationship becomes distorted – first by his fear of her power, and then by his determination to be in charge. What was possibly a love relationship, at least potentially, turns into a relation of power:

> Power of this kind, concentrated in one sex (the woman) and exerted at the outset over both, is far too potent and dangerous a force to be allowed free sway in adult life. To contain it, to keep it under control and harness it to chosen purposes, is a vital need, a vital task, for every mother-raised human.[6]

Men do not seem to have this power, although of course they do, so men do not become the object of male and female projections of power.

We all retreat to the world of men because it looks safer, calmer; we cannot see the 'nature of this link'[7] between woman-centred childcare and the constructed divisions between women and men. It is what Dinnerstein calls 'societal despotism': the 'female rule over childhood' and the 'male rule over the historical process'. The one ensures the other. Women and men become distinctive power bases, not because of any fundamental differences between them but because our lack of insight forces us to demand and construct separate roles for women and men. But as well as keeping us in infancy it also keeps us sub-human[8] and locked into neurosis. We do not see what it is to be human because we are so busy protecting ourselves from the power of women.

Men not only marry women to conform to society's demands of them but also to return that original place of charm; women marry men to escape to the place where men, not women, will be in control. At the core of this need to marry is a neurotic desire to remain locked in the mother's arms, but not so enclosed that escape is not sometimes possible. Yet it is in the nature of neurosis to seek for a resolution, a healing, and that will often mean a re-enactment of the original wounding until enough awareness is gained to allow for a conscious change over time. A man may marry and divorce several times and never see that he is repeating a pattern which is longing to be ended. He does not see that his infantile psychology is pressing him to confront the nature of his humanity and to move into a new psychological state which will give him the option truly to be human. As long as he goes on falling in love and acting on his condition he will not see that he is putting on to the outside world what is unresolved on the inside. And this is all because he has, like everyone else, projected the infant fear of his vulnerability on to women. He may posture strength but it is unlikely that that is how he really feels; with an infant inside him, he will feel terror in the face of danger.

A man needs, therefore, to protect himself from love and to muster all his defences against it. This is why, I believe, a man tries very hard not to marry a woman he feels he really does love. He sticks with convention and the convenience that convention gives him; convention provides all the rules for the appropriate behaviour in marriage, whereas love confronts all the rules and begs all questions. So convention comes to the assistance of men and can be seen as the device by which to perpetuate their fear of love. It helps them contain their fear of love. This fear is reflected in the lengths to which men will go to keep love away, so strong is the man's fear that he will marry a woman he doesn't love to escape someone he does; or he may simply try to build up his psychological defences.

The conventional modes of male behaviour seem to me to be one of the ways of self-protection. Married women say that their husbands are cold and distant and make demands on them which they do not return. Men do not listen or pay attention to their wives. Many men stay away from home as long as they can to avoid their wives; they feign duty to their jobs so that they don't have to get involved in confrontation.

The kinds of difficulties which have been examined so far

seem to deny the possibilities of a good, long-lasting and deeply satisfying marriage. Though it is true that they may be exceptional, it is for that very reason that they deserve attention. Good marriages are the result of a lot of hard work and those couples I talked to said they couldn't stress too much the effort they put into their relationships.

One couple, Rosie and Trevor, have been married now for 12 years and they admit that it has not been plain sailing. It is Trevor's second marriage. He was almost destroyed, he says, by his first relationship. After his first marriage ended he spent a couple of years in therapy and he says that this helped him tremendously to see what had been going on. He and Rosie put a great deal into their marriage, making sure that they spend weekends together even if their different jobs keep them apart for much of the week. They try to talk over problems when they arise rather than hold on to them. Trevor told me that they sometimes need to say hard things to each other to get through a problem, but that they respect each other so much that they always listen to what the other has to say, even when it is painful. When they are together at weekends they try not to socialise too much but to do the things they both enjoy – walking, gardening, going to their local pub, things which do not require a lot of planning and energy. They have both sacrificed – though they do not see it in terms of hardship – a great deal of personal ambition for the sake of their relationship.

Trevor is atypical, though. He is not afraid to confront what it means to him to love Rosie and go on loving her. In my view, this makes him very open. He is not closed to the possibilities that might come up. When they talk about their marriage they both say that they could never have imagined that it would have been so good, even though they loved each other very much at the beginning.

Tim and Liz have been married for nine years. A couple of years ago, Tim told me, they nearly split up. He had to make a decision about whether he took on more work or put more time and energy and commitment into their marriage. He said he feels he almost had a nervous breakdown about it: 'I was in such a crisis over my job that I couldn't see anything else. Liz held everything together for a long time until finally I saw what was going on.' Tim resolved not to work any harder but to give much more time to developing his relationship with Liz and spending as much time as possible with their three children.

A perception of the power relations that exist in traditional marriage and a desire not to perpetuate them may also have saved the situation for Tim and Liz. Tim said he got locked into believing that all he had to do when things got difficult in the relationship was to exert his power. Phyllis Rose writes about this kind of power in *Parallel Lives*[9], her study of five Victorian marriages.

> Traditional marriage shores up the powers of men in subtle ways which I believe few men – even sensitive men of the greatest goodwill towards women – appreciate. When you are playing tennis and the wind is blowing from your back, you may not be aware of the wind at all and think only that you are playing very well. All your shots go in swift and hard. It isn't until you change courts and the wind is blowing against you that you appreciate the force of the wind. Power is like that. You feel it most when it is working against you. Women sometimes marry to find that the wind is suddenly blowing against them. I am speaking now of spirited women, strong women, who are the most likely to resent the sudden change. They feel overwhelmed in marriage by husbands who have been raised to act, if not to be, strong in their dealing with the outside world and to expect devoted care from a woman in the family.

Good marriages, whilst rare, seem to be characterised by change and by the ability to recognise that a degree of conflict is both necessary and enriching to a relationship. They do not seem to be idyllic, necessarily, but are marked by good and strong friendship as well as deep respect. They are psychologically alive, and about as different from the expectations of conventional marriage as it seems possible to be.

Over the last 20 years much has happened to change the nature of modern marriage. For one thing, most married women do waged work.[10] This means that many women are economically independent, so they now have options which were denied them in the past. Many women nowadays question what husbands are for when men do not come up to expectations; even women with children say they find it easier to manage on their own, provided they have enough financial support or earning power to do so. Men, they say, make it much more difficult to bring up children. On a day-to-day level many women find being a single parent much more rewarding and interesting without the difficulties a man often brings.

Women's lack of satisfaction in marriage is one of the reasons so many are seeking divorce. Just under 75 per cent[11] of divorce petitions are now initiated by women, though this figure varies throughout Western society. It is as though women have finally allowed themselves to think the impossible thought: that marriage is not all there is. There are other things. Women in the West can make the kind of choices which were impossible for them until 20 years ago. When they have a good job, a marriage and children, it is the marriage that they are often prepared to abandon when it is unsatisfactory for them over a long period.

But while women are seeking both to divorce and stay divorced, men in the same situation go on to seek another partner and often remarry in a very short time.[12] It is as though aloneness is something they can tolerate less than a difficult marriage. But if they could tolerate, or even enjoy, living alone, they would make much better marriage partners. Interestingly, from the research conducted and published by Dorothy Rowe,[13] single men and married women are the most depressed people; the implications are self-evident.

Women also leave marriage because their needs to be loved are simply not met by men. Shere Hite's report on *Women and Love*[14] shows how women find much greater love amongst other women. When they leave a marriage they often prefer to spend their time, sometimes on a live-in basis, with other women. Women find the companionship and love they hoped for in marriage with other women. The reverse is true for men, however. Marriage benefits and supports men and male lives in a way it has never benefited or supported women. Marriage still is the place where inequality between the sexes is most clearly exposed and lived out, though many women are no longer willing to live like this.

Women begin their lives as unequal to their brothers. They learn in infancy – from the superior treatment their brothers and fathers get – that they are unequal. It becomes clear to them also that there is something wrong about themselves. This happens because their developmental needs are not met, and when needs are not met children do feel bad about themselves.[15] Mothers pass on to their daughters this sense of inferiority both in the way they see themselves (as women) and the way they serve men and their needs. Girls are also denied their need to be nurtured because of the prior claims of men and because of their future role as nurturers of men. Girls realise that being a boy is more important and they internalise their inferiority. When women marry they unconsciously hope that the needs that have been denied in childhood will be met by their partners. Instead they find that marriage is a relationship where they do most of the caring and men make most of the demands. Women lack good mothering and pass on to their daughters the lack which they themselves experienced and continue to experience. In marriage women are often very disappointed when they see how one-sided is caring. Many hope all their lives to find the 'right' man who will attend to their needs.

Women feel guilty, in the way that anyone who internalises a sense of inferiority feels guilty. They tend to assuage their guilt by extending their care for others even further. They get more and more self-denying. It is a vicious circle which keeps many women ensnared for the whole of their lives. What saves some women is the care they receive from their friends and the self-respect they gain from their work in the public domain. Marriage often works against women, undermining their confidence and separating them from the world.

The inequality of marriage pushes a woman to see the fault as hers and to make light of her own need to be herself. Societal expectations insist upon her being a 'good wife and mother', rather than a well-integrated and creative individual. Everything encourages her to focus upon the needs of her husband, and to support him in his endeavours at the expense of her own possibilities. This backdrop can never make a marriage good or happy: it only frustrates one partner and encourages resentment and repression. Moreover, when women are so out of touch with themselves – as often they are because of their own sense of deprivation and personal unhappiness in marriage – they try to control and define the structures of their relationship in order to get some kind of grasp on themselves. This puts a great deal of pressure on a marriage and pushes a man to look elsewhere for some pleasure. Marriage becomes a battlefield, with both partners grasping for their own individual survival. This is not to suggest that women are responsible for making men look elsewhere but rather to show how powerful are the structures which limit the power of women within marriage and society and therefore impose impossible burdens on individual marriages.

As long as this situation persists – where women's needs are not met, and their feelings of inferiority are internalised – nothing can move, or even begin to change. The structures of male dominance in marriage and outside it are maintained, along with the myths of women's domestic role in life. The only thing that will save the situation, and save marriage, is shared parenting and women's equal participation in public life.

The consequences of these kinds of changes will be profound for the human species and will transform marriage. Marriage will no longer be an escape from one state of infancy to another, but could allow adult women and men to continue their development in company with one another and in full support of each other. Marriage will not be merely a support to a man's job.

Men's fear of love, and fear of women, frustrates their need to be human in the way that marriage demands. It simply is not possible to live in the same place and share the same bed and table while maintaining an attitude which is partly hostile. It reduces a man to the frustration of infancy: on the one hand he is longing to become a fully self-creative person; he is at the same time hampered in his desire by his unwillingness to go beyond his infantile state. The only way such a marriage can work is when both partners settle for the mother–son relationship (she cares for his needs and is essentially his home-based boss).

This kind of marriage is much more common than one would wish it to be and represents a form of incest which has common links with the more traditional form of father–daughter marriage, where all the outward appearances of power rest with the man (the 'father'). Some marriages are still conducted on this basis and are often contracted between an older, wealthy man and a younger woman who is conventionally beautiful or sexually desirable. This father–daughter marriage is based on a power relation which stems from money and the woman here is often reduced to the position of a 'legalised prostitute'[16] with few rights or freedoms. The appearance may be beguiling; in reality, however, a woman in this kind of relationship has no life of her own.

Since so many men are split from the feelings that would normally guide their decisions and actions, they stick to what they know best: the conventional models of marriage. And since they are split from their feelings, they cannot really tell who they love, or who they don't love. So they allow themselves to be drawn either to the one who best suits their external needs (the 'eye to the main chance' option) or who touches in them the compulsive need to return to the mother's side, the mother's body.

But how can a woman tell why a man wants to marry her? How can she know the reality of the situation without knowing also his internal reality? These are impossible questions to ask before a marriage: the state of being in love is blinding. Only after some time together can the woman see what was at the root of her partner's desire. When women then begin to question the status quo, men become very confused – especially if they believe themselves to have obeyed all the outer commands of marriage. A man's lack of relationship to his own feelings gives him no other way – just rules – by which to measure the state or condition of the relationship. Men are often bowled over to learn how unhappy their marriages have been or are, particularly when they believe they have been 'good husbands' and have abided by all the rules.

After 18 years of marriage, the woman to whom Jack was married suddenly disappeared. That was the way he saw it and explained it to me. He could not have been more confused or perplexed by her action, and he believed she had gone mad. He knew he had been a good husband, according to the traditions of British marriage and the church. What more could a woman ask of him? Couldn't she see that she was being impossible and dreadfully flighty? How could he force her to return at once? He wanted me to engage in his tussle with him.

Jack's pride was terribly wounded and he fought for months to make Melanie 'see sense'. But Melanie refused every request to return and even to meet with Jack. He found her hard-hearted and cruel. What Jack couldn't understand – though Melanie was very clear about it – was the fact that Melanie had been telling him for years that she was troubled by their relationship, that things were wrong with the marriage. He had refused to listen to her, or to join her in discussion at the time when it would have been possible to look at the issues without risking the marriage. He had been denying all along that Melanie's feelings were real because he had no sense of how good or bad the marriage was. He was prepared to stay married simply on the grounds that his sense of convention and his religious beliefs demanded it – not because of his feelings. And he clearly had little respect for her feelings.

During our work together, it became more and more apparent to us both that Jack had never really felt anything for Melanie as a person. He saw her only as 'wife', and in that regard honoured and cherished her. But as he tried to describe her and tell me about her it became clear that he had very little idea of who she was, apart from being married to him. This was further authenticated by the way Jack then fell in love with a number of other women within months of Melanie's leaving. In their life together Melanie had done what many women are forced to do: she had carried all the feelings of the relationship. Jack had been so busy being good at his job that he had left the marriage to her as though it was her responsibility. This is because he saw marriage as a set of roles – the woman's role, the man's role. So when she felt hurt by something that he had said to her and wanted to discuss it with him, he just didn't understand what she was talking about. When she wanted to discuss a problem concerning one of the children, he could deal only with the practical side of the issue – not the feelings. When Melanie was so convinced there was no longer any hope for the marriage, she went to live somewhere else and established, very quickly, a new and independent life for herself. She had prepared herself for this over a number of years by realising the impossibility of saving the marriage.

Jack eventually saw that not only had he been untrue to the marriage, but that by making Melanie responsible for the emotional side of the marriage he had robbed her of her own life. Once she no longer had the problems of the marriage, she could at last have a successful job. What troubles Jack now is the way he is much less able to deal with his work: his success is at risk.

Jack belongs to an ever-growing group of men who have been divorced by their wives. Like most other men, he is dealing with it badly because he has never learned what it is to live with feelings. From my point of view, Melanie did Jack (and herself) a big favour: he has been forced to look at himself in a way he has never allowed before. I hope that Jack will not marry again until he has resurrected his own feelings and dealt with the split in himself so that he will never again have to make a woman live that disowned part of himself.

Marriage means many things to men but, from my perspective, it really is often not much more than an institutional framework – rather like the nursery where they took their first steps. Men need marriage because it not only gives them a solid base from which to conduct their lives, but also because they rely on the women to whom they are married in the way they once relied upon their mothers. They need these women to help them develop and to support them in their comings and goings, with warm socks and simmering soup.

But this is not real marriage: that is a state which relatively few of us know about or understand. We shall have no clearer perspective on it until we are all clear of the nursery.

8. Men and violence

To protect against the pain wrought by this radical shift in
his internal world, he builds a set of defences that, in many
important ways, will serve him, for good or ill, for the rest
of his life. This is the beginning of the development of ego
boundaries that are fixed and firm – barriers that rigidly
separate self from other, that circumscribe not only his
relationships with others, but his connection to his inner
emotional life as well.

Lillian Rubin, *Intimate Strangers* (Fontana, London, 1985)

The statistics and the details about the violence which men
perpetrate make very unhappy reading, whether they concern
the kind of violence that takes place inside the home, on the
streets, or the type of collective violence that happens around
sports grounds. In all of its forms violence is an unacceptable
part of male behaviour which is rarely seen for what it is; more
often than not, it is accepted as a normal part of maleness, part
of a tradition which has been established over centuries and
expresses natural male aggression.

Men commit most of the murders in Western society.[1] Men
rape women and other men and sometimes children. Men sexually
and physically abuse children, girls and boys.[2] Men appear to
be gratuitously violent and therefore create fear in society,
making many of us feel uneasy about living our lives fully and
freely. Men put constraints on the access we all have to our free
and creative self-expression. The degree to which violence is
part of daily life makes many of us feel unsafe, even in

our own homes.[3] We all live with violence, even if we do not directly experience it.

While it is perfectly clear that men's violence is rooted in the social and cultural systems of the West – and is to some extent the outcome of those systems – what is necessary is some deeper understanding of why it is men are so violent. Do social and cultural constructions of men bear all the responsibility for this? More particularly, since violence in men is often acted out in the home, we need to ask why it is that men are violent with those they claim they love. In England,[4] for example, 'homicidal violence . . . is linked to those most basic and unchanging institutions, heterosexuality and the nuclear family.'[5] In other words, homicidal violence is culturally based, with the members of the family most at risk:

> Of the murder victims over the age of 16, seventy per cent
> are female, and of these females nearly half are killed by
> their legal husbands and a quarter by other relations and
> lovers . . . The commonest murders are those of a wife by
> her husband, a child by one of its parents or a woman by
> her lover.[6]

Rape is often thought to be an act committed by male strangers, though in fact more than half of all rapes occur either in the victim's home or in the offender's home. In more than half of the cases that are reported to the police, the victim 'at the very least, was acquainted with the attacker'.[7] Very young female victims of rape, those 10 years or under, most likely are related to their attacker.

The battering of women by husbands or lovers takes place in the home and, according to all the evidence, becomes systematically more brutal the longer the couple stays together. Estimates,[8] which appear to be very conservative, suggest that 1 per cent of all women who live with a man are victims of violent assault, much of which begins with pregnancy.[9] The estimate is considered to be very conservative because it is based upon only those incidents of violence which are reported, while it is now widely accepted that women often feel too ashamed to report an incident. Contrary to popular belief, this kind of battering is not class-based but crosses all class boundaries.[10]

What do men make of the violence that they see all around them, that many of them take part in, and that makes them afraid of other men? I put this question to all the men I interviewed, though none of the answers – most of them very brief – left me feeling that the real issue at the heart of my question had been addressed.

Mike, a 35-year-old actor from a working-class background, answered quite simply that 'men are more violent'. By this I understood him to mean 'more violent than women'. He went on to point out that he felt that the difficulty with men's violence lay in masculinity:

> Men feel that their masculinity gives them the right to
> behave in a certain way and that makes me very angry. I see
> it a lot in rehearsal. When I think about it, I mean that men
> have a kind of attitude which allows them to behave very
> badly.

Mike sees that masculinity and violence share common ground. It is as though violence is the inherited right of masculinity and allows the 'masculine man' to exercise that right over others, and particularly over women. Mike believes that it really gets in the way of his work with other actors and clearly it makes him feel very uneasy about the men who take up violent attitudes.

Gerry works in a computer firm, which is an unexpected centre of violence. He sees his office colleagues having punch-ups with one another every few weeks and he says that he has taught himself a way of dealing with it so that it doesn't cause further disruption:

> I distance myself, shut up, clam up, and wait until the
> emotions have gone and then I go and point out the problem
> and the basis of my complaint and try to come to a consensus.
> Otherwise, it is impossible to try to talk to them.

It is not at all uncommon for violence to erupt in the work-place: in factories, mines, offices, large organisations. A good deal of research has been conducted on this subject, particularly in relation to the violence against women in the workplace.[11] A trade union organisation in Britain, the National and Local Government Officers' Association (NALGO), carried out some work to discover why women were at the receiving end of violence and harassment at work, violence which causes 'anorexia, sleeplessness, and in extreme cases, nervous breakdown, and is always a source of stress'.[12] What is clear through these studies is that men resent women's presence at work, become hostile to them, and so ridicule them.[13]

When I asked Gerry why he thought that men couldn't discuss rationally their office problems but had to resort to expressions of physical violence, he said

> it is because men are incapable of rationalising an emotional
> response – everything is to react. It is a bashing-out against
> the incomprehensible. There is no social structure which
> allows a man to deal with heavy emotional material. I think
> if I could get away with it, I would go and shoot people
> who have done me wrong.

The image of the men in Gerry's office – and his self-definition – presents a very different reality from the picture men usually like to show of themselves: as essentially logical and rational and coolly discerning. Gerry's observations confirm a number of points: that men often do not deal with their experience in their internal reality, but seek other kinds of solutions – revenge and retaliation being just two. Men do not seem to be able to deal with their emotional issues (their hostility towards the presence of women at work, for example) in an open, non-aggressive way. Gerry shows men becoming paralysed whenever their feelings are aroused and being socially disabled in coping with them in an acceptable way. What happens in Gerry's office, and in offices and factories all over, is that tempers first have to cool before anything can be said, and very often once tempers have cooled the issue is left unaddressed because of the shame the men feel at having behaved so badly. While to leave something until tempers have cooled is a pragmatic response to difficulty – and obviously a sensible one – it does not allow anyone to look at the fears that are aroused when violence occurs. It means that everyone in the office lives with a low level of fear all the time, never knowing when there might be another eruption, and on what scale.

Gerry told me about the other men who seem cool enough, but at the end of the working day go off to the pub and then return to the office 'to speak their mind'. What they really want to do is fight out the difficulties they were unable to verbalise during the day when they had to try to keep their feelings under wraps. But they were guarding against their violence. Only when, he said, they were 'half plastered' could they speak their real feelings. In speaking out, they became highly irrational, aggressive, spoiling for a fight.

Another man who often follows this course of action – remaining calm at work during the day but nipping off to the pub as soon as his shift is over – told me that he has to keep such a tight rein on his feelings because he is sure he would get violent. What he doesn't realise is how clearly his violence comes through, even though he believes he has it controlled. His feelings are so transparent to everyone he works with that they have to placate him endlessly in their efforts not to arouse his violence.

At the end of his shift he goes to the pub and then returns to speak up. It is unpleasant for everyone, sometimes dangerous, and he is mortified the next day when he remembers his behaviour. He is quiet for a day or two before breaking out again.

The split in this man is so clear that he is aware of it himself, and can, on occasion, talk about it. He relates it directly to what he calls his 'wounded feelings' – he says he has been so badly hurt in the past that he cannot now allow himself to have any genuine feelings, so he has to seal himself off. In the workplace, then, he tries to hold on to that sealed-off part, though he nevertheless acts it out unseen to himself; at night, he gives himself access to his hidden side when he has had sufficient to drink to put aside the daytime personality.

When I asked Chuck what makes him so upset at work, he didn't find it difficult to respond. He feels he is not appreciated enough by his workmates, by the company he works for, and so he needles everyone to get a bit of praise. He has a strong belief in his own ability and thinks no one recognises his work. He is highly competitive and always comparing himself to others and their work. At root, it seems that his insecurity makes him violent. He is so determined to be noticed, to hold the number-one spot, that he will fight to make himself noticed. It is very infantile behaviour. Chuck feels he has to keep on proving himself. It isn't enough that he is sometimes told he is good at his job. He needs constantly to be praised. He feels he has to be excessively 'masculine' to prove himself; so he fights.

There appears to be a very considerable connection between violence, the demands of masculinity, and this kind of 'proving'. In an essay entitled 'The Army Will Make a "Man" out of You', how these connections merge in the training men receive – in this case, in the United States Army, is described in a very powerful way:

> In [Marine] boot camp, there was a Private Green who had a good deal of difficulty with the rigorous physical regime. He was slender and light complexioned. Private Green was a bright, well-intentioned young man who had volunteered and yet lacked the composite aggressive tendencies thought to comprise manhood. Although not effeminate by civilian standards, he was considered so in boot camp. He was

> continually harassed and called girl and faggot. We began to
> accept the stereotyping of him as effeminate, passive, and
> homosexual.[14]

Because of this stereotyping, Private Green was attacked and
beaten up by between 60 and 70 men, under orders from the
top. He had offended the sexual identity of his fellow Marines
and paid the price by being beaten almost to death and hurled
on to a 'concrete wash rack'. A fellow-Marine later reported, 'We
had been ordered to run around Private Green in order to
equate passivity and nonaggression with being a clear and present
danger.'[15]

So men see danger, and are encouraged to see danger, where it
does not exist – in this instance, in a young, bright man.

Rick, now in his early thirties, is not at all surprised by men's
violence, though he does not like it:

> From an early age boys are taught to be aggressive. It is
> socially acceptable for men to be violent. There's no
> contradiction in the fact that most people think it is all right
> for men to box or to play rough sports – it is just that most
> people don't see how it is conditioned from the beginning of
> a boy's life.

Rick's comments are upheld by a study undertaken by the
government of Victoria (Australia) published in May 1988. The
study was set up after a brutal murder and aimed to assess the
basis of community violence. In this study, it was found that
'70% of people believe violent behaviours in young boys to be
acceptable', just as '20% believe it is acceptable for a man to
beat his wife'.[16]

Many boys are conditioned to violence from infancy. In the
nursery playground, little boys often bash little girls. (Little girls
sometimes do bash back, too.) They are often not stopped by
their parents because parents 'know' and 'accept' that life is
violent and brutal and therefore children have to be prepared
for it.

Spencer, a man in his fifties, believes that men's violence is more the result of biology than social conditioning:

> I think that men are much more aggressive than women, and
> I think that this is a virtue as well as a vice. I mean, I think
> that aggression is what makes things happen. You only get the
> world to work if you attack, I think. You have got to do things,
> you have to go at it. I don't have enough aggression, which is
> what makes me less effective in the world than I might be.

Spencer is of course right to believe there are forms of aggression which can be a virtue. And aggression does not need to be violent. It becomes, as he says, 'a vice' when it is used against the purposes of creativity. But I question whether what Spencer really means by 'aggression' is 'high motivation level' – which is certainly necessary to get things done in the world. There is a vast difference between the kind of attack that is made through aggression and the one inspired by motivation.

I believe that it has been our inability to separate generations of learned behaviour from what we see to be 'innate' violence. Boys are not innately violent, as girls are not. But being raised as a boy in Western society generally means being raised as a violent boy and becoming an observer of violence, if not a practitioner. Parents do sometimes encourage boys to be violent in order to display the so-called necessary characteristics of 'masculinity'. 'No boy of mine is going to be called a ninny – go for him!' I heard one father say to his small boy.

Clearly, we each have a potential for violence which can be either encouraged or not. In the case of girls it is discouraged, on the grounds that femininity requires passivity, receptivity, and gentility; in boys it is a characteristic which is often purposely developed, as though it were an art form. Young boys are taught methods of self-defence in their after-school hours, some of which (Aikido and Judo) stress techniques of violence. Those parents who do not encourage masculine qualities in their sons are often ridiculed; their children also suffer from derision as well as the violence they won't adopt for themselves.

So, when psychologists claim that male violence is innate and there is nothing to be done about it, they generally argue their case from the standpoint of the social biologist, forgetting any question of conditioning. Boys *per se* are violent. Aggression is part of masculinity. In their arguments about why boys are violent and girls are not, these theorists hold the hormone responsible for much behaviour, thereby neglecting the research that has been conducted on gender construction. This research shows that gender behaviour is taught rather than being 'natural', or biologically determined as many people seem to believe (see also Chapter Four). The reason boys tend to be more violent than girls is because they are encouraged and taught to be so. They are being 'masculine'. The passivity of girls is as conditioned as the activity and aggressivity of boys. The social biologists do not pay enough attention to the way in which behaviour is learned from the moment of birth.

The same potential quality in infants and children – the ability to nurture and care for others – is the one which is not cultivated in boys because it is seen as being contrary to masculinity. Boys are the object of female care. Nurturing is the prerogative of girls and women; violence of men. When we look clearly at violence it is obvious that it is not a natural component of male psychology; rather it has been imposed upon men to identify their male difference. But for what purposes? And by whom? While it is impossible to lay the blame directly at any particular door, it is apparent that the purpose is to identify gender roles by 'masculine' or 'feminine' qualities, qualities which in themselves may bear little relationship to real human qualities. Men, therefore, are more powerful; women are powerless. Men are strong; women are weak. Men are violent; women are peaceable. These false dualisms are not only fundamentally groundless, but they contrive to manipulate human behaviour – and therefore human beings – into particular moulds which accord with acceptable traditions. These traditions have been the way in which men have gained power and held on to it ever since. What, though, does it profit a man to be powerful if he loses his real capacities to be truly human?

One of the most coercive acts performed both today and throughout history has been to identify men and war with masculinity. Men who refuse to fight are subject to ridicule and humiliation. One woman told me how her son, born in London, refused to go to war. He had been a student and had never worked at anything besides his studies; he conscientiously felt it was wrong to fight. He was punished for this and sent to work in a coal mine where, in the first week, he was involved in an accident and had to have both his legs amputated. In Australia, a young priest who refused to identify war with patriotism lost his job in the church. His sermons on peace made his position untenable. In his book *Sexuality and Homosexuality*, Arno Karlin reported an anti-pacifist incident:

> In 1968 pacifists set up coffee houses to spread their word
> near military bases. A Special Force NCO said to a
> *Newsweek* reporter, 'We aren't fighting and dying so these
> goddamn pansies can sit around drinking coffee.'[17]

The potential to nurture and take care of infants, children and men is cultivated in women, who are taken to represent the qualities of love and tenderness. A firm boundary is marked between women and men. Men see caring as women's particular contribution to life and therefore see themselves as separated from the women's part. They are in a separate camp, where the 'opposite' qualities are cultivated. Power is set against love; violence against tenderness. Since power and love are not compatible forces, men tend to use their strength to deny love; sometimes they even have to be violent in their effort to deny or avoid love. Sometimes, it seems, they have to kill the love for others which they feel in themselves. They have to murder a part of themselves in order to conform to the social stereotypes. Sometimes they are so threatened by their emotions they even have to murder other people, people they say they love.

The destructive capacities of gender construction are nowhere more apparent than when men feel the need to kill others because they cannot deal with their own inner feelings, which have been murdered by the divisions of gender. As a direct result of this, women, children and other men are their daily victims.

Men often lose their capacity to feel. They learn to rely on rules and laws. They foster discipline and obedience in themselves, believing these qualities will see them through their tasks. But all this does is to separate them further from their essence; it makes them rigid and hard and controlled. It also puts men in positions where they no longer need to ask the kind of moral and ethical questions that must always be asked. How else could men kill? How else could they drop bombs on other human beings? How else could men have been trained to torture other people, women and men? In order to do these things, they *must* be cut off from love and tenderness. How else does a torturer leave home in the morning and go to his torture room? To him, he is only obeying the commands of his job. He is able to do this because he is rigidly compartmentalised, and his power to feel has been so diminished as not to exist at all. He has been thoroughly subverted. Thoroughly split.

Psychologists sometimes claim that the kind of treatment that we (and by 'we' they mean all of us) receive in childhood is the treatment that we pass on to the next generation. The evidence that they use for this is based upon the knowledge they have of men who sexually abuse children. Men who sexually abuse children were very often abused themselves in childhood. But why should this be? Why should it be men, and not women, who pass on their own terrible treatment? Why is it that women and men respond to life-experiences in such different ways?

As we have seen, the psychology of men is very fragile and formed by the need to be separate and to keep up a strong defence against any possible attack of intimacy. Hence, they violate that which threatens their separateness. Their own psychological foundations do not encourage men to nurture good relations. The only reason their behaviour is seen as 'normal' lies in the fact that male behaviour is understood to be the appropriate model for human behaviour; more than that – it has become, over the centuries, systemic. In other words, the pathological problem displayed in men cannot be seen for what it is because of its universality. It makes the need for a new model that much stronger.

The violence of men is, I believe, a manifestation of that 'original terror of helplessness'[18] – the need to reach out in eternal frustration against someone who made us feel so vulnerable. If there were not just one single despot, but a pair of them to be reckoned with, the child could face the fact that his difficulties are human difficulties, not simply problems with women. It would then be much more possible to see these human problems in himself rather than to cast them on to women. Tyranny would find its place at last.

During the 1980s about half the women who divorced their husbands said that the men had been violent.[19] Violence was the reason over forty per cent of women divorced their husbands in Britain, according to the sample studies by Burgoyne, Ormrod and Richards.[20] Given that in 1984 more than 170,000 petitions for divorce were filed, it can be estimated that around 75,000 women in Britain in 1984 were the victims of home violence. The Select Committee on Violence in Marriage reported its findings in 1975 that slightly under one per cent of all married women might be battered. Elizabeth Wilson points out in her book *What Is to Be Done about Violence against Women?* that this is a very conservative estimate. It is as though the men who are violent in marriage display two personalities, one of which they show to the outside world and the other of which they keep for home. The men who batter and rape women appear, in other situations, 'entirely normal'. 'Normal' men sometimes talk about the fear that they have that they might rape or brutalise women, rather as if they really do possess two sides, one which they know as 'themselves' and another over which they have no control. Women often have to be on their guard against 'normal' men who might, without warning, become gratuitously violent towards them – in the same way that they might, on another occasion, be responsive and attentive. This is how the split in men functions.

Men manifest their 'shadow' personalities whenever there is a real threat to the side of themselves that they know little about. When someone or something gets close to that part of them they erupt and head for shadowy territory. When men are together in groups this aspect can reveal a collective darkness which is all the more powerful than the sum total of the individuals. Often this characteristic is seen rioting at football games, sometimes out of control and murderous. While it is said[21] that such collective violence has no obvious social origins other than class, it seems to me that the group violence that is now commonplace – and which, for example, has brought British followers of football into such disrepute – is generated by the immense force of collective violence. When men are together the repressed aspects are forced out and the powers of the unconsciousness they share are let loose. This kind of behaviour, though, has its origins in the active encouragement of aggressive behaviour by boys though the authorities rail against such mass displays of violence. It seems to depend on the kind of occasion it is though before it is either condemned or honoured. Mass violence is punished when it comes from a football ground but rewarded when it takes place on the battle field. But the root of the problem stems from men's denial of their own problems. In essence they are fighting with themselves, and projecting their own issues on to the other side's team or the other country.

Whatever it is that we do not face realistically and squarely in ourselves, we project on to others. Only when we can accept that not only do we have difficulties, but we must also learn to deal with them, will we be at peace. Only then will we have understood that the real 'enemy' is not the one outside us, but the one who lies deep inside us. When that enemy within is befriended through self-reflection, it turns another face towards us – not the face of an enemy or shadow, necessarily, but more often the face of a small and vulnerable child.

When men realise and accept that they have split off from themselves a very important side of their human nature, they too will be able to see the root of their conflicts. They will no longer need to impose violence upon women and children but will understand that they have a lot of catching up to do.

At that point, it will be possible to deconstruct the systems of violence as they operate within Western society, whether in the organisations where male dominance – a kind of violence in itself – is systemic; whether in the way violence is used to control women's behaviour (down to methods of childbirth); or whether in the way men are violating themselves through over-work or the physical abuse of drugs or alcohol. Violence is self-perpetuating and, until it is uprooted from our society, it will go on living in men's inner world and having its expression in their behaviour.

9. Men at work

Male public culture gets caught up with machines and puts
emphasis on things that are not alive. The decision-making
of males in power tends to happen in a vacuum with little
reference to the needs of life. Paradoxically, the public
leaders who are supposed to help us deny death become
increasingly oblivious to life and show increasing contempt
for it.

Naomi Goldenberg, *Changing of the Gods* (Beacon Press,
Boston, 1979)

Work is the place where men's self-evasion is most carefully
concealed. Men at work join together in a mutual task of self-
evasion. They collude to keep themselves safe in the arms of
whatever organisational father they work for, and out of reach of
mother. (For 'mother' read also 'wife' or 'lover' or anyone who
makes a man aware of his feelings.) In other words, whether it is
in a factory, a university, an office, a school, work is a safe
refuge for men. Until very recently, it was also possible to avoid
women at work but many men now find themselves working
alongside women.

Few men would deny that work takes the major part of their
energy and their interest, even when the job they have is not
fulfilling or is even repetitive and boring. As Carol Gilligan
convincingly shows in her study of the moral development of
women and men [1], men define themselves in terms of work (see also
pp. 89–91). Where women define themselves in terms of attachment or affiliation to others, men do so in relation to work – even
when they do the same kind of work and have the same status.

I asked all of the 120 men I interviewed for this book two leading questions: What is the most important thing in your life? and, What is your most important achievement to date? Around 80 per cent of these men (as distinct from the men I see in my professional work) told me that work is the most important part of their life and their achievements were generally in relation to some kind of work. Some men, though, did say that the most important part of their lives was their self-knowledge and their inner life. Tony was one:

> As far as I'm concerned, not just now but over different
> periods of time, two things are important, one is
> relationships and the other is work. Sometimes they go
> together, sometimes one gets one at one time, sometimes
> one gets the other at another time. At the moment work is
> good – it's there and always has been.

Tony is very lucky. He does not know the deadly boring work of the production-line, and he is rarely unemployed. He is an artist and freelance, so he is not bound to an organisation in the way that many, or most, men are. This gives him, in my view, a very great psychological advantage. He has choice, something which is often denied to those who work in big factories or for large organisations; and it means that he has to deal with the problems of work within himself and does not often have the possibility of projecting work issues outside himself. Nevertheless, work for Tony, as for most men, is the one continuous aspect of his life. In that sense, it is the only 'compartment' that he can be certain about. Everything else in his life is subject to change. This is a very important factor in men's lives: security.

But what kind of security does work bring men? Is it only economic security, or is it something much deeper (which isn't to deny the importance of economic security)? In other words, is it more to do with personal identity? And is this why few men wish to retire, even when they reach the age of retirement? Is work for men a substitute for personality?

Even though so many men told me that their relationships were very important to them, when I asked them to discuss the energy they put into their work and relationships there appeared to be a substantial discrepancy. Michael, for instance, told me that his relationship with a woman was the most important thing in his life. But when he turned to the subject of his achievement he told me:

> Well, my biggest achievement would be if I could get a
> book published on comedy which I'm working on now: that
> would be my biggest achievement. There are other things
> I've done which, on paper, are not without merit but don't
> really excite me. Work, being a director, or a barrister, all
> those types of things – they haven't given me that sense of
> fulfilment which other things might.

Michael works incredibly hard: very long hours, international telephone calls through the night, travelling a great deal of the time to international film festivals. But, he says, it is not what gives him satisfaction. Creative work on his book would do that. So what, I wonder, apart from economic necessity, makes men stick at work which they don't really like, when doing what they like would give them real satisfaction?

Although Michael doesn't get much satisfaction or achievement from his very high-powered job, it does give him a particular identity. He is somebody because of his work and this gives him access to the world of men where his identity as somebody is secure.

Russ works as an engineer. He hates it, and he has always hated it. He does it because it was what his father wanted him to do. The kind of things he has to do in his work also go against his political ideals. He has to design city centres, large concrete jungles, when he is committed to life on a small scale. But he hasn't been able to see his way through this dilemma and so he goes on doing what he hates. He works against himself and against his values for society. He told me that the reason he does this is because his father's voice keeps ringing in his ears (Russ is now in his late forties) and keeps him doggedly pursuing what he doesn't want to do. But, like Michael, he gets his identity from his work and his position of power within his company. He acknowledged to me that this was where the only strength in his life comes from. He made that comment even though he lives in what he describes as a happy relationship with a woman. All the other areas of his life are very fragile and wouldn't stand up to much testing if they were put to it. So Russ needs his job because his sole source of strength comes from it, and he recognises that fact.

As I see it, Russ's work is psychologically destructive to him. If he were to lose his job he would very likely lose his identity. His job separates him further from himself, as he is the first to admit. But as much as he acknowledges this, he also recognises that without his work he would be totally destroyed. His conflict might sound peculiar to his personal situation but I think it is a common problem for men. They are lured into a position of believing that this is what they most need when in fact what they most need (and possibly even want) is to be themselves and to do the work that will most usefully direct them to become themselves. But the amount of time that most men spend working also points to their dedication to self-evasion. This is why retirement comes as such a shock to so many men and why so many men die within a short time of retirement.[2]

I suspect that one of the reasons why Russ and the other men like him direct themselves to work as they do stems from the unresolved conflict which they have carried with them from infancy. In casting all difficulty on to the women in their lives – at that time, on to the mother – they falsely interpreted the father's position as the one which would give them safety. To them, father represented mystery, excitement, adventure, autonomy, self-creation – all the things missing from their experience of the company of the mother who wielded such power over them. But in making what is apparently so false a deduction, men have landed themselves in a no-win, no-move position – what is commonly called a closed system of possibilities.

Once having opted to be with the 'father' – in adulthood represented by the factory, the corporation, or whatever – men find it impossible to move, psychologically speaking, from this position. Either they are locked into a situation with the 'mother' or the 'father'. What looked like a safe situation at work turns out to be nothing of the kind. It is another battle-ground, where hierarchies are sought after, power is everything and the return of satisfaction is often minimal.

Work becomes a treadmill, even for those men at the top of a corporation. They get great financial returns but at the cost, often, of little time away from work, ill health, stress, and poor relationships. They have to put in a great deal for scant rewards.

Unemployment also brings hazards for men, apart from the economic hazard. While men in management jobs suffer from stress and burnout, unemployed men often suffer from mental illness. A six-year study conducted by the British Social Science Research Council and the Medical Research Council[3] into the effects of unemployment found that the most vulnerable group of people are middle-aged men. The researchers found that the contributory factors which make unemployed people twice as vulnerable to mental illness are 'the work ethic, financial strain and being male, middle-aged and working class'.

Given that unemployed men are so vulnerable, why should it be that women seem to escape the devastating consequences of unemployment? The majority of women now work in paid labour but unemployment does not strike them in the same way. This is because a woman's primary identity does not come from her job, but from her relationships. When a man loses his job he loses much more besides his income. He finds he does not have the inner resources to cope and so runs the risk of becoming psychologically ill.

One question I ask myself all too frequently is whether men, because of their identification with work, have not lost their ability to feel and identify with people. I often find myself wondering whether their ability to feel may not have atrophied.

I can only allow myself to suggest this half-seriously, since it would create a dilemma about the very nature of what it is to be human. But a French man, quoted by the British psychologist Phillip Hodson, puts forward a similar thesis in the suggestion that 'work insanity has turned men into unemotional zombies'. The executives he studied in the United States

> were not what he called human beings, nor did their world
> have a human dimension. Not that he saw them as science
> fiction computeroids, simply as people lacking the ability to
> show warmth or sadness or even delight. They had schooled
> themselves never to feel dependent on another person.
> Thirty-six of the forty insisted that they hardly ever felt
> dependent. Thirty-two of them said that when they did,
> they would not let anyone know they felt that way.[4]

Although it seems an extreme example of particular men in a particular part of the world, I do not believe that this is so. This is rather the atmosphere which is cultivated by the notion of masculinity: isolation, separation, independence. These men appear to be in control but it is only their identification with their work which gives them this image. If they were to lose their jobs or get divorced, they would run the kinds of risks which I have described above. If they were to lose their jobs, all appearances of strength and control would disappear.

It is not enough, though, simply to recite the known facts about men's relation to their jobs. We need to go behind these facts and ask why it should be that a man feels he has lost everything when he loses his job. I suggest that he feels this way because everything for him is dependent upon his external world: how he appears to himself to be and not how he really is in his internal reality. It is possible to say that he really has very little regard for his internal reality – if, indeed, he knows that it exists – for in his effort to identify with his work he has lost the capacity to be a self-reflective person. So if he has not integrated his experience into his internal reality before, then he is very unlikely to do so when he loses his job.

In their identification with their work, men often destroy their bodies as well as their psychological capacities. Many men now suffer from a syndrome known as 'burnout', others from stress-related problems such as heart attacks, strokes, alcoholism, and so on. It may be that the illness forced upon them springs from an unconscious desire to get well: the unconscious will often force people to be attentive to their problems. Although women also sometimes suffer from burnout and stress, and some even from heart attacks, the figures are barely significant when compared with those for men.

Men who take early retirement often do so in the hope of starting another career. The thought of occupying themselves with gardening is often daunting and they frequently have little relationship to their domestic environment except as handymen. Some who retire early are forced to take a very close look at themselves and to concentrate on their internal reality in a way they had previously – and successfully – tried to avoid. They were too busy, they say, with their work.

Joseph took early retirement a few years ago. He did this so that he could explore other avenues, particularly writing. He says that if I had asked him about what was most important to him a few years ago I would have received a very different answer. Nowadays, he says:

> Impossible. I don't know. I mean I suppose my relationship.
> My work. My inner life. I think probably the real answer is
> my inner life. So it's all those things in particular
> relationship to me. But, in a way, my relationship with my
> partner and my work are all interrelated with my inner life,
> and if they aren't all tied up, and if they aren't internal and
> external, nothing works.

Joseph says he could not have said this a few years ago. And I am sure that this is right. Outside his organisation, his life has changed dramatically. Within his organisation, he had terrific status and he had been what is known as a 'high achiever'. But he has an entirely different relationship with his work now; it is no longer a question of status and achievement, but of the work and its value for its own purposes.

The new view that Joseph has of his work seems to me to be like the attitude many women take to their work. Clearly, not all women do the kind of work they wish to do, just as men do not. But their attitude is often more concerned with their relationship to their work rather than their achievements. In contrast to men, women are much more likely to want to work with people, often in service industries or the caring professions. They often – though not always – want to work co-operatively rather than hierarchically, and they share their work problems with one another and with male co-workers much more readily than men do. They are also much more likely to try to find better ways of doing jobs, rather than always following the old order.

This, then, is where I believe the crux of the problem lies for men: in their relationship to the kind of work they wish to do, especially as it concerns whether or not that work assists them in pursuing their real purpose in life. There are some – more often than not, artists or poets – whose work allows them to develop psychologically. They are lucky because they have seen beyond work as status or achievement and have withdrawn their projections from 'out there' and so deal with things on the inside. Their work and psychological development are one.

Sadly, these men are in the minority and their lives are made more difficult because of their perceptions. They are often marginalised because they do not measure up to the demands of masculinity in stereotypical terms; and economically their lives are generally difficult – art and poetry rarely pay an adequate living wage.

If work represents, as I suggest, an escape from the mother to the father, then a recognition of this will change men's attitude to their work. As it is, men say that they cannot participate in domestic life because they need to uphold the financial status quo and so the burden falls upon the mother or other women (the nursery worker, the childminder, the nanny). When men acknowledge the flight from mother to father as a psychological reaction, the result of their own psychological heritage, they will be able to take the step which will free up a good deal of the economic, political and social systems. They could take on job-sharing, for work status will not have the same significance. Nor will they be driven by the same mad desire to achieve things for the ever-demanding father.

It comes down, I believe, to what it means to be human. If work, through its demands of objectives, makes a man less human or less than human, then its ends can only be harmful. It must divide the man from love and his capacity to love and be loved. Only when love is present in work can the work itself be of value to a man personally and to the community in general. This is not to say that this is an easy task to achieve. It demands a radical reappraisal and a penetrating connection to the inner world, and the ability to hold a tension between the inner and outer realities.

10. Men and the world

Recently I listened with horror to a group of international
scientists discussing on radio their feelings about global warming,
what we know as the 'Greenhouse Effect'. Environmentalists
from Washington DC, the United Nations, Geneva and the
United Kingdom spelled out in words of terrifying clarity the
full meaning of the Earth's warming. These particular scientists
give us as a species between 10 and 30 years before our extinction: that is the time-span we appear to have if we take no
immediate action to slow down or to halt the kind of ecological
disasters that will occur.

Other scientists take a less optimistic view on time. Vandana
Shiva, an Indian physicist and ecologist, said we have only five
to ten years before some violent disaster will occur. She emphasised that we will have to stop thinking about time as we
have known it. 'This isn't geological time' she emphasised, 'nor a
slow process of extinction; but a sudden end to the possibilities
of life'.[1]

Most countries are now experiencing, at least in part, some of
the effects of global warming, whether it is in the form of
changes in the established weather patterns, crop failures, more

skin cancers, or floods. Countries in the Southern Hemisphere will, it is said, experience more rapid changes. Already Australia and New Zealand have a greatly diminished ozone cover, as well as a disturbed weather pattern.

While many people now state that the problems with the environment and the damage to the eco-system cause them more disquiet than anything else, it seems we have succumbed to a state of psychic numbing. We have entered the realm of the unthinkable. I hate writing about this subject. I hate acknowledging that the damage that has been done is perhaps irreversible. I want to be able to have confidence in the governments of the world (who clearly know the extent of the damage) and the environmentalists who understand what it is we have to do to make human life possible on the planet. But at the same time that I recognise these things, I also have to look at the psychological underpinnings of this destruction which has brought our world to this moment.

Some economists might argue that people in the so-called Third World need to consider the benefits of cash crops. But their arguments do not take into account the many other factors. If, for instance, a forest is destroyed for cash crops it is not only that some trees have been lost, but a series of species, perhaps a whole society whose livelihood and culture depended upon the forest. One example of this comes from the Chipko Movement in the Himalayan forests which worked ceaselessly to maintain the forests because they are a natural resource for everyone and maintain a complete eco-system. In the 1960s a group of loggers came in to the forests and began to cut down the trees and soon after this landslides began to occur in the Himalayas. Then the water began to dry up, even though the residents had always had plentiful springs in the area. Then the agricultural workers in the fields noticed that the forests weren't able to provide the usual fertilisers. Everything which sustained life was being lost until the women of the Chipko Movement started their actions of hugging the trees, telling the loggers that if they wanted to fell the trees they would first have to kill the women. After a long, hard struggle the women of the movement won their contest, and in 1981 the government banned commercial logging in those forests.[2]

When I take hold of the facts I then have to acknowledge to myself – and publicly – that it is the will and the actions of men in positions of power that have brought us to this point. Those men might be the industrialists in charge of their chemical factories and plants, the farmers desperate to produce even more abundant crops through the use of chemical agents, or government ministers who have allowed their rainforests to be hacked down to further the production of paper and paper products such as tissues.

There is a false equation at work in our world which says that power and greed are greater than health and life. I ask why it is that the environmental scientists do not have more power to change the equation. I have only to look at the statistics which show how the world's scientists are employed to realise that the majority of them work in the field of destructive technology: half a million military scientists invent and develop ever-more complex weapon systems, which arms manufacturers then produce in great numbers.'[3] The number of scientists working for a sustainable environment and future is pitifully small. It is more than likely that any hope we have for the future is founded on a lack of knowledge of the real dangers, and our psychic numbing.

How is it that we have arrived at this point in our history? How is it that we are so apparently capable in some areas and so immensely disabled in others? What lies at the root of the destructive powers in the world that have not only robbed us of our most precious gift, but also stand in the way of our reclaiming that gift of life?

Geoff believes that the world is in a mess at the moment:

> On the whole I get very worried about the thought,
> particularly at the moment, of what is happening in Brazil
> to such enormous areas and the dispossession of the natural

habitat of the inhabitants and all for no reason. It's going to damage the whole climate of the world, and I believe this is really happening and I hate it. And I hate it when the water I try to bathe in is polluted and unpleasant and, yes, I am worried about the seals too. I'm getting an increasing sense of what I had as a small boy – a feeling of the oneness of organic life on the planet and that everything is affected by what we do. What the answers are in many cases I am not sure. I mean, somehow it should be made possible for the Brazilians to stop burning down the biggest rainforest in the world.

When I asked Geoff what he sees at the root of this wholesale destruction, he was unhesitating in his reply: 'Male greed. I bet you there aren't many entrepreneurs making a fast buck out of the rainforests who are women.' So, what, I put to him, is male greed about?

It's about getting power and money in order to get women. If I am becoming an old man then I had better have lots of money to gets lots of young women. Men think young women are more desirable, and it may be (though I am on delicate ground here) inbred in them that, genetically speaking, it is better to choose women in child-bearing years and so they are attracted to younger women. Otherwise, I can't see any value in it, for the evolution of the species.

Geoff's argument is particularly interesting in its return to a socio-biological perspective. But, even if it were true that men are biologically conditioned always to want to go on reproducing the species, why would 'nature' have implanted the contrary desire: to destroy the planet on which to nurture the species?

Geoff also has a belief in the spirit of the Earth – Gaia – who he believes is presently trying to make herself known on the Earth (in the form of the many apparitions of the Virgin Mary) to get us to change our ways and to restore the Earth to its ecological balance.

Roger, who feels very strongly about the state of the world, says he has been overtaken by a sensation akin to psychic numbing:

> I sometimes wonder whether I shouldn't be thinking about
> these things much more, and talking about them, and
> although I don't discuss them very much I am aware of
> them and I do think one of the biggest frustrations with
> looking at the way things are happening is the way it makes
> me feel almost helpless. As an artist, I feel the real difficulty
> is to have the kind of information I need to take action.
> There is a tendency, I think, for people to discuss things
> that they don't know enough about.

Roger expresses the views of many men. And it is certainly true that it is very hard to get hold of accurate information. The kind of material that would allow appropriate action to be taken does not come from the traditional political parties or their members. When accurate information does appear, it is more often than not denied. If the message is unpalatable, it is to be avoided – hidden. But the wealth of accumulated data is contrary to all the dubious whitewashing that governments continue to do in order to remain in power. Not only do governments have difficulty in telling the truth, or the whole truth, but some of us have developed a selective method of hearing, sifting out the favourable from the unfavourable.

Women, it seems, are much better at recognising and working with these realities; whether it is the Pentagon Women and their recognition of the senselessness of war and nuclear pile-ups, Greenham Common women in their desire to reclaim the common land and be rid of any threats to life, the women of the Chipko Movement in the Himalayas, or the women in the now international Green movement. Women seem not to employ the same mechanisms of denial as men, though clearly this is not true of all women, just as it is not true of all men. Women also see the paralysing effects of male domination very clearly. Women have, for thousands of years now, been in the vanguard of the peace movement, of social reform at the most grass-roots levels, in medical research. At the source of this is the role of women in life-sustaining and life-supporting systems; women listen to each other and take each other into account in a way that men, because of their compartmentalisation, seem unable to do. This is not to say that women and men are 'naturally' either life-sustaining or life-denying, but have been part of social conditions which see women and men as polarised.

In this twentieth century there have been, to date, 237 wars, some fought on ideological grounds, some economic, others in order to deflect trouble at home. In any event, men seem to find that war is the way to deal with something they cannot face in another way – around-the-circle discussion, for example. What is it that men cannot confront, either in themselves or in one another, that forces them to take up arms to kill? Are they really seeking to protect 'national sovereignty' or does there exist in men some unfathomable desire to hit out at whatever they do not understand or anything that resists control through power?

The women who protested at the Pentagon in 1980–1 put this question in another form when they addressed the following statement to the men of the Pentagon. In doing so, they expressed the view of many women in the world:

> We are in the hands of men whose wealth and power have
> separated them from the reality of daily life. We are right to
> be afraid . . . We want to know what anger in these men,
> what fear, which can only be satisfied by destruction, what
> coldness of heart and ambition drives their days. We want
> to know, because we do not want their dominance, which is
> exploitative and murderous . . . we do not want that sickness,
> transferred by the violent society from the fathers, to the
> sons.[4]

There are many ways to look at the statement: economically, politically, historically, socially. But on the psychological level it has to be acknowledged that since fear of love seems to have men in its grip, it is more than likely that this same fear drives men away from any contact with love – except in the purely formal sense – and towards a destiny which will be marked by cold competition and, ultimately, death through destruction. Fear seems to lead to the desire for power over the feared ones and power seems to lead directly to destruction, whether it is destruction of equality, love relations, the environment, or human life. Fear is the result of the separation men are conditioned to see as their true state of being. In my view, the end-result of separation is the kind of destruction we have been witnessing as part of the arms race and the disintegration of the global environment. Power and disintegration go hand in hand.

How does one face the enormity of the issue, given the potential for destruction that is clearly present? How is it possible to address the kind of fear that pushes away all the creative choices in favour of the end of human life as we know it and have known it over millennia?

One thing is true and very apparent: that if there is enough male energy and power to bring the world to a devastating end, there is also the hope that the equivalent energy and power could be used to bring about the necessary changes for good. All, it seems, rests on a mighty change of heart and will. Or, to put it another way, men need to change their attitude and to examine their fears.

There is a parallel, I believe, in some marriages. Fragile men, perceiving themselves to be as strong as the macho stereotype, find themselves at a loss when their relationships begin to get out of control. They have to assert themselves in order to make it appear that they are in control; that they have the power in the relationship, as they are supposed to. Because they are so unwilling to look at the reality of the situation, they convince themselves that the problem lies with the woman. She is denigrated – she is an incompetent fool and, what's more, she is fat and ugly. The loved one is turned into an enemy, even though she may be quite blameless (unlikely, but possible). He may turn to violence, to battering her, or he may cut her off from any sources of finance to prevent her leaving him because he knows he would be utterly lost without her.

Countless marriages exist on this basis. His sense of being 'up' depends on keeping the woman 'down'. The weakness that is unconscious in the man is projected on to the woman. He hates what he cannot recognise in himself. Because he now perceives his wife to be weak, he cannot bring himself to the negotiating table to talk things over. He feels he has to resort to keeping her in order by wielding force and brutalising her. And all the time he diminishes himself. His wife and children begin to hate and fear him. What he is unable to recognise in himself is his own self-hatred. His marriage is, in effect, a battle-ground and he is so stuck in his isolation that he can do nothing about it. The kind of violence which is enacted in the world on a daily basis has its roots in this psychological weakness where enemies need to be created and then fought: all to keep at bay the confrontation with the inner psychological split. The universalism of the pathology makes it that much more possible for men to perceive a common enemy where none exists and to wage war against the imagined foe. Men have for centuries perceived this threat in women and have, through their collective action, managed to keep women powerless and under so-called control.

Male relations with women are reflected in male relations to nature. Where women are seen as sex objects to be dominated, so nature is perceived as that which is to be stripped – or, to use another sexual metaphor, raped. All that nature had to offer through co-operation with humanity has been obliterated. Another parallel with marriage can be drawn: just as marriage demands or necessitates co-operation between partners, men so often deny this reality and set themselves over their female partners, as men have set themselves over the world of nature, expecting it to serve them.

Women and nature are seen as subordinate to men and men's will. In the early European settlement of Australia (many would say the invasion) the landscape was encountered as female – as infertile, elusive, to be 'penetrated'. When Thomas Watling, in exile in Botany Bay, wrote that 'The face of the country is deceitful; having every appearance of fertility; and yet productive of no one article in itself for the support of mankind⁵, he was saying what many explorers of the time also felt. The fear of, and desire for, the land that is gracious and submissive can be identified in many of the letters of the early explorers in Australia, Sturt and Mitchell amongst them.⁶ The dual reactions provide an insight into the relation between women and nature and men's need to conquer both. What the first settlers did to the Australian land was to clear it, to take away part of its threatening character (its graciousness?) to enable them to do with it what they wanted. Although Aboriginal people had lived in Australia for 40,000 years and had destroyed nothing, the first Europeans wrecked species after species in the need to dominate. From the beginning, it was a relationship of abuse; in the 200 years since that time, the environment in Australia has become one of the most damaged in the world. Where Aboriginal people live in harmony with the land and have developed a powerful mythology based on the dignity of nature, European men have raped and plundered the continent in every way possible, avoiding in their actions the knowledge that they are as responsible to the land as the land is to them. The denial of reciprocity seems to be at the root of men's psychological troubles. Is 'denial' the only possible response to the profound lack that men seem to feel in themselves? Is it their 'lack' which stirs their need to plunder and fosters the desire to subdue and control?

Perhaps the key to this crucial psychological issue is the question of men's relationship to nature. Where Aboriginal men in Australia recognise their integration with nature and have fostered a loving attitude to their surroundings, colonial men came and 'conquered' the land, asserting their rights and dominion over it, as they did over women, European and Aboriginal.

What is disheartening is that so many men seem not to have learned anything through their failures. Seeing that it is the damage to the rainforests that destroys so much of the climate, isn't it possible to imagine – as Geoff indicated – that restitution might be the most appropriate form of action? Should not our knowledge that chlorofluorocarbons (CFCs) are so damaging to the ozone layer inspire new forms of technology? Instead, however, those who perpetuate destruction seem only to go further and continue their acts of madness, while at the same time denying the proof in front of their eyes and thus furthering their isolation from their actions.

In recent years, there has been an almost overwhelming degree of media attention given to the rainforests of the world, particularly to those in the Amazon Basin in Brazil and Australia. It is impossible to believe that we are not all aware of the dangers to the whole world because of the folly of some of the state governments in Australia and the federal government of Brazil. And yet they go on being destroyed. Economic arguments are pulled out as though they have a far greater weight than those which seek other solutions. Numerous schemes to save the forests – and therefore the future of the world's environment – have been devised, but so far none has been taken seriously (even when they have allowed for the financial situation of the Brazilian government).[7]

When this intransigence occurs, it is possible to see a psychological split in full view. Men's experience and the understanding of their experience fail to connect. Hence there can be no insight. In psychological terms, this is a state of pathological disturbance, of regression.

Men have become, as Dinnerstein puts it, 'proverbially subhuman'.[8] Instead of reflecting on their actions, they have left that task to women and children. Thus, it is the children who are the most vulnerable, since they have few resources for self-defence and protection. They are not yet psychically numbed. This means, then, that children, while being unprotected from the acts of men, are able to perceive the devastating effects of their fathers' actions (sometimes their biological fathers), whether manifested in the kind of work they do or in their violence. Children all over the world are deeply concerned about the possible effects of nuclear war, as their dreams and conversations attest. Children feel powerless to accomplish any change. They know that it needs just one mad finger to touch one small button for their lives to be brought to a horrible end.

Today's children and those of the future will have to contend with terrible psychological realities which have never before been faced. Children 'describe weird nightmares and fears that the earth itself will disappear and there will be nothingness'.[9] They also realise that they will inherit the future and have the responsibility for it.

When individual men speak up against the destructiveness of other men they are often attacked by a group of men backed up by some ideological framework. I think, for example, of the attacks made upon individual men of some ecological organisations and peace groups who have been publicly vilified as betrayers of national security, enemies of the public conscience, and so on. These individual men stand out on the side of life and creativity. They are enabled to call destructiveness by its real name and not by any euphemism. The world, in their view, is in a mess and must be perceived in its reality in order for change to take place.

Joseph believes the world is in a mess and that original sin is at the root of it: 'I'm not being serious in the theological sense, but I am serious in another sense – I think that human beings are extremely imperfect and the mess of the world is due to our imperfection.' So I further put to Joseph whether he saw any destructive tendencies in himself:

> Yes. There's a mixture of the creative and the destructive in
> everybody and the business of life seems to me to be about
> trying to encourage the creative and discourage the
> destructive aspects, but this can only be done by diminution

of original sin. It's perfectly clear that some social
circumstances are more in favour of the development of the
individual in a creative way than other social circumstances.
I think one has to create social circumstances which allow
people to function better and I believe that democracy is the
best solution which anybody has yet come up with for the
free development of human beings and the destruction of
the democratic system – whether by the left or the right –
seems to me to be the greatest possible evil.

Joseph's perspective on the destructive aspects points to some
necessary reflection on the nature of humankind. He sees that it
is possible to encourage the creative side of human nature and I
am convinced that this is so. It is also true, I believe, that it is
just as possible to encourage the destructive side and I propose
that this is one result of sex-role stereotyping. The creative
aspects of a boy's life are encouraged less than the destructive
and the hostility of the boy's environment – separation, isolation,
silence – distracts him from a close engagement with the creative
world.

Given the state of the world at present, I asked Joseph to
comment on whether he thought that creative or destructive
forces were uppermost now:

One can never know the answer to that question – the
creative and destructive sides are always there. The trouble
now is that because of the development of modern
technology, the capacity of the destructive forces to destroy
everything is much greater than it was before and we are
working with a system of checks and balances which before
worked because it could be contained. The trouble now is
that when things go wrong they go wrong on a scale that
would destroy everything and that does worry me quite a
lot.

Like much of humankind Joseph is worried about the future
of the world – its peace, stability and environmental security. It
is as though the world and the world's inhabitants live now in a

shadow. How is it that we all live in a shadow? It is a psychological truism that whatever is pushed down into the unconscious forms an unhappy deposit of rejected experiences; it forms what the Swiss psychologist Carl Jung named 'the shadow', the 'other' personality.[10] Jung also taught that the reclamation of the shadow brought the greatest possible richness to the personality and I am convinced that this is so. Over and again it is possible to see the way in which split-off parts can be brought back into the conscious personality and enhance it. Because men live with a split in themselves, they in fact live in a kind of shadow-land which they have created through their refusal to examine their own experience – particularly their destructive experiences, whether these appear to be simple everyday issues like hurts and angers, or more complex questions about investment policies, to use an example. It is not only that individual men live in their own personal shadows but that men have formed a kind of collective shadow which is responsible for the present state of the world.

Yet if it is possible on an individual basis to reclaim the 'other' side of the personality, then it figures that it must also be true that the collective shadow of men can be redeemed. Clearly, it is an immense task which has to be undertaken but it is one on which the future of the world – and men's individual and collective lives – hangs. It demands the greatest degree of courage on the part of men – to examine their internal realities and reflect on their personal, social and political experience – and there is not much time left.

The possibilities for humankind have barely been sighted. The transformation which is within the grasp of men – if they choose to reach it – spells the transformation for us all. This is not because men have the social power to confer change upon us all, but because of our interdependence. If men reclaim all that they have denied in themselves, or repressed, because they believed there were qualities in themselves which do not meet the standards of masculinity, they will no longer be separate from themselves, their loves, their children; their 'essential self' will be restored to them and, with it, their capacities to see that they and the world are one.

11. The phallic state

Women cannot exist: the category of women is by definition
that which does not fit into existence. So women's activity
can only be negative, in opposition to what currently exists,
saying 'that's not right' and 'there's something more.'
I mean by 'woman' what is not represented, what remains
unspoken, what is left out of namings and ideologies.

Julia Kristeva, quoted by Rosalind Coward in *Female Desire*,
(Paladin, London, 1984)

Although this chapter appears towards the end of the book, it
was its starting-point. The ideas about the book began with a
dream I had where I encountered an older woman who wanted
to discuss certain psychoanalytic concepts with me. The more
attention I gave to the dream the more I understood that this
woman represented one who had not only learned the patriarchal
value systems as part of her own training, but who had thoroughly internalised them and lived by them. She was in conflict
with a new psychological understanding. Unlike some other
women, she had not questioned her theoretical framework, rather
she sought to make other women fit within it. My thoughts about
this dream gave me a way of perceiving the systems of thinking
which have preoccupied and governed us all for thousands of
years. These systems of thought are all 'patriarchal' and they all
lead to patriarchal attitudes, whether they are taken up by men
or women. The work of deconstruction is to examine their
appropriateness for women and men today.

Whilst it is true that we all – women and men – use the same
language, it is also true that the language we use is based on

male values. And although women and men use the same language, the same words convey different meanings. We have what Carol Gilligan has named 'a propensity for systematic mistranslation'.[1] As well as this, we all see life through the eyes of men. We have become accustomed to see things according to male values because they are the dominant values. What many women are doing now, though, is giving voice to the lie behind this. Women are now expressing the desire to be heard as women, not as substitute men. For women's experience of life is utterly different from men's, though there are experiences which are clearly shared human experiences, such as our feelings for children, for learning, for music and creativity. This is true even though our social conditioning tends to emphasise one aspect of an experience or another.

Sharing in a common humanity may well be the one thing that will in the end bring us together and save us, but until now that shared humanity seems to have been acknowledged only by women. Men's view of women has been as inferior and 'other'; to a degree, women are the untouchables in Western society. Women have not taken up the position of defining others, for they have been too busy unravelling what has been said about them.

So it is that women have learned the language of men and have heard what men say about them. Women have understood that they are not fully human and the reasons for it; in every century they have spoken up against this. In medieval times women were said to be without souls; they were persecuted as demons and witches, put to death. They had to defend their honour against the theologians. In the past two centuries women have had to speak out against the false labelling that defined them as short on brain and intelligence. In this century they have had to work for the legislation to give them equal rights at work, though even now women are subject to sexual and economic discrimination in the workplace. Religious dogma and psychological theory together worked to define women as 'being' people, rather than 'doers' – no doubt to prevent them from assuming positions reserved for men only. Women are to be passive and receptive, like (dare I say it?) the rainmakers of old. Only exceptional women are capable of performing scientific tasks – women with the minds of men, women rather too masculine.

The same is true of women as artists. How many women composers and painters get exhibited and included in the catalogues? The list is endless. In psychology women are defined as those who 'feel' (for men?) and those who 'intuit' (about the needs of men?). Intricate theories abound: that women should stay at home with babies; take care of elderly parents; teach piano in their sitting-rooms; grow vegetables. If they don't they will be responsible for ruining their children's lives, to say nothing of their husbands'.

Why has it not been possible to dismiss these theories and get on with life? This is an important question, but it is also one which many people, women particularly, never have the time to answer, or even bring into focus in their thinking. Their lives have been so defined and constructed by male authority that they are generally too busy to take on such a task, even if the question were to impress itself upon them.

But there is another side to this, a deeper, more subtle, more pernicious side. Since woman has been defined as 'other', as inferior, as temptress, and the one who brought sin into the world, as the one who cannot think, only feel, then the inner world of women is so filled with these feelings and thoughts that they are hard-pressed even to begin to deal with them. This is why I say that men do not accept that women share humanity. This is why a psychology devised by men cannot wholly apply to women; the first task of a woman is to deal with all the untruths about herself and her kind that she has internalised, that she feels to be true even if, rationally, she knows they are subterfuges.

Woman is not represented, even in her own psyche. What goes

on there is a reflection of what men say and believe about her. It is as though all women have been subjected to a kind of psychic implant: before they can begin to know themselves, they must first perform the operation to remove the foreign body that lies within their own. This is the task of women therapists and analysts and all the women who are involved in working with women psychologically: to help them to offload what does not belong to them as women, and to begin to perceive what it means to be a woman in Western society. This is a very arduous task which requires scrupulous examination of a woman's internal reality and the ability to put aside what does not belong there.

Women who are trained in psychology and psychoanalytic theory learn about themselves through the words of men and other women who have themselves internalised patriarchy. How other women have done this is not hard to imagine; it has in fact been necessary for them to capitulate to the male system in order to enter the profession. Once they are in they have to toe the line or risk being humiliated. Women who don't capitulate tend to be kept outside.

What I am speaking of, then, is a subtle form of unisexuality – a homosexuality of the mind, which, of course, has a great deal to do with uniformity of thought and not a little to do with heterosexuality. It is what Kate Millett might call 'phallic state'[2] of mind, where the whole culture has to take on the value of the phallus – that is, of male power and domination. This state is logical and rational and sees feeling as something inferior. Women and men are both socialised to see that this phallic state is the superior state to live by, though the problem for women is that they can't, 'because they are so dominated by their feelings'.

Because women are dominated by feelings (it is argued), they are precluded from taking part in any phallic enterprise – that is, the enterprise of life. So they, women, are said to represent all those things to do with family. Even when women have no family, they are still held to represent 'family' kinds of things; in professional organisations, they get put in charge of housekeeping arrangements (as secretaries) and coffee-making (social secretaries). No matter how skilled a woman is in terms of her equality with men, she is still relegated to the inferior 'feeling' tasks. And women do them so well! A woman's nature is defined by her functions; her functions are limited to her biology.

The American psychologist Jean Baker Miller points out that women are 'caught with no real power in a situation militating towards failure'. On the other hand, men 'are encouraged from early in life to incorporate and to aim toward living up to the highest values of their society. They are much more thoroughly and internally formed by these precepts than are women, much more in tune with the *status quo*.'[3]

The phallic state directs men towards achievement (success) and women towards supporting that achievement. A woman's life is successful if the man to whom she is attached is successful. In reality, though, she is not living her life but merely supporting a man and, through him, the whole structure of our patriarchal (phallic) society. It means a kind of annihilation of the psyche and the state of psychic being. The responsibility for this must be laid directly at the feet of men who have constructed this state (not a life) for women.

But what possible reason have men had to desire to keep women out of life – not just public life, but the state of being alive: that is, alive to themselves, and not just to men's needs? How can this serve them? Apart from giving them the obvious power, all it does in the long term is to separate men further from themselves. Men are closed off from the needs of others, closed off from themselves.

Notwithstanding such inadequacies, it is a phallic model which has been used to describe the appropriate pattern of psychological development. It is little wonder that psychology has not been nearly as successful as it might, that a good many therapeutic systems have had a deservedly bad press.

Despite the degree of evidence to the contrary, men still seem to go on believing that they are the true models of human development and human potential. They have believed as much untruth about themselves as they have about women, even though wherever they look they can see the evidence to belie their ideology. But men seem much more disposed to take on ideologies than to observe facts. Do they do this to the same extent that they have been damaged by falling for the ideologies in the first place? This clearly is an impossible question to answer, although one thing does seem to be apparent: men who come into therapy – as the male therapists I interviewed told me – rarely do so because they want to explore their own development; rather, they come because they are sent, or driven by a problem, generally a problem in relationship. One of the male therapists told me that he thought men didn't come into therapy until they were pushed because they try to deal with their relationships with their heads. 'Men don't know that they have hearts', he said, 'and that is why they become so isolated. This problem leads to all the boundaries men set up around themselves so it becomes a kind of prison for them.' Another male therapist who runs groups for men was very expansive about their behaviour. He said he thought men behaved so strangely with each other and needed a great deal of help to look at themselves psychologically. Whenever he absented himself from the group he ran, the other men couldn't cope. Only when he was there did they function well. And my own experience suggests that women are more psychologically disposed; that women somehow are much more keenly in touch with unconscious processes and give themselves up to psychological development with much greater interest and concern. Perhaps men fear that if they did begin to do some psychological work on themselves, they would be exposed to a degree they would find difficult to tolerate.

What I question, therefore, in examining the structure of patriarchy, is what it does to the souls of men. Does it, as it appears to do, diminish their humanity? Or, as the poet Andrew Harvey expresses it, rob them of their capacities for love and tenderness? Is there a way to get back what is lost? Is there a means of preventing further generations from being so disabled?

Our primary concern as humans must be to others, to ourselves, and to the world which allows us to sustain human life. This means that we must develop – quickly, for time is running out – a new way of living, one that is far from the phallic state and intimately connected with love and tenderness. Whatever splits there are must be healed if our future is more than an unrealisable Utopian ideal.

Inevitably, this means that men must now take their full and equal part in generative processes – not in the harsh and authoritarian ways they have trained their children in the past, but in the knowledge that it is only by opening themselves to their children that they will reawaken the human capacities in themselves.

Confronting the problems that men have created for us all is without doubt the greatest human task which we as a species have ever had to face. It is possible to see the first stages of this encounter in the work of the environmentalists, the peace groups, the women's groups; however, even those who are active in such areas need to be aware not only of what they are doing, but also the reasons which brought on the destruction in the first place. It is not enough to do the work without being conscious of why it is necessary. Lack of awareness will lead only to a fresh set of problems. If men's need to be separate ultimately causes them to become destructive and if, as I suggest, an equal share in child-rearing will alter this state, then it is a very small social change to make. It may seem to be monumental, given that it will involve men in working for different periods and for much shorter times – the inevitable result of equal parenting – but we have made much greater changes in the past for much less significant gains.

When this change happens, women will then be free to enter the public domain – not as trespassers on men's territory, but as those who can contribute equally to the enterprise of the community, just as men can contribute to the life of their children. This allows us the possibility of going beyond the state of eternal infancy to a place we have not yet been able to experience. Going beyond that infantile paradise may indeed lead us to an experience of consciousness – even conscious paradise – where phallic power is as unnecessary as the fear of women.

Phallic power has led men to see hierarchies as the natural mode of living. It has led them to see that decisions can be made only on an 'either/or' basis, an exclusive rather than inclusive model. It has suggested to them that love is not a gift which goes on developing and growing according to its infinite nature, but has to be contained and limited. What we need for our new social arrangement is a horizontal rather than the old outmoded hierarchical model of power relations. Equality and mutuality will be the model for the future, based on the equal and mutual roles of the two parents.

12. Men and fathering

Psychoanalytic theory, whether Freudian or Jungian, gives singular primacy to the mother as the basis of life. This is an error.

E. Monick, *Phallos* (Inner Spring Books, Toronto, 1987)

If any subject could be said to be underrated it is surely the subject of men and fathering. As fathers, men are best understood by their absence. In the psychological literature, one of the most popular themes today is the absentee father and his relation to the psychological development of his children. Twelve minutes is the amount of time most men spend with their children in the course of a day. But these men are not understood necessarily as 'bad fathers'. It is just accepted that the role of parenting is the woman's role, even if and when both parents work in full-time jobs.

When they talk about their fathers, grown men – often fathers themselves – reveal ambivalent feelings. Andy remembers his childhood very clearly. His grandmother lived with his family in their tiny house:

> I loved my mother very intensely as a child and I think I enjoyed my mother as a child, but I was brought up in an extended family and my grandmother was there as well and I absolutely adored my grandmother. I think I had a smashing relationship with my mother. She was the one who wanted me to do well at school and she was the one who said that if I wanted to do my A-levels she would go and get a job when my father was saying, 'Bloody well go out and get a job and bring some money in.' I owe a lot to my mother.

Andy barely mentioned his father in his response to my question although I had asked him about both of his parents.

Harry said he had very strong feelings for both his parents:

> I loved them both. I was more intimate with my father but
> I loved my mother more. And yet I realised that they didn't
> get on at all and early on my father would tell me about
> their disagreements. I was very concerned that they should
> be together and so I adopted a role of peacemaker, trying to
> reconcile. My father said to me, 'Your trouble is that you
> always want to run with the hare and hunt with the hounds.'
> That's the truest thing anyone ever said to me because I try
> and bring things together whenever possible.

Harry's father said those words more than half a century ago but Harry still remembers them as though they were spoken yesterday. He recognises his father's wisdom although he loved his mother more.

Jason spoke very openly about his relationship with both of his parents:

> I was very fond of both of them; I was passionately attached
> to my mother, very physical with my mother until almost in
> my twenties, I would say. We were a happy family. They
> never tried to limit me in what I tried to do. They were
> always very insistent that I did a lot by myself.

Of his father Jason commented:

> My father loved me very much. I always loved my mother
> more than my father. I feel a bit guilty about that but not
> very, because I thought it was natural. There is something
> for which I feel I blame my father and it's something to do
> with not having supplied me with a sufficiently masculine
> image. He was a very sensitive, very intellectual man, very
> idealistic; he didn't like taking responsibility and I think I
> have some feeling that somehow he didn't provide a male
> image.

Jason says that he believes it is because his father didn't give him a male image that he feels that there is something lacking in himself:

Yes, that is exactly so. I still attach myself to people who I
feel to be more active, more effective than myself, people
with the capacity to lead, the capacity to sustain things which
I have great difficulty with, the capacity to keep cool and
the capacity to do masculine things – playing games and
playing the masculine role in running things.

Jason's view of the 'masculine' role is very traditional, though he
admits that what he might well be describing is temperament
rather than particular attributes of masculine or feminine roles:

It may well be that I associate masculinity with one kind of
temperament and femininity with another kind of temperament
and that neither of these things is absolute – they are just
tendencies.

All but one of the men I interviewed said that they felt they
loved their mothers more than their fathers. They all found
problems with their fathers and not one of them, except for
Luke, felt closer to the father than the mother. Luke describes
his relationship:

I felt very close to my father and I now don't feel I was as
close to my mother as I thought I was. My father and I had
a very loving, warm relationship and I have never looked up
to anyone as I did to him, but in a totally objective, calm,
non-hero-like way. I was always very glad that he was my
father, and very proud of him. And I feel as close to him
now as I did when he was alive – he died four years ago.
There are many things I respect in my mother which she
has passed on to me, but against that there is a kind of
perversity and stubbornness in her, so I am caught in a
situation – whether it is love or a very close bond or
something – I have got used to. I am tied by obligation to
that person, or tethered. It may be one yard away, it may be
a hundred miles, but there is always a connection, so I feel
very ambivalent towards my mother.

But while most men feel that they love their mothers more
than their fathers, while they feel that their mothers did good
things for them for which they feel very grateful, this does not

change their attitude of fear towards women. Sometimes, this fear is expressed by the view that women might devour them or laugh at them or demand things of them. Certainly, it makes men keep their distance and fosters their wish to keep women under control.

The child's experience of his father is bound up with the kind of time and attention his father gives him. The father comes in when the child is happy; the father plays with him. The child is unable to judge whether or not his father would be willing to wash and iron his clothes for him, to spend all night pacing up and down; all the child knows is that for a few precious moments the other figure enters in and life is blissful. Or his father takes him for an outing on Saturday afternoon; he shares what his father loves, whether it is football or swimming or walking in the forest. Some of the best and most exciting moments are with his father.

Through his relationship with his mother the boy is set in ambivalence. His most important and powerful life-experiences come to him in and through her presence. While she is his great love, however, she is also the one whose will stands in the way of his, whose power overrides his.

Although Leo has no children of his own he has thought about child-rearing a great deal in his work as a teacher:

> I think future generations could be much more sensitive, much more creative, if there were equal influence from both mother and father, and I would say not just influence. There needs to be a change of attitude to child-rearing and a combination of the two would be a marvellous new future if this could be arranged.
>
> Actually, I feel very strongly about that. If I look back on my childhood this whole thing about 'women do this and men do that' was very difficult. If you were a boy you had to do things in this way, and that represses some of those feelings one has, whether one is a boy or a girl. I've had some interesting experiences recently – not exactly role-reversal. Two of my friends, where the woman is a dancer and goes out to work and the man now stays at home and

takes care of the children, have developed an absolutely
marvellous relationship and the children are beautiful
children.

Leo's experience is not an isolated one. A number of men now
stay at home and care for children, but this is rarely because of
the belief in equal parenting. Often it is because the woman has
the greater earning capacity or because the man has suddenly
become unemployed. Moreover, role-reversal does not get over
the difficulty that women-only parenting brings up. If men were
suddenly to give up their jobs and do all the things that women
have always done, it wouldn't mean that children's psychological
status would be enhanced. It is very likely that the situation
would merely be reversed and that would be as dangerous as
woman-centred child-rearing. The real benefit of equal parenting
will be to allow us to see women and men as they *really* are,
and not only through the distorted gaze of our childhood
projections.

But that is just one beneficial spin-off amongst many, foremost
of which is the psychological advantage it will mean to a child to
have to deal with those feelings of frustration within its own
internal reality instead of projecting them on to women. If these
feelings, which are normal and natural, occur in relation to both
parents they will have to be dealt with in the child's inner world
at the appropriate time and not at some far-distant (if ever) time
when life is collapsing all around him. The problem, then, is
trying to get at such deeply embedded and repressed issues that
should have been confronted in childhood.

When children see that women and men have an equal share
in relation to them, they will not tend to undervalue feelings
which at present they see as belonging to women only. This, I
believe, is the most obvious human reward in equal parenting,
since it will allow men to develop in themselves the kinds of
feelings which have been the prerogative of women – feelings of
love and tenderness for a vulnerable child, who depends on their
care. For as long as women are in charge of the feeling factor,

men will tend to isolate themselves from feeling and be hurt by their isolation from it. When feelings are hurt, it is impossible to see things clearly in relationship and men are doubly reduced by this. They are damaged enough by their own child-rearing which has forced them to have a distorted view of women. When a man sees a woman taking responsibility for the feelings towards their child, his own negative feelings are aroused. But just as he, as a child, had no way of dealing with his frustrations, so now he is even less able. He feels inadequate and turns his feelings of inadequacy in on himself, even if he doesn't recognise what he is doing – and it is more than likely that he doesn't.

This may be one of the reasons – though only one – why men look upon fathering as somehow 'optional'[1] to their lives, as though they are not an essential person for their children. Their feelings of inadequacy and inferiority then make men authoritarian in relation to their children. This is not, of course, for the sake of the child, but for the reason of protecting all those difficult feelings inside which might reveal themselves as tears if they were not so carefully disguised. Rigid authoritarianism is very unpleasant when it is dispensed in place of feelings of love and tenderness and it is just as unpleasant in what it does to the one who dispenses it. It distorts the inner reality even further.

For children, though, caught between their feelings of passion and fear in relation to their mother, the rigidity and firmness of paternal authority can look like a 'sanctuary'. Dinnerstein describes this as

> a sanctuary passionately cherished by the essential part of a
> person's self that wants to come (like Andersen's mermaid)
> out of the drowning sweetness of early childhood into the
> bright light of open day, the light of the adult realm in
> which human reason and human will – not the boundless
> and mysterious intentionality, the terrible uncanny
> omniscience, of the nursery goddess – can be expected, at
> least ideally, to prevail.[2]

Terry is 35 and he has a young son, David, who is now 4. When

Terry's child was 10 months old, Terry realised he was becoming increasingly frustrated by the little time he was spending with David. So he gave up his full-time job and became self-employed, working just half time. That is more than three years ago. Since then, Terry and David have had the same kind of intimate relationship that Christina (David's mother) and David have enjoyed. Like Terry, Christina works half time and spends half time with David. David relates equally well to women and men and challenges authority, regardless of whether it comes from his mother or father or another woman or man. He helps his father in the kitchen and the garden as well as in the garage. Sometimes Terry takes him, with a picnic, to collect Christina from work. Both parents equally share 'roles' as they share responsibility.

Terry has become the most human of men and he has developed a side of himself which might have got very damaged in fathering. All three have been lucky that Terry recognised this feeling in himself and was able to act upon it. In financial terms, it has meant a lot of hardship but neither Christina nor Terry mind this because it has allowed them a totally new experience of intimacy as a family. Both of David's parents see child-rearing as an adventure rather than as a response to their marriage and social conventions. The time David spends with each of his parents is qualitatively superior, since neither of them sees him as taking time away from their own personal needs which are often denied in the ordinary course of child-rearing.

I see that David's response to life is different from other children's. He is often struggling with real issues, even though he is only 4. He has already established a relationship with his own inner world and his feelings. He discusses his feelings of sadness and happiness, frustration and anger when they come up.

Shared parenting also brings men into the realm of friendship, that area which they generally find so hard. In letting go of the stereotype of the traditional father, men become exposed to the friendship of their own children and their children's friends.

Men are put on equal terms with other parents and can have the kind of friendships that usually only happen between women who are mothers. Terry says that this is one of the most interesting aspects of his new life – socialising with other parents and children.

One of the most pervasive errors of our Western society has been the idea that motherhood is in some mysterious way related to 'mother love'. Elisabeth Badinter explores this relationship in her book *The Myths of Motherhood*, where she questions the whole philosophy behind the notion of 'maternal instinct'.[3] It is so often thought, particularly by people influenced by ethology (the study of behaviour of living organisms in their natural environment), that women are endowed by the 'gift' of maternal love that is denied to men.[4] But the ability to nurture and take care of children is no more innate – and I do not believe that it is innate – in women than in men. My view of the maternal instinct argument is that it is essentially a political argument dressed up to convince women that their right place is in the home and in charge of children. It keeps women out of the workplace and denies them access to economic power. Many women speak about their feelings of failure in child-rearing. They say that they felt nothing for their children when they were born, but that the feelings developed as their babies grew. It is the way in which parenting – whether fathering or mothering – is conducted, that allows the skill of nurture to develop. But I am sure that many men believe that it is a quality they do not have and that this lack in themselves automatically disqualifies them from intimate contact, as well as from the ability to learn how to care for children.

When men are absent fathers – whether through the so-called demands of their jobs or through divorce – they set up very real psychological difficulties for their children, unless, of course, as sometimes happens, divorce actually encourages a man to see his children very often. These problems do not diminish with time. The problem of the absent father is one of the most common

163

syndromes in therapy and it often requires years of therapeutic work to bring it into full consciousness. For on the inside we each need to have good parenting and if one of the parents is absent for some reason there is a gap in both the internal reality and the psychological development of the person. Every problem which is not resolved on the inside does not merely diminish our human capacities but actually creates other problems as well.

But what is also true is the kind of psychological development that can take place when an issue in the internal reality is resolved. Just as equally shared parenting brings good things to father and child, so it also diminishes the difficulties of gender construction and thus, in turn, issues of social power and domination by men. I look on men's need to control and dominate the public domain as a way of expressing their regret at feeling locked outside the private sphere. It may be a very desperate way of stating their regret but the sooner we face the fact that fathers need children as much as children need fathers, the sooner our world will be a place not of destruction but of creative possibility. As Greg said when I asked him for his observations about child-rearing:

> I think that children who have good relationships with their mother *and* father probably come out better. I mean, I had a very intense relationship with my father. He used to take me to bed every night and he used to tell me a story which he used to make up and I loved that. I think that some parents are not good at looking at their children as though they are individuals. Their individuality and their individual development get trapped quite quickly.

13. Men and religion

We have a civilization in which males in high places imitate
a male god in heaven – both think themselves above the
petty concerns of simple nurture and delight in generative
life.

Naomi Goldenberg, *The Changing of the Gods*,
(Beacon Press, Boston, 1979)

Although on the surface of Western society religion appears to
play a minimal or even insignificant part, behind the old traditions lies one of the most powerful forces in our lives, subtly
directing many of our actions, and not just the major events of
birth, marriage and death. However insignificant they appear to
be religious traditions die hard in the mythic heritage which
lingers on at a number of levels: in our collective unconscious
and in the heritage of culture. Even when we say we have no
'religion', most of us have some kind of attitude to it, perhaps
because we have rejected it or lapsed from it or reacted
against it.

At the unconscious and cultural levels there is one religious
story which dominates the lives of those of us who live in
Western society and which informs and perpetuates the tradition
of patriarchy. This is the story of the Creation and the Fall as we
know it from Genesis 2 and Genesis 3. A number of false and
naive interpretations of some of the passages contained in these
two chapters have been responsible for women's sense of inferiority and men's moral superiority, certainly since the early
Christian era. Many women, not only Christian women, have

been taught that since Eve was responsible for the presence of sin in the world, all women somehow must share in that responsibility. Eve was tempted and gave in to temptation. She was, therefore, morally weak. Further, she tempted Adam. She could not be trusted. Women are thus responsible for the fall of creation. In sum, women are betrayers, cannot be trusted, are temptresses. Men had better be on their guard in case, like Adam, they too succumb. This kind of teaching has been at the root of the mistrust men have of women, even though it is based on untruth, according to contemporary biblical exegesis.[1]

Although both female and male theologians have long ago put the 'difficult' passages from Genesis into their cultural and historical perspective, this doesn't mean that the tradition of women as the inventors of sin has died in the popular accounts of women's place in the world. Nor does it mean that women have been able to put aside thousands of years of untruth in their unconscious lives. They may know, at the level of rationality, that they are not solely responsible for wrong-doing, but this doesn't mean that they don't still feel badly about themselves on the inside. Whilst this is a problem for Christian women in particular, it does not mean that women from other religious traditions have escaped the conclusions drawn by Christian teachings, because of cultural overlaps which impinge upon each other. In popular Christian traditions, women have been accused not only of bringing sin into the world, but of being responsible – along with the Jews – for the deicide, the killing of Jesus.

Christianity has been the main dispenser of the popular image of women as weak and therefore easily led astray, as sexual fiends always on the look-out, hoping to seduce men from their path of righteousness. The New Testament lays the blame squarely upon Eve. 'Adam was not deceived, but the woman was deceived and became a transgressor.'[2] Over the centuries, as a direct result of this kind of passage, women have been viewed as slaves, people without souls, as witches or specimens of incarnate wickedness; in every respect contemptible.

How much has the murky history of the church to do with the psychology of men? In my view, the two go hand in hand. Biblical literature has always been, until very recently, that which men studied on their own, and as such has been subject to false interpretation, at times malicious. It is only in recent years that religious teaching has lost its central place in Western society, though that to some extent has been replaced by the rise of fundamentalism, particularly in parts of the United States and Australia.

By holding women, following in Eve's footsteps, responsible for sin, men have been able to look on themselves as the 'other', as infinitely superior in human terms, set above women to keep them in order. Women have been admonished to keep silence and maintain a position of invisibility. In Christianity, men were to be the 'head' of women as Christ was the head of the church. The Jewish tradition has in some senses served women better. For example, the Genesis story has a different significance within Judaism, and the burden of guilt from Eve is not systematically transferred to all women. But as an American woman rabbi told me, she still feels that the religion to which she is deeply attached really belongs to men. 'Even though I am a rabbi I still feel that I am trespassing on territory that does not belong to me, even when I am preaching a sermon to a large congregation in the synagogue. I have inside me so many feelings of guilt and inferiority which are there because the men make me feel I am trespassing.'

By internalising their own superiority over women, men have put themselves in a situation whereby they have been able to read biblical texts uncritically. They have not seen their own lack of impartiality. But biblical texts are as much a part of the social, cultural and political concerns of the time in which they were written as are the religious accounts and stories of our own time. Yet no one would interpret what is written today uncritically. It seems that over the centuries men have been able to suspend their personal experience and knowledge of women in favour of traditions which they have misapprehended, whether wittingly or not. What men read in Genesis 2 and 3 allowed them to believe that Eve had been tempted. Eve, rather than the 'human couple',[3] has had to bear the burden and the guilt of that action.

Guilt is a very strange emotion. It often falls upon the innocent to carry. Women feel very guilty about what is said to be their legacy from Eve. They meet it on two levels: in the popular accounts through which they 'realise' their part of the Fall, and in the hidden message they receive through the unconscious. This means that if they fail to experience their guilt on a personal level it still reaches them from the unconscious layer and has its effect. It is rather like a level of anxiety within, hard to detect and very hard to heal. So while many women realise consciously that it is ridiculous to feel bad about themselves for what they never participated in, they do nevertheless retain feelings of guilt which get in the way of their enterprise and self-creation. It is hard to act freely when you feel bad about yourself. You tend to want to cover over the guilt and women often do that by making themselves feel small, and apologising for themselves.

Men's feelings of superiority over women, and women's feelings of guilt, have maintained a kind of status quo over thousands of years, both before and after Christ. The patriarchy of Judaism is no less harsh in its critique of scripture and women's position than Christianity, even though Judaism has never cast all women in the role of Eve's sisters. Judaism does not need to place so much emphasis on the 'Fall' and therefore does not need to hold any one person responsible for the Fall.

But if, from a generalised male perspective, women are guilty of allowing sin to enter the world, then it follows that women must be excluded from any position of power that would allow further contamination. Men, clearly, must be put in charge of the overall operation. This is true, still, of the administration of religious institutions, even though a number of women do have a place in some traditions within Judaism and Christianity, and can become rabbis, ministers or priests. But the question here is whether men truly believe that women are responsible for sin, or whether men act from irrational fear of women and perceive – wrongly, in my view – power in women where it does not exist.

Even in those branches of Judaism and the church where women are supposedly accepted, they are rarely welcomed openly. It seems, rather, that their acceptance is grudging and half-hearted. A woman priest in the Episcopal Church in the United States told me of the way she had been treated in the diocese of New York. There were a number of male priests, she said, who were personally very welcoming, but she experienced great hostility from others, and never had what she felt was job security. She didn't know when she might get moved from her work in a parish to some kind of administrative post where she wouldn't be so visible. This has been the experience of many women ministers, not just in the Episcopal Church but in a number of Protestant denominations. A woman Baptist minister told me that, even after 20 years of serving in a parish, she was still subjected to hostile acts by male ministers – there were still little jokes made about the presence of a female minister. Women rabbis experience similar treatment. They are much more closely scrutinised by male superiors when they are doing their theological training, their sexuality is often discussed openly by their male peers, and they rarely enjoy the same status as their male contemporaries. A male rabbi in the English Midlands told me how furious he was when some other male rabbis called a meeting to discuss the sexuality of one of the female rabbis. 'But the women were not invited,' he told me. 'We were acting unilaterally as though we were in charge and therefore had some kind of authority over our women colleagues.' A young woman in training for the rabbinate outside London said that she was aware that she was always having to protect her position within her course. She could never just accept that she had the same freedom as the men, and she said she felt the decisions concerning other women rabbis might depend upon her behaviour.

Throughout the centuries, popular theology has prevailed. Within Christianity, one of the particular problems has been its close association from earliest times with Greek philosophy and philosophical traditions, traditions which have never been displaced even though they perpetuate fundamental problems for Christianity. Rosemary Radford Ruether, the American theologian, is quick to point out how the concept of 'divine Logos' (the Word of God) set in motion a 'chain of being',[4] or, in other words, a hierarchy within Christianity. Thus it is in Christianity, as in the context of Hellenistic Greece, that just as the 'Logos of God governs nature . . . the Greeks must govern barbarians, masters govern slaves, and men govern women.'[5] The application of this false logic is apparent in every age of Christianity, regardless of the culture in which it is based. When this logic is taken a step further it is possible to see how women then become equated with nature over which men also govern. What must be clear is the lack of concern with love. Hierarchy is about order.

But the hierarchy built in to systems of philosophical thought is contrary to the underlying ethos of both Christianity and Judaism; in neither religion can there be superior or inferior. In God's world there is equality between women and men. But popular theology, like popular tradition, rarely concerns itself with deeper implications – such as equality – and tends to hold in place the structures which are considered necessary to maintain popular dogma.

What appears to have infected many of the world's major religions – Judaism, Christianity and Buddhism did not escape – is the system of dualistic thinking which has not only maintained its place in religious traditions, but has deeply touched psychological teaching too. Dualistic philosophy seems to be one of the most dangerous and simplistic of all explanations for holding the world in place. Beginning with male and female, divisions are made between 'light' and 'dark' aspects of a whole. It follows from this that light has a certain quality, as does dark: one becomes associated with good and the other with bad, or even evil. So it is that a train of polarisations follow: men and women, heaven and hell, spirit and body, good and bad. Maleness and femaleness are not seen as like but as opposite qualities; men and women become opposed to each other, rather than linked in some mutual project because of their similarity. No longer are they human persons separated biologically by one chromosome but part of a different cosmic order. The danger for women is further constructed.

So, regardless of the religious tradition and its scriptural teachings, men get to be seen as those who belong to the order which connects them with goodness, light, objectivity, action, heavenliness and the spirit. Women become associated with sinfulness, darkness, death, nature and the body. Male and female have come to stand for 'cosmic principles', which cannot be applied to different human beings. Through this system of dualisms men have been able to retain the upper hand and have thus been able to have dominion over the lower orders, which include women and nature, the body and death. In one swipe of dualistic thought, it was possible to see women and nature as inseparable and inferior, not only through philosophical domination and quasi-religious teaching, but through actual exploitation and rape as well.

These false dualisms lie at the root of the misunderstandings of the nature of women and men. Dualism is today equated with complementarity, a dogma based on dualistic thought but with a deceptively 'human' appearance. For behind the notion of complementarity lies the old syndrome of superior men and inferior women. Men represent mind and objectivity, women the body and subjectivity; the evidence has not been examined.

Religion has failed women and fooled men. And where religion has failed – namely, in its capacity to connect women and men with their mythic and sacred traditions – psychology and psychoanalytic thought has taken over in the West. But women present the same problems to psychoanalysis as they did and do to biblical scholars. Psychoanalysis is not value-free when it comes to women.

In their need to flee from death, men have cast the responsibility for the body on to women and have made women pay the price for sexuality. When a woman is raped there are thoughts about her responsibility in it. Did she encourage the man? Was she dressed to provoke him? Did she 'ask' for it? Male behaviour is often put aside because of the widely 'understood' notion that women somehow tempt men; besides, men's sexuality is so instantaneous in response that the man does not necessarily have to be asked to be responsible for his behaviour: 'the female, as the cause of human suffering, knowledge, and sin . . . represents the most crucial argument of the patriarchal tradition in the West.'[6]

But where does this leave men, apart from the recognition that they have in some way needed to separate themselves absolutely from women? The psychological question is why they felt that it was so necessary. In order to find the origin, we need to go to that first garden to see the resemblances that it has with the infant's nursery. Eden's garden was a place of delight, a place of innocence and beauty. A woman and a man. But consciousness, in the form of sin (it is said) intervened, and the man's beloved fell from grace. She, and he, were expelled. From then on, she has known pain in childbirth – she brings forth in pain, which is her due. In the 'nursery', the same human couple – a mother and her son – are as one until his need to become a man intrudes; at this point, she falls from grace and he *feels* expelled. The loss of the beloved is the loss of the mother and it must feel very much like the moment when sin enters in.

Each of us for a time inhabits a 'garden', until the necessity of growing up forces us to leave it. At that time, we must take responsibility for our own self-creation. But if we are forced to leave behind just one beloved person as human parent, we will cast on to that person all that we cannot face in ourselves. We will unjustly blame the woman. But we gain nothing by blaming, by seeing her as responsible for what has happened. In leaving the garden (the nursery, the body of the mother), a man sets himself in flight from the body to the spirit in his 'need to escape something essential in himself'.[7] And that is the reason why man wants woman to be 'outside of him'.[8] He wishes her to be 'all that which he cannot grasp inside himself'.[9] So, by casting sin on to the woman or the mother, he evades sin in himself, and thus evades responsibility for life. But by evading responsibility he is set upon the path of destruction, destruction of his own personal psychology and of all that he regards as inferior.

As I see it, the place of religion is to provide the appropriate framework to allow human beings the most apposite means of finding their harmony in the world. Religion has failed us lamentably in this; only by a re-examination of its own roots will it be able to make good the damage it has done to us all.

14. Is there a future for men?

Today even the survival of humanity is a Utopian hope.

Norman O. Brown, *Life against Death*
(Wesleyan University Press, Middletown, Conn., 1959)

If it is true, as I believe it is, that all human actions leave their own impressions, whether visible or invisible, then we all live our lives amidst the repercussions and traces of those whose actions preceded us as well as those amongst whom we now live. Every action goes rippling on, filtering in to the unconscious at various levels. Some are positive, others harmful. One action can in turn damage the whole world; just as another can change it for the better.

Many men in Western society bear the scars of past actions which have never been resolved or even acknowledged, but which have simply crept through the centuries creating the world we now know. Not many men, it seems, allow the buck to stop with them, or stop to consider that although we cannot be held personally responsible for the actions of individuals or societies long gone, we must still act responsibly towards the present and the future.

Gabriel is one man who, although his daily work concerns the analysis of society, does not stop to take account of his part in its present destruction. Gabriel is now in his mid-forties, a moderately successful academic who teaches at a British university and, sometimes, at a university in the United States. He grew up in a small town near London, received an excellent education and has always understood himself to be amongst the intellectual if not the social elite, behaving as if his views were superior and better informed than those of others.

In the 25 years since he graduated, Gabriel has been married and divorced twice and has been involved in sexual affairs amounting to many dozens. He has sworn fidelity to his many partners, feigning horror at the suggestion of any other involvement. The two women he married both divorced him because of his intolerably duplicitous behaviour towards them.

Gabriel argues that he deceived these women in order to save their feelings. Could he help it if they were possessive? Why do women want to 'own' men? Isn't he allowed to develop his emotional life? In truth, Gabriel's position is one of self-evasion and self-deception and a kind of murderous abuse of women. For in deceiving and lying to so many, he also denies the integrity and reality of every individual woman, binding her into a power relationship with himself. He has the master-control. For without possessing the facts of a situation, no woman could make a real decision about the relationship.

Gabriel's behaviour – psychotic when interpreted psychologically – is almost impossible for women to understand. Everyone stands to lose so much, Gabriel included. So why continue in this vein? In his teaching job in England and the USA Gabriel has assumed a good deal of power, particularly over women students. He sometimes boasts to his colleagues about his 'conquests' amongst the young women in his classes; his sexual promiscuity is lived at their expense: emotional, psychological and, nowadays, physical. He seems not to care. They can make their own decisions, he says. But no one is free to make a decision when they are held in such a power wrench.

Gabriel's life is a model of the failure of men in Western society; constructed by the society which he spends his life reviewing, he can be judged to reflect its values – even though that means a construction by false values. He lives, in microcosm, all the issues that have never been confronted collectively, but which in macrocosm hurt us all. His failure, like the failure of many men in Western society today, can be seen in his inability to connect his head and his heart. His head, often so plausible in argument, has no relation to his feelings, and even though he claims to have deep feelings, those who know him realise that his deep feelings are all for himself. Western society gives scant attention to emotional or psychological needs: its basis and motivation stem from a concern with hierarchical power and personal and collective economic growth, even at the expense of half the world, or life itself.

But power and control, wherever they are, are about unrelatedness. Gabriel does not have relationships with women; he has management of them in much the same way as a pimp manages a group of women in a brothel. Behaving as he does, Gabriel not only diminishes any ability he has for relationship, he changes women from what they naturally are into people they can hardly recognise as themselves. This happens because he forces them into impossible positions where they have to compromise themselves and question their own integrity. By having associated with a man like Gabriel, they feel sullied and abused. And they are.

Psychologically speaking, Gabriel lives on the edge of, if not fully inhabiting, a psychosis: that is, he lives in multiple realities which are not connected to one another and where people do not count except as adjuncts to himself. But while living on the boundaries of psychosis, he is still able to hold down a reasonable job with a good salary at a respectable university. This fact indicates another aspect of the failure of Western society: that psychotic behaviour in men can be seen as 'normal' because of its prevalence. Psychotic people live in a number of realities and are so compartmentalised as to be unable to recognise the rigidity of the boundaries which separate the compartments. So Gabriel, even as he dissembles, only barely glimpses what he is doing. And his behaviour is defended by his male colleagues: he is, after all, one of the 'lads', a good bloke.

Gabriel's views are upheld by the values of Western society.

Let us, however, consider the damage that this psychological proposition – that intellectual capacity and ambition are the keys to what it's all about – has effected. Like the emotional vandal that he is, he has abused dozens of women, and sometimes three or four at a time. By convincing them that he is utterly devoted to them, he places them in severe self-doubt; something tells them that things don't quite add up but, when they probe, they are met by Gabriel's hostile ridicule. One of his acquaintances dubbed him the 'Sniper'. At any moment when his game is about to be revealed, he snipes; all his behaviour is directed towards keeping his lies masked; by concentrating the focus of disturbed behaviour on the women, his real life stays concealed.

Fortunately, there are a few men who have seen the signals of a failed society – like those reflected in Gabriel's life – and have noted that the central issue is the nature of men. These men claim that the male preoccupation with the past and the future has laid waste the present.

Daniel is nearing 40. He has devoted the last ten years to work in an organisation which studies the ecological problems of industrial society: 'I feel compelled to try to make some inroad which will get the environment to function as it was intended. And I can see that the heart of the problem lies with the way men have been conditioned.'

When Daniel articulates his feelings about men, he is often attacked by other men – men who believe that without the 'profit motive' all is lost. But he is sanguine about their hostility, knowing that he too once held the same opinions. What has changed him is his perception of the interrelatedness of all things, particularly the so-called First and Third Worlds: 'How can I be happy in my comfortable life if I know that it is at the expense of someone in another country?' Daniel says that unless he can be personally contented in his marriage and a good father to his children, he will have made only a negative input into life. What he wants to do is try to make the interdependency of everything clear so that there will be no gaps between his personal and public life; his relationship with the woman he lives with, and his colleagues at work.

Jim is a much younger and less public man, an environmental scientist of 28. He has lived in Central America for the past few years, helping formulate solutions for saving a devastated environment. Like Daniel's, Jim's life knows no rigid boundaries. The decisions in life are made jointly with Liz, who is as committed to her life in Central America as her husband, though they work in different fields. They both feel themselves to be part of a collective and individual struggle to create an atmosphere of mutual caring and reciprocity which extends beyond them towards the direction of political and environmental life.

Daniel and Jim are men who could both have immense power in the world; they have the ability and education to gather the confidence of millions. But they both, thousands of miles apart, have taken a turning which they believe and trust is the only viable one for men if they wish to make some positive contribution to the future. Both agree that power corrupts and distances them from what they really want in life – good relationships and a clear sense of what it means to be human.

There are stark differences between the lives of Gabriel, Daniel and Jim. For a start, Gabriel's life is one of self-evasion: he has no real self-knowledge and therefore no relationship to himself. In consequence he can have no real relationship to anyone or with the world. He wishes only to control and organise things to his personal advantage. He has no real sense of being a living part of human society, one of a species which is in very real trouble. For him, to come to this realisation would mean a complete capitulation of his life and his values – and, as he says, he has already 'made his investment'.

Daniel and Jim, and the women who share their lives, have given up their old investments in the ways of the past. These two men have taken account of their personal 'shadow' lives and have enough awareness of the collective shadow of men to enable them to be clear-sighted in their vision of the future. They both know that they can neither control nor organise the future but must let it unfold in the way their personal relationships unfold and grow deeper and richer.

By seeing themselves as part of the world, in intimate connection with all other living things, men like Daniel and Jim are restoring the possibilities for men, and for all of us. In recognising the splits in which many men live, they are seeking to recover themselves: to make themselves available where they were formerly closed off. As Jim said:

> Unless I do this, I am only contributing further to the chaos
> in the world. But I also know that the greatest pleasures I
> have had recently are all connected with my place in the
> world. I used to feel on the outside if I wasn't at the centre
> – crazy, I know – whereas now I have the feeling of being
> attached to everything.

Notes and references

Chapter 1 Masculinity

1 A. Metcalf and M. Humphries (eds), *The Sexuality of Men* (Pluto Press, London, 1985), Introduction.

Chapter 2 Sexuality: a problematic zone

1 A number of studies, most informal and unpublished, have been conducted to attempt to estimate the number of bisexual men in Western society. ('Bisexual' is defined as men who have sexual relations with both women and men.) Much of this research has been conducted since the spread of the HIV virus and has been done in conjunction with a number of clinics. Some researchers put the figure as high as between 50 to 70 per cent, whilst others say it is more like 20 per cent. One of the main difficulties in identifying these men is due to their self-perception. Various AIDS councils have interviewed bisexual men: the AIDS council of New South Wales, Australia found that 16 per cent of men identified themselves as bisexual. Another researcher, Dr Viv Cass, a clinical psychologist, believes that there is a hidden population of men. She estimates around 50 per cent of men have ongoing sexual relationships with men (The *Australian*, 23 March 1987). A psychotherapist in London who works almost exclusively with men in groups estimates the number to be 60 to 70 per cent. Michael Ross of Flinders University, South Australia, looks at this issue in his book *The Married Homosexual Man* (Routledge & Kegan Paul, London, 1983) and is presently conducting more research.
2 Lillian Rubin, *Intimate Strangers* (Fontana, London, 1985).
3 Charlotte Wolff, *Bisexuality: A Study* (Quartet, London, 1977).

4 Ibid.

5 Jean Baker Miller, *Toward a New Psychology of Women* (Beacon Press, Boston, 1976).

6 Russell Vannoy, *Sex Without Love: A Philosophical Exploration* (Prometheus Books, New York, 1980).

Chapter 3 The split in men

1 See Nancy Chodorow, *The Reproduction of Mothering* (University of California Press, Berkeley, 1978); Dorothy Dinnerstein, *The Rocking of the Cradle and the Ruling of the World* (Women's Press, London, 1987); and Susie Orbach and Luise Eichenbaum, *What Do Women Want?* (Fontana, London, 1984).

2 Marianne Graubecker, *There's a Good Girl* (Women's Press, London, 1988).

3 See Dinnerstein, op. cit.

4 Lillian Rubin, *Intimate Strangers* (Fontana, London, 1985).

5 Ibid.

6 Ibid.

Chapter 4 Sex and gender

1 See Susie Orbach and Luise Eichenbaum, *What Do Women Want?* (Fontana, London, 1984); Robert Stoller, *Sex and Gender: The Development of Masculinity and Femininity* (Maresfield Reprints, London, 1984), vol. 1.

2 Stoller, op. cit.

3 Robert Stoller, *Sexual Excitement: Dynamics of Erotic Life* (Pantheon Books, New York, 1979).

4 Ibid.

5 Ibid.

6 Dorothy Dinnerstein, *The Rocking of the Cradle and the Ruling of the World* (Women's Press, London, 1987).

7 Ibid.

8 Ibid.

9 Ibid.

10 Ibid.

11 Rosemary Radford Ruether, *To Change the World: Christology and Cultural Criticism* (Crossroad Publishing, New York, 1981).

12 John Ruskin, *Sesame and Lilies* (1865; Homewood, Chicago, 1902), 'Of Queen's Gardens'.
13 Dinnerstein, op. cit.

Chapter 5 Men and friendship

1 See Barbara Rogers, *Men Only: An Investigation into Men's Organisations* (Pandora, London, 1988).
2 Carol Gilligan and Susan Pollak's research is quoted in Carol Gilligan, *In a Different Voice* (Harvard University Press, Cambridge, Mass., 1982).
3 Gilligan, op. cit.
4 Ibid.
5 Ibid.
6 See Chapter 2, note 1.

Chapter 6 Men and love

1 Dorothy Dinnerstein, *The Rocking of the Cradle and the Ruling of the World* (Women's Press, London, 1987).
2 Ibid.
3 Ibid.
4 Lillian Rubin, *Intimate Strangers* (Fontana, London, 1985).
5 Milan Kundera, *The Unbearable Lightness of Being* (Faber & Faber, London, 1984).
6 Shere Hite, *Women and Love: A Cultural Revolution in Progress* (Alfred Knopf, New York, 1987).
7 Ibid.
8 Carol Gilligan, *In a Different Voice* (Harvard University Press, Cambridge, Mass., 1982).
9 Ibid.
10 Ibid.

Chapter 7 Men and marriage

1 Tom Wolfe, *The Right Stuff* (Jonathan Cape, London, 1980).
2 *Marriages Australia 1986* (Australian Bureau of Statistics, Canberra, Catalogue Number 3306.0).
3 Australian Institute of Family Studies, *Newsletter* (Melbourne, December 1988).

4 Ibid.

5 Another interesting finding concerns the duration of marriage. In one study, half the divorcing couples stated that the difficulties in their marriage arose before two years. This confirms the theory advanced in Chapter 3, pp. 51–2. For statistics, see Jacqueline Burgoyne, Roger Ormrod and Martin Richards, *Divorce Matters* (Penguin, London, 1987).

6 Dorothy Dinnerstein, *The Rocking of the Cradle and the Ruling of the World* (Women's Press, London, 1987).

7 Ibid.

8 Ibid.

9 Phyllis Rose, *Parallel Lives: Five Victorian Marriages* (Penguin, London, 1985).

10 Dinnerstein, op. cit.

11 See figures compiled by Relate (National Marriage Guidance Council), Rugby, England. The Office of Population Censuses and Surveys, St Catherine's House, Kingsway, London WC2 publish the figures every year.

12 Burgoyne, Ormrod and Richards, op. cit.

13 Dorothy Rowe, *Choosing Not Losing: The Experience of Depression* (Fontana, London, 1988).

14 Shere Hite, *Women and Love: A Cultural Revolution in Progress* (Alfred Knopf, New York, 1987).

15 Orbach and Eichenbaum, op. cit.

16 Phyllis Chesler, *Women and Madness* (Avon Books, New York, 1972).

Chapter 8 Men and violence

1 E. Gibson and S. Klein, *Murder 1957–1968* (HMSO, London, 1969); E. Gibson, *Homicide in England and Wales 1967–1971* (HMSO, London, 1975).

2 *Inquiry into Strategies to Deal with the Issue of Community Violence: First Report* (Parliament of Victoria, Social Development Committee, May 1988); Elizabeth Ward, *Father–Daughter Rape* (Women's Press, London, 1984).

3 Elizabeth Wilson, *What Is to Be Done about Violence against Women?* (Penguin, London, 1983).

4 See (a) British Association for the Study and Prevention of Child

Abuse and Neglect (BASPCAN) (1981): *Child Sexual Abuse* (BASPCAN, London, 1981).

   (b) Jasper Gayford, *Wife Battering: A Preliminary Survey of 100 Cases* (British Medical Journal, 25 January 1975).

   (c) Rape Counselling and Research Project, *First Annual Report*, London, 1977; and Rape Counselling and Research Project, Submission to the Criminal Law Revision Committee (London, 1977).

   (d) Report from the Select Committee on Violence in Marriage, Vol. 2 (HMSO, London, 1975).

   (e) *Criminal Statistics, England and Wales* (HMSO, London) published annually.

   (f) E. Gibson, *Homicide in England and Wales 1967–1971* (HMSO, London, 1975).

 5 Deborah Cameron and Elizabeth Frazer, *The Lust to Kill* (Polity Press, Cambridge, 1987).

 6 Terence Morris and Louis Blom-Cooper, *A Calendar of Murder* (Michael Joseph, London, 1964).

 7 *Inquiry into Strategies to Deal with the Issue of Community Violence.*

 8 Wilson, op. cit.

 9 Ibid.

10 Ibid.

11 Ibid.

12 Ibid.

13 Ibid.

14 Wayne Eisenhart, 'The Army Will Make a "Man" out of You', in Pam McAllister (ed.), *Reweaving the Web of Life* (New Society Publishers, Philadelphia, 1982).

15 Ibid.

16 *Inquiry into Strategies to Deal with the Issue of Community Violence.*

17 Arno Karlin, *Sexuality and Homosexuality* (MacDonald, London, 1971).

18 Dorothy Dinnerstein, *The Rocking of the Cradle and the Ruling of the World* (Women's Press, London, 1987).

19 Jacqueline Burgoyne, Roger Ormrod and Martin Richards, *Divorce Matters* (Penguin, London, 1987).

20 Ibid.

21 An article in the *Australian* (April 1989) argued that there is a strong class basis for collective violence, particularly football violence.

Chapter 9 Men at work

1 Carol Gilligan, *In a Different Voice* (Harvard University Press, Cambridge, Mass., 1982).
2 The statistical analysis of the death rates of men of the same age in Britain show that those who have retired are twice as high.
   (A. J. Fox, 'The role of OPCS in occuational epidemiology: some examples'; *Annals of Occupational Hygiene*, Vol. 21, 1979.)
   In the USA, 25 per cent of the suicides are amongst the retired over 65, even though they represent just nine per cent of the population.
   (K. Hopper and S. Guttmacher, 'Rethinking suicide, notes toward a critical epidemiology', *Int. Journal of Health Service*, Vol. 9, No. 3, 1979.)
3 Study jointly published by the Social Science Research Council and the Medical Research Council, Sheffield, 1977–83.
4 Research conducted by Dr Fernando Bartolomé and quoted by Phillip Hodson in *Men* (Ariel Books, London, 1984).

Chapter 10 Men and the world

1 Radio interview with Vandana Shiva, Director of the Research Foundation for Science, Technology and Natural Resource Policy, Dehradun, India.
2 Vandana Shiva, *Staying Alive* (Zed Books, London, 1989).
3 Frank Barnaby (ed.), *The Gaia Peace Atlas* (Pan Books, London, 1988).
4 Quoted in ibid.
5 Quoted from Delys Bird, 'Gendering the Landscape: Metaphors and Myths of the Land in Australia' (unpublished lecture from English Department, University of Western Australia, 1987).
6 Ibid.
7 A number of plans to save the Amazon rainforest have been put to the Brazilian government by international environmental organisations. One of these suggests that individuals and groups buy parts of the forest to help with the Brazilian debt.

8 Dorothy Dinnerstein, *The Rocking of the Cradle and the Ruling of the World* (Women's Press, London, 1987).

9 Barnaby, op. cit.

10 Carl Jung, *Memories, Dreams, Reflections* (Fontana, London, 1963).

Chapter 11 The phallic state

1 Carol Gilligan, *In a Different Voice* (Harvard University Press, Cambridge, Mass., 1982).

2 Kate Millet, *Sexual Politics* (Hart-Davis, London, 1971).

3 Jean Baker Miller, *Towards a New Psychology of Women* (Beacon Press, Boston, 1976).

Chapter 12 Men and fathering

1 Phillip Hodson, *Men* (Ariel Books, London, 1984).

2 Dorothy Dinnerstein, *The Rocking of the Cradle and the Ruling of the World* (Women's Press, London, 1987).

3 Elisabeth Badinter, *The Myth of Motherhood* (Souvenir Press, London, 1981).

4 Elisabeth Badinter discusses this fully in ibid.; see also John Bowlby's theories, which are closely aligned with the theory of ethology.

Chapter 13 Men and religion

1 See Phyllis Trible, *God and the Rhetoric of Sexuality* (Fortress Press, Philadelphia, 1978).

2 New Testament, 1 Tim.

3 Trible, op. cit.

4 Rosemary Radford Ruether, *To Change the World: Christology and Cultural Criticism* (Crossroad Publishing, New York, 1981).

5 Ibid.

6 Kate Millett, *Sexual Politics* (Hart-Davis, London, 1971).

7 Dorothy Dinnerstein, *The Rocking of the Cradle and the Ruling of the World* (Women's Press, London, 1987).

8 Ibid.

9 Ibid.

Index

A Selected List of Non-Fiction Available from Mandarin

☐	7493 0109 0	**The Warrior Queens**	Antonia Fraser £4.99
☐	7493 0108 2	**Mary Queen of Scots**	Antonia Fraser £5.99
☐	7493 0010 8	**Cromwell**	Antonia Fraser £7.50
☐	7493 0106 6	**The Weaker Vessel**	Antonia Fraser £5.99
☐	7493 0014 0	**The Demon Drink**	Jancis Robinson £4.99
☐	7493 0016 7	**Vietnam – The 10,000 Day War**	Michael Maclear £3.99
☐	7493 0061 2	**Voyager**	Yeager/Rutan £3.99
☐	7493 0113 9	**Peggy Ashcroft**	Michael Billington £3.99
☐	7493 0177 5	**The Troubles**	Mick O'Connor £4.99
☐	7493 0004 3	**South Africa**	Graham Leach £3.99
☐	7493 0254 2	**Families and How to Survive Them**	Creese/Skynner £5.99
☐	7493 0060 4	**The Fashion Conspiracy**	Nicolas Coleridge £3.99
☐	7493 0179 1	**The Tao of Pooh**	Benjamin Hoff £2.99
☐	7493 0000 0	**Moonwalk**	Michael Jackson £2.99